MAKEREADY

A Prepress Resource

DAN MARGULIS

MIS: PRESS

*A subsidiary of
Henry Holt and Co., Inc.*

MIS:Press
a subsidiary of Henry Holt and Company, Inc.
115 West 18th Street
New York, NY 10011
http://www.mispress.com

First Edition—1996

Library of Congress Cataloging-in-Publication Data

Margulis, Daniel
    Makeready : A Prepress Resource / by Dan Margulis.
        p.   cm.
    Updated selections from the author's column in the magazine Computer Artist.
    ISBN 1-55828-508-3
        1. Pictures—Printing—Data processing. 2. Color-printing—Data processing. 3. Desktop publishing. I. Title.
    257.M37   1996
    686.2'5445369—dc20   96-32534
                                                                                                          CIP

10 9 8 7 6 5 4 3 2 1

Associate Publisher: *Paul Farrell*   **Production Editor:** *Anne Incao*
Executive Editor: *Cary Sullivan*   **Technical Editor:** *Peter Fink*
Copy Edit Manager: *Shari Chappell*   **Copy Editor:** *Suzanne Ingrao*

Contents

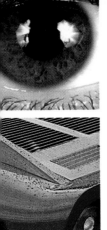

PART II   L*a*b* MEETS THE MATADOR
colorspaces, curves, and a consistent correction philosophy

PART III WHAT GOES AROUND, COMES AROUND

the ground rumbles beneath the feet of the professional photographer

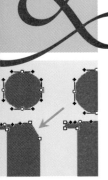

PART IV TYPOGRAPHIC FASHION FOR OUR TIME
after 500 years, the architecture adapts to the age of color publishing

Introduction

Publishing in the nineties is like the Wild West.

Looking at the current situation in the most positive way, it is a time of colossal growth and opportunity. On the other hand, it is a time fraught with danger and sudden death for the unwary pilgrim. There are adventures unlike any seen before, and new outposts, like the Web, open rapidly.

The specialists have stayed back east. On the frontier, every barber is also a surgeon, every photographer a typesetter. The uncertainties of such a situation leave the door open for the frock-coated stranger with a string of fancy degrees, peddling elixirs that promise to cure everything from hangnails to cancer, and color management systems guaranteed to bring new life to one's complexion.

It's a cowboy culture, greatly different from the factory mentality of the past. Now, we are independents, though we have loose alliances, perhaps, with certain of our neighbors, the local blacksmith, and a service bureau or two.

Riches are there for the taking, but the territory is an uncharted one. Though no one can guide us unerringly through such a wilderness, we are grateful for all advice and suggestions.

The accuracy of this metaphor may explain the extraordinary response to the columns you are about to read, or re-read. *Computer*

Artist and I were both taken by surprise by their success, which shows how little we understood what the new frontier was all about.

In early 1993, Tom McMillan, the editor of *Computer Artist* magazine, asked me to write a regular column, but far longer than most: four or five thousand words apiece, with lots of graphics. His idea was to call it "Makeready," and to limit it to the practical prepress matters of our digital age.

I thought this a very attractive name but a stupid idea. I felt computer artists as a group were dreamy creative types who enjoyed constructing complicated but useless abstractions and had about as much interest in practicalities as I have in the etymology of Sanskrit.

That, of course, ignored reality, and on further consideration of just where the DTP revolution was going, I decided to do the column. I am one of the very few people with a traditional prepress background who saw the writing on the wall virtually as soon as desktop publishing was introduced, and made the switch in the eighties. It is true that such a conventional background is of limited help in areas like vector graphics, which is a completely new field. On the other hand, such concepts as trapping, type legibility, and color correction haven't changed. The problems are the same, the techniques to correct them are slightly different, but the more experience one has the better.

Since I was running a desktop publishing department for a New York prepress house at the time, I started off with a piece discussing the most common

errors that cause jobs to fail to run properly. That is always a useful thing to discuss, but boring. I felt bad about it, and resolved to loosen up the next time. Here is how the next column opened:

A six-year-old, a color scientist, and an electronic retoucher were each given the same test in logic. They were asked, what do the following terms have in common: RGB, HSL, YCC, LAB, and HSB?

The six-year-old said, they all have three letters. The scientist said, each is a paradigmatic construct enabling expression of empirical visual data in the form of unique normative values of probative color equivalence. The retoucher said, each is a color-space, but not CMYK, so to hell with 'em all.

That the six-year-old gave the most coherent and technically useful response is the theme of this column, in which we will discover how to make a weapon of the anomaly that sets CMYK apart from and above other color models: the presence of black ink.

This introduced two columns on GCR and its implications in color correction. I quote it at such length because it epitomizes "Makeready" in several ways.

Gray component replacement was a concept understood by practically nobody in the industry, not printers, not Photoshoppers, not the folks at SWOP who propound industry standards, and most assuredly not by some of the authors who write desktop publishing books these days. Yet it is not difficult to grasp, and can be explained in plain English, not the pseudo-scientific academese made fun of above, the use of which, in most cases I have observed, is a reliable indicator that the speaker doesn't know what he's talking about.

Profanity excepted (for I am from New Jersey) I see no reason to write much differently from the way I talk—and no reason to avoid having fun doing so. I am disinclined to flourish knowledge of mathematical concepts that have nothing to do with the bottom line of quality. I take some pleasure in exposing those who misuse color science, who hype worthless technologies, or who spout panaceas and nostrums based on ignorance.

As the above example suggests, the reader need not have a tremendous amount of knowledge, apart from being able to execute simple commands in the various programs under discussion, but I do assume an urgent desire to learn more about the why of things. By most definitions this is an expert text; but most of us are experts in certain areas and total novices in others. Therefore, I've tried to express almost everything in terms that even a non-graphic artist can understand.

This is not a style that appeals to everyone, but those who like it like it a *lot.* "Wow," a reader faxed Tom that first year. "Dan Margulis's article on color correction was spectacular. I've been reading computer graphics trades for as long as they have been around, and this was the first successful attempt to deal with this complicated topic that I've ever seen. Articles such as this which assume that the reader has a fairly high level of intelligence and expertise are a welcome relief. Please, give us more!"

Or: "It's happening again and again. The articles written by Mr. Margulis are just a joy. Like the last one about type-setting. His articles are on a level of their own in the business…Every time I read one of his articles I feel like I have gained permanently. The topics, the way they are written, and there's never a wasted word. He cares about what he writes. Maybe his articles should be compiled?"

Comments like that not only make authors very happy, they make book publishers offer them contracts. My *Professional Photoshop* (John Wiley & Sons, 1995), which is about color correction, drew heavily on material that first appeared in *Computer Artist.* (None of the columns that were the foundation of *Professional Photoshop* appear in this book.)

Unimpeded by the space limitations of a magazine, I have added many new graphics, upsized others, and in some cases replaced the ones originally used with better examples. I did some rewriting, restored cuts, and added information. Not as much as you might think, though. In an industry where a year is an eternity, the editorial content aged surprisingly well. That is by design: I deal in concepts, and rarely review specific products. Trapping principles will be just as valid ten years from now as they are today—and just as simple.

These selections range from quite complex (Column 7, on retouching and color correction using the LAB colorspace, which contains information available nowhere else) to rote learning (Column 4, a simpler LAB correction recipe) to completely nontechnical (Column 10, on what typifies typefaces designed this decade.)

And some columns are technically

easy and yet challenging to the expert. The Prologue was a lengthy article written for a special issue on color correction. In it, I tried to examine what makes human beings like certain renditions of color photos and not others. There are three versions each of several images, and I invited a group to determine which was best in each case. You can compare your own opinions to mine, or to the group's—nothing that involves the question of taste requires the evaluator to be an expert.

For those involved in the prepress industry, one can hardly imagine a more fundamental question. Millions of dollars are thrown away every year by companies who needlessly remake work that their clients might well like. But in spite of the fact that anybody capable of stating a preference between three versions of a picture can participate in such a discussion, it's never been written about before, as far as I know. Now, how stupid is that?

The Epilogue was the column that accompanied it, which expanded on the idea of what makes desirable color by inquiring what makes *professional* color. I think that these topics, with their mixture of science and subjectivity, form an appropriate set of bookends for this endeavor.

It's an honor to have been allowed to do a book on, for want of a better definition, general desktop publishing for the would-be expert; there isn't another such title available, to my knowledge. More than half of this book pertains to the proper reproduction of color, but it is neither a sequel to nor a replacement for

Professional Photoshop. Those who have read that book are familiar with some of my conventions and prejudices, which, in fairness, I should spell out here.

• Among my readers, the big growth group is professional photographers. And no wonder: the increase in usage of Photoshop by photographers is staggering. According to Adobe, in 1994 around 10 percent of Photoshop users identified themselves as expert photographers; only two years later, the figure was 25 percent. My own background, however, is prepress, not photography. Keep this in mind when you look at some of the corrections. In presenting color, a photographer tries to please the largest number of people. A prepress person tries to displease the fewest. Think about it.

• In showing curves, the convention is that left to right equals light to dark. Photoshop and other programs permit users to set it either way. If you are accustomed to the other way around, you'll have to keep that difference in mind. When I say, for example, "raise the midtone," in my terminology this will yield a darker, not a lighter, image.

• Most of the images in use here come from commercially available CDs of royalty-free photography. There is now a terrific selection of such disks available, but I also use it to avoid the charge of setting up straw men. When a correction is shown, the original image is just as it comes off the disk, without any sabotage, the same image the vendor expects you to pay good money for.

• The fact that certain maneuvers are explained using Photoshop terminology is a sop to Photoshop's commanding market share. It does not mean the techniques are not useful in other image-manipulation applications. None of the techniques here require the use of Photoshop 4, and for that matter very few require even Photoshop 3.

• Data, data everywhere, and not a thought to think! This should be the motto of my favorite patsies, the calibrationists, who make occasional appearances in these pages. For those unfamiliar with the term, calibrationism can roughly be defined as an overweening, blinding confidence in numbers, nostrums, and repeatability. Calibrationists tend to have just enough of an academic background to convince themselves that their theories are valid and should be implemented by the world at large, yet not enough to realize what constitutes building on scientific quicksand. Disciples come in many shades and strengths. In the most extreme incarnations, calibrationists would rather have predictable scans than good ones; rather have a good-looking histogram than a good-looking image; rather have how something looks aesthetically be decided by densitometer than by human observer; and, where there are several output devices, rather have equal color on all of them than acceptable color on any.

*   *   *

The columns are arranged in what I consider a logical order, as opposed to the order in which they appeared in the magazine. The columns that make up Part II, for example, present a cohesive general philosophy for color correction, in spite of the fact that they originally appeared over several years.

In each case, there is also a newly written Afterword, summarizing general developments since the column was written. Specific changes are generally cited in side notes to the text; I tried to retain the flavor of the columns by not incorporating confusing updates.

The question and answer sections at the end of many of the columns are all actual correspondence, which has been edited freely for space and understandability, as well as to eliminate profanity, gratuitous plugs, ghastly grammar, and excessive acronyms. Because so much of this correspondence is e-mail, which encourages give-and-take, I've set it up in dialog form. Some is from readers of *Professional Photoshop;* some also derives from threads where I participated in various on-line settings.

The topics in these Dialog Box sections range from very simple (why do they call it *unsharp* masking; should I buy a Mac, or a Wintel machine?) to alarmingly complex (5-color trapping, the ins and outs of UCA, proper flesh-tones for disparate ethnic groups). Column 3, on dot gain, was inspired start to finish by a message from a reader. At the end of it comes 20 pages more, all on how to make a proper conversion to CMYK in Photoshop.

*   *   *

The technical terms in use are those that I believed *Computer Artist* readers understand without further explanation. Given magazine space constraints, however, there would in any event be no room for lengthy definitions. Without that limitation here, a Jargon Watch follows each column except for Column 8, which is in absolutely unexceptionable English. The stuff in the Dialog Boxes, however, which can be a little more specialized, is not included.

To summarize: this book presents practical how-to on a number of graphic topics. There is an emphasis on color and how to manipulate it. As Column 9 indicates, I advocate using consensus software, meaning that used by the majority of professionals. The techniques discussed, however, are broadly applicable to any program. There is no requirement that you be an expert in Photoshop or any other application to benefit from the majority of the content.

This is neither a Windows book nor a Macintosh book. It does not show spiffy special effects. It does not have a "hot tip" on every page. No dorky-looking logos are in use. It is a graphic arts book for thinkers, people who are willing to read ten pages or more at one sitting. It is, as the title indicates, a pre-press resource, but it is not intended to be your only such resource.

If you have purchased this book because you think it is a sequel to my existing one on color correction, you will find more than enough hard-core technique here to justify the price of admission. Column 7, in particular, justifies the words with which I closed *Professional Photoshop*, almost exactly two years ago, and which apply with equal force to *Makeready*:

"Two years from now, I expect to be much better at color correction than I am today. If you are uncomfortable with some of the methods discussed here, don't worry. The basics can be acquired. Improvement will never stop."

The enthusiastic response of the past readers of these columns is what made this book possible. If you are one of them, my thanks. If you are a new reader, I hope you find the topics worth attention. In the frontier culture, common-sense solutions will always be at a premium, and there are several to be found here, I think.

Happy pioneering! ●

MAKEREADY

makeready Term, unique to the professional graphic arts, implying the step immediately before the final product, especially 1) in metal typography, the leveling-off of forms to get a more consistent impression during printing; 2) in film stripping, the creation and assembly of intermediate elements prior to burning composite final films; these intermediate elements are often referred to as *the makereadies;* 3) the process of preparing a press for printing, including washing the units, loading inks, and mounting and registering the plates.

Prologue

Hard Facts, Hard Choices in Color

Is what's best all a matter of taste, or can correcting color be reduced to rules? A professional jury considers the evidence, and renders a verdict.

his is a test.

Please find a place where lighting conditions are favorable. Have a look at images A, B, and C. Decide which one you consider to be the best, and which the worst, of the three. When you are done, turn the page and do the same for images D, E, and F.

Color correction is a slippery subject, because there is so little agreement on what is "correct." We all perceive color differently. When an image is complex, we all see different things in it and apply independent, individual judgment in deciding what's important.

This article will explore the truths and consequences of color correction. When we find truths, certain techniques will be unhesitatingly recommended. When there are pros and cons, as there usually are, we will try to give them a good airing.

Back to the test. You should have selected B and D as the best versions of the two images, and A and E as the worst. Such, at any rate, is *my* opinion. Unfortunately, that does not make it right. I am subject to at least as many vagaries, ficklenesses and personal prejudices as any other human. Why should you rely on what I say?

To the extent that it's my aesthetic judgment versus yours, you probably can't. Then again, if my opinions about the merits of these

3

images can be shown to be those shared by the overwhelming majority of professionals, you probably *should*.

At the prepress house in New York where I was working when I prepared to write this column, I empaneled a ten-person jury to give the final verdict on these two sets of images, plus several other sets that we will see later. The three versions of each were isolated and placed in standard viewing conditions with a white background. The jurors were not allowed to consult with one another, nor did they know my opinions, nor the purpose of the evaluation.

This was, incidentally, no slouch of a jury. Every member was a full-time color professional of many years experience: retouchers, scanner operators, color supervisors. All had excellent to outstanding color perception, as measured by the industry-standard Munsell test, and around half actually got perfect scores on it, which is rare. Therefore, one can consider this jury's findings quite authoritative.

Unanimity—and Dissent

With impressive monotony, each juror marched into the viewing booth and marched out affirming my judgment on the first set (and yours, too, I hope), giving ten votes to B as best and A as worst. The second set, alas, was another story.

Four panelists joined me in endorsing D. Each of these agreed with me, furthermore, that E was the worst of the lot. Unanimity fragmented, however, when three jurors chose F as best and two E. The tenth said he had no preference between D and E, but that F was the worst. Of the five who chose either E or F as the best, three said that D was the worst.

How can we make sense of *that* verdict? Why is there such striking unanimity among experts in the first case, where the versions are nearly identical, and such a ridiculous splitting of the vote in the second? Why does D provoke such strong feelings, both positive and negative, that only two put it in *second* place?

B won a unanimous decision because there was no reason at all to vote for either of its competitors. C was the original, a stock photo digitized using the Kodak Photo CD format. As commonly happens with such scans, the full range of possible colors was not forthcoming, and the image did not seem to be sharply focused. B is the routine professional response to these problems: an application of unsharp masking plus a curve-based adjustment of each color channel. A is just the opposite. It is an anti-correction: curves applied to C that intentionally limit color range and thus, contrast.

The two variations on C did nothing to overall color balance, nor did they stress one part of the image at the expense of another. Consequently, there is no area in which it could be argued that C is better than B; no area in which one might reasonably say that A is better than C. This across-the-board superiority is not found in DEF.

That set tests three methods of transforming a Photo CD image into CMYK. The differences in approach are moderately complex. Unlike the first set, therefore, this one's members have clear strengths and weaknesses. Those jurors who placed D last were critical of its left side. The boy's shirt is not blown out the way it is in E, but it doesn't have the detail of F. And even D's defenders found the boy's face too light, although it does have good contrast.

As against that, the girl's face in D seems much more realistic than in either of the other two. The boy's hair is also superior. And F has a green cast, which is probably why the girl's red ribbons seem strangely muted.

Our choice, therefore, depends not just on personal preference and taste but on how important we find each of these items to be and on who we expect our audience to be. If we have been led to believe that the girl's face is of paramount importance, we should probably vote for D. If this is a clothing catalog where we are selling the shirts the children are wearing, F is best. If we know that the person who will give the final OK to this image favors full, rich colors, we should stay away from D. If, as here, those judging the color are notoriously eagle-eyed, expect the green cast in F, modest though it is, to get a harsh reception.

Of course, in real life we would try to come up with an image that combined the strong points of all three. This is what color correction is about, and this is where we have to start thinking about tradeoffs. If we are working on F, for example, there are two major problems: the green cast and the girl's face. Eliminating the cast is unconditionally right; it will improve the image in the eyes of nearly every beholder, at no cost.

Attempting to liven up the girl's face, however, is likely to reshuffle the whole color balance of the picture, and it is unlikely that we will get a unanimous jury in favor of our changes. Fortunately, *we* get the deciding vote.

Compensation and Cheating

In attempting to reproduce a photograph by means of the offset printing process, we are fighting long odds. The original will have far more of a color range than a press can accommodate, so the printed product is apt to look flat and lacking in detail. Because of the lack of range, slight color casts will seem more pronounced, more offensive, than they would be in the original.

The art of color correction largely consists of countermeasures, which some might call cheating, against these deficiencies. If contrast is a problem, fine; we will make sure we maximize it in every image. That means having the largest range we can get away with, particularly as regards the most important parts of the image.

In DEF, there is a pure white, in the children's shirts, and a pure black, the girl's hair. It surely makes sense to make these as light and as dark as our process can handle while still showing detail. This will mean values of from 1 to 5 percent in the CMY inks for the white, and from 70 to 90 percent in all four colors for the black. The exact numbers will depend on the kind of printing we are doing, and on what paper.

In ABC, there are dark areas in the trees and light areas in the water, but these are hardly the dramatic blacks and whites of DEF.

The successful color technician pretends that they *are*. We find the darkest area in the trees, and set it to be exactly the same value as the girl's hair. If there is an area in the water that we can reasonably expect the viewer to evaluate as white, we will give it the same value as the children's shirts. A photographer can afford to have his ABC shot print flatter than his DEF. We cannot.

When, unlike our two examples so far, an image clearly has one object of prime importance, correction choices become considerably easier. In series GHJ, the pig is just such an object.

A pig wallowing in mud does not exactly present us with a lot of bright colors—certainly not with anything that the viewer will accept as white. Nevertheless, anybody who knows anything about color will attack this image in approximately the same way, although the final results will vary somewhat.

G is the original scan here, and we may take it to represent the flatness of the original photograph fairly accurately. The lightest areas in the mud are around 25 percent in all colors but black. You might think it makes sense for a relatively dark image like this one to have its values so concentrated at the dark end of our range. A more appropriate view, in my opinion, is that a quarter of our usable space is being thrown into the trough.

There is nothing much technically wrong with G. The pig, the mud, and the background appear to be of about the right color. The darkest area of the image, the inside of the near ear, is also fine. Improvement is certainly possible, though, as H and J, which were done in one of my color correction classes, demonstrate. These adjustments were made in Photoshop, but the technique would be the same regardless of what system was in use.

H is a sensibly conservative approach. The operator applied a set of curves that forced the lightest values down, although not to an extreme. Throughout the image, this pushed colors further apart from one another, resulting in a crisper and better-focused image. Notice how much better defined the pig's bristles are. You might take this to be more unsharp masking, but it is not: just better use of color space.

The operator in J took a bit more of a whole-hog approach, as it were. He made the lightest areas lighter still, but that does not account for a difference this large. Instead of adding contrast to the image as a whole, he targeted the pig, giving it more range at the expense of the rest of the picture.

You may certainly feel that the image is now too brilliant. Three members of my jury did, and voted instead for H as best hog of the litter. The other seven went for J, as do I.

The lessons of the ABC set were underlined by the jury's unanimous selection of G as worst. The swashbuckling techniques used in J may not be to everyone's taste, but where possible, a quiet extension of color range—which is the only difference between G and H—is almost always right, period.

Contrast on a Budget

Once there is a full range, however, further improvement is possible by better allocation. Contrast is much like a paycheck. There is only so much there. The bank will not give us an extra ten percent just because we are graphic artists. We can, however, compensate. If, depressed by the weather, we decide we need an island vacation, we can set aside money for it, but it may require certain economies: spaghetti at home instead of a restaurant dinner, foregoing that latest CD-ROM game, etc.

In short, being thinking individuals, we are capable of distinguishing what is important in life, and of making sacrifices in less significant areas. That is what the operator did in J. He looked at his contrast budget and found some pork in it. Here is how he trimmed the fat.

In H, the pig got more contrast, but this was incidental, because the entire image had its range increased. In J, a deliberate decision was made to allocate contrast to the pig and not elsewhere.

This process starts with an analysis of the minimum and maximum color values. In G, the pig weighed in at around 30 percent in all colors except black, magenta being heaviest. There was a range of almost 50 points in the magenta, 30 in the yellow, and 15 in the cyan. The operator so finagled J that these values became 80 in the magenta, 60 in the yellow, and 50 in the cyan. He achieved this in a most swinish fashion, by stealing contrast from less important parts of the picture.

He found the minimum values for the pig in each color and forced them lower; he found the highest values and forced them even higher. This maximized variation in the pig, at a certain cost. Everything that was either lighter or darker than the pig was hurt. For example, he forced values of 40 percent cyan up to 60. Saying for the moment that 80 percent is the maximum acceptable value, his action compressed anything that was formerly 40 to 80 percent cyan into half the space. Naturally, such objects, if there are any, must lose contrast, and similar losses can be expected in the dark areas of the other colors. If you don't believe this, look in the dark part of the pig's near ear. H has more contrast than J there, because in J, the operator sacrificed it in the interest of putting it in the pig.

Note that these tactics resulted in some color variation, which the operator was willing to accept. He pushed the lighter magentas down further than the other colors. Since magenta makes greens look muddy, the background became much brighter.

He was not, however, able to increase the heaviest magentas in the pig as much as the other two colors, since those magentas were already near maximum. This meant proportionally heavier increases in both yellow and cyan, especially yellow. So the pig became more orange, less pink.

This technique of selective contrast enhancement is one of the most important tools the professional has. A startling amount of detail can be pulled out in this way, and not always for the better. K and L are competing corrections of part of a familiar Kodak image, and there is the question of whether L goes too far. It is more realistic, for sure: look at the shape of the nose, for example.

Unfortunately, in fashion shots like this, "flawless" skin is currently in vogue. The feminine ideal is not supposed to be encumbered with such disgusting imperfections as pores, not to mention acne scars, obvious facial powder, or a spot under the right eye where the makeup artist missed with the eye pencil. L is certainly more lifelike, but some art directors might not accept it.

Older skin looks especially bad when subjected to this kind of treatment. When Franklin Roosevelt was President, there was an unwritten agreement among news organizations never to print any photograph that showed him in a wheelchair, or otherwise alluded to his disability. When Ronald Reagan was President, something similar occurred. Retouchers would *not* put this kind of contrast into pictures of him, not wishing to make his weathered face look more aged than it was.

Not that the technique was unknown. Less popular figures than Mr. Reagan did not fare as well. One newsmagazine managed a bloodcurdling cover of Leona Helmsley by ratcheting up the contrast and sharpening. Thanks to such creative color work, the Queen of Mean appeared with an alcoholic's bloodshot eyes, a ruined complexion, and jowls and wrinkles that would have done honor to a bulldog.

When Choices Are Possible

So far, we have encountered a few absolutes in color correction, and several cases where tastes vary. We will now consider pictures that may be treated differently in different contexts.

If L is a lipstick ad, for example, we would have to go for an exact color match. If the context is something else, it is unlikely that anyone will care if there is a small variation in lip color.

GHJ has only one object of any importance, so it is hard to come up with an alternative to trying to improve the pig. ABC, a nature scene, also seems unambiguous, unless for some reason we want to make the greenery less attractive and more forbidding. In that case, we'd boost magenta so that the greens would not be as clean.

DEF has distinct objects of interest in the two children. As the two faces have different color ranges, it would be possible to accentuate one at the expense of the other. Unless it is a movie ad in which one of the children is a great star and the other is not, it is hard to think of a reason for doing so.

MNO is a much better example. There are three major objects of interest: the walls, the greenery, and the sky. The sky and the grass have just about the same amount of cyan, so it is likely that any improvement of one will also help the other. The walls, though, are lighter than either. If we elect to put extra contrast in the walls, we will hurt the rest of the picture, and vice versa.

M is the original image. What we do with it will now depend on how we rate the importance of these three elements. This is the kind of decision that comes up a lot.

N and O may be considered to be the extremes. N assumes that the priority is to accentuate the walls and that everything else is unimportant. O goes for good grass and sky at the expense of the walls. Again: short of selecting and correcting each half individually, which rarely looks natural, there is only so much contrast that we can put in this image. Most of it can go to the walls, most to the environment, or it can be divvied up.

The method used to achieve each effect is the same as in GHJ. We find the minimum and maximum values for each item of interest, and then try to engineer in a greater range.

In M, the values in the wall range from 2 to 30 percent in all three colors, with traces of black. In the sky, cyan ranges from 15 in the clouds to 70 at the top, and magenta is about half that. There is almost no yellow or black. In the grass, yellow is near maximum (75 percent and higher); cyan goes from 50 to 70, and magenta from 15 to 25, with slight amounts of black.

If the idea is to produce N, therefore, we increase the quartertone value in all colors. This is the only way of getting more range into the walls, since the lightest areas are at minimum already. The downside of this move is that the sky becomes heavier, and the grass loses detail, becoming almost a green carpet.

If we are instead concentrating on the grass, we still increase the quartertone in both magenta and black, since that will give them more range in the green; but we drop the yellow three-quartertone to make a longer transition to max-

imum yellow. We drop the cyan highlight, to get whiter clouds. For better grass, we drop the cyan midtone, but increase the cyan three-quartertone.

P

Q

Thus, what used to be a range of 50 to 75 percent cyan may become, say, 40 to 80 percent.

Of course, the moves in cyan and yellow hurt contrast in the lighter ranges of these colors, which is why the walls in O are so tepid. But if good grass and sky are what we want, look how much better O is than N.

It may seem that this is another one of those sets with no right answer, where one's personal views have to be the deciding factor. This is not quite accurate. True, I don't know where on the continuum between N and O the best treatment of this image lies, but there is at least one right answer. Increasing the magenta quartertone is certainly correct, since it improves *both* the walls and the background. Even if you have decided that the overall feeling and balance of M doesn't need adjustment, this move in the magenta will help.

The Bright Blue Problem

The bane of the professional color technician's existence is the art director who, parrot-like, repeats the phrase "Match the art," as though such a thing were possible.

On the printed page, as compared to a photograph, there is such a vastly smaller range of colors and image data that certain details are sure to be suppressed, and the picture is apt to look out of focus to boot.

More than that, the colors we must work with on press are weirdly misshapen. We can get a pretty good red and a fair green, but we're in big trouble when a rich blue is needed. The cyan inks we have to work with are quite inferior. To ask us to "match the art" when we have such a grievous inability to print blue is approximately as reasonable as asking us to match a color if we are printing black and white.

Color theory says that blue is made by

equal amounts of magenta or cyan ink. If you open QuarkXPress and look at the default color "Blue," you will see the glorious azure that 100C100M really ought to be. Regrettably, you have a better chance of seeing Quark ported to CP/M than of seeing that particular blue reproduced with process inks. In color-scientist heaven, 100C100M is blue. In our vale of mortal sorrows, however, it is purple.

This deplorable fact means that we will have to make some decisions whenever we have to handle pictures that contain bright blues. For example, series PQRS features a participant in New York City's annual parade saluting the culture of the Caribbean. Her costume includes (in the original photo, that is) some extravagant feathers of a brilliant blue that we have exactly zero chance of matching on press. The question is, what now?

There are at least four plausible solutions for this problem, and each image illustrates one of them.

P. What problem? If we ignore it, the feathers will go purple. So what? The viewers of the eventual printed piece will have no idea what the original was like. They may think purple looks nice!

Q. Match the blue or go down trying. If there is something significant about the color, let's say it is found in a national flag, there will be no choice but to make the feathers blue. Unfortunately, by cutting back magenta and/or adding black, the color will be more subdued, if more accurate.

R. We need detail in the feathers. With good control of the yellow plate and some unsharp masking tricks, much better definition within the feathers can be had.

S. The important feature of the feathers is not so much their color as their brilliance. The green trees and blue uniforms in

the background compete for the viewer's attention. If we hammer these, the blue we are interested in will seem brighter in comparison. We will leave alone the orange feathers on the woman in the left of the background, since orange sets off blue nicely.

Sabotage in a Good Cause

It may seem the antithesis of color correction to sabotage a portion of the image, which is what was done in S, but sabotage is an important part of the professional arsenal. We'll see it again in the TUW series. Which do you think is the best? The worst? How do you think the professional jury voted?

As you may have guessed, T is the raw image here, and U and W are two very different attempts to correct it.

Personally, I was flabbergasted that fully half of the jury voted for U as the best. To me, and to the other five jurors, W is a clear choice. The woman first, and the water in the background second, are the principal objects of interest. They stand out far better in W than in U. No wonder: the artist sabotaged everything else. The rocks in the background have been blurred and desaturated. Meanwhile, skillful application of curves have put far more life into skin and bathing suit than was the case in T.

Some of those same concepts were at work in U. There, however, the artist elected not to reduce or eliminate the yellow cast that pervades this image, though he did knock out the offensive bright yellow areas in the woman's neck and shoulder. He also decided not to

T

U

W

indulge in the ambitious move of dulling the background.

The jury fragmented over which was best, but its unanimous selection of T as the worst of the three shows how well U succeeds in adding snap to the darker areas of the image. Once again, the two artists who did this had different conceptions of where they should go, and of what fleshtones should be. The relatively golden flesh in U is perhaps more sensible than the pink in W, which two jurors said suggested that the model would shortly be spending time in the hospital, recovering from sun poisoning.

What Is Taste, What Is Truth

We have hardly exhausted the basic repertory of color correction here (one could write a book about those) but the fundamental concepts should be clear. Expert interpretations of individual images, though, are often counter-productive. If I tell you that W is better than U, yet it looks to you like it should be the other way around, you are no doubt going to be confused and think that color correction must be an incredibly deep field.

To some extent, an individual's taste can be predicted based on past preferences. Recall that four individuals agreed with me that D was the best of the DEF series, and a fifth said it was tied for best. The six of us were the same six, *the only six*, who thought that W was the best of TUW. The odds against this being a coincidence are pretty large. Although we voted completely independently and without consultation, we are clearly a bloc. If you analyze what we voted for

here, you can pretty well guess what we would like in other circumstances, and, if we happen to be your clients, you can modify your taste to suit ours.

Variances of taste only go so far. Certain values are accepted universally. Maximizing color range appeals to virtually every viewer, as shown by the jury's unanimous rejection of images A, G, and T. To see how powerful a factor contrast is, go back to the first set. You doubtless agree that B is best, but what about a comparison between A and C? The differences are very subtle (indeed, two jurors said they at first thought that A and C were the same image) and yet all ten wound up voting the same way, that C was better.

The modest adjustments made to create B, H, and U, therefore, may be considered *corrections* in the literal sense of the word, in that no one can dispute that they make the image better. J and W incorporate these corrections, which is why nobody voted them worst, but the overall thrust in both is not so much correction but speculation. The artists made major changes in the pictures on the theory that this would make it more attractive. I think they both succeeded. You may disagree.

In image enhancement, we need to learn to distinguish between taste and truth. Range adjustment can be emphatically the right thing to do. The artist will frequently elect to embark on something considerably more ambitious. Such adventures can be rewarding—as long as we remember that they are adventures, not requirements, and that not every adventure is to everyone's taste. ●

Dialog Box

I've recently been given the assignment of producing 4-color seps at a commercial printing company. Our graphics department has been trying, unsuccessfully, to do color correction for a couple of years now—with no prior training—and the task has been given to me. My background is in prepress (stripping and camera), and I have been producing quality black and white halftones on a scanner for some time now (by reading highlight and shadow percentages and adjusting using Levels in Photoshop). I learned not to believe the monitor a long time ago. After doing some preliminary research, I found many people touting your book.

How and why deep blues go purple during the conversion to CMYK

I'm with you 100 percent on your theory "forget the monitor, use dot percentage readings and adjust accordingly." Our graphics department has tried monitor guessing and it just doesn't work. By the way, I have basically no color sep experience.

So anyway, here I am in Photoshop following your procedures: Photo of two college tennis players (in foreground) with navy blue windbreakers and white skirts.

This is the classic CMYK problem. Everybody has trouble with this picture, not just you.

Adjust the highlight to 5C2M2Y—it's looking better. Adjust the shadow to 80C70M70Y70K—better yet. Adjust fleshtones—OK. The navy blue windbreakers read roughly 90C89M30Y5K. Since I'm totally new to color I'm pretty much clueless as to how much cyan when mixed with magenta will make navy blue. And also I have to guess how much yellow and black, if any, should be in the mix. So I look up the mixture in the Pantone colors and find that 100 percent cyan and a percentage of black and no yellow give me dark blue more or less.

Don't use the Pantone mixes. They are based on what might be called maximum GCR, meaning that, just as in this case, the unwanted color (yellow) is always zeroed out in favor of more black. If you are making a spot color that is a perfectly valid way of doing it, but if you are trying to apply that color in the middle of a photograph, you are asking for trouble. Right now your yellow is at 30 percent, which is about what I would expect for navy blue, if your separation method is at all normal. If you try to zero out the yellow, you may be able to get the kind of blue you want but you will find that the rest of your image suddenly has more problems than the California system of justice.

I pull a proof and it's not too bad, but the blue jackets are now purple.

Welcome to the infuriating, lopsided world of CMYK.

So now I have to go back and do what? Decrease the magenta, increase the yellow, add black…

Any of these might be correct, depending on circumstances.

…add cyan?

That would be choice number one, but it will be awfully difficult if you are near 100 percent already.

This is my dilemma: Don't I need to have a strong understanding of color mixes and color theory before I can apply your percentage theory to color images? Are you oversimplifying or am I just missing the boat? I thought I was semi-intelligent but maybe I am just an ape. This problem of purple blues has been consistent on a number of preliminary scans—for some reason the scanner is putting too much magenta into the dark blues.

It is not the scanner, it is CMYK itself. Cyan ink is terrible. This is why, to make a neutral color, you need extra cyan, when one would think that equal amounts of CMY would be correct. But the big problem is deep blues. If all inks were perfect, adding equal amounts of yellow and magenta would make red. It does. Adding equal amounts of yellow and cyan would make green. It does. Adding equal amounts of magenta and cyan would make blue. No way. The magenta overpowers and makes a purple where color theory wants a blue. This is a fact of life, and what we do about it really depends on the image. If we are talking about a light blue, we can add more cyan. But in a heavy blue like the one you have, cyan will be near maximum already. That's out, so here are the remaining options:

1. Ignore the problem: This is the correct decision most of the time. Most images don't have big globs of deep blue. Those that do, many times we are willing to just let the sweaters or whatever go purple.

2. We need a blue but not a rich one: in this case we subtract magenta and add black. This pushes us toward navy. There is no way of getting a bright blue in CMYK in the same sense that we can get a bright red.

3. Blueness is critical: so we drop magenta and get something that is clearly blue, but somewhat lighter than we would really like.

4. Brilliance is critical: so in addition to the approach in either #2 or #3 we also knock down the intensity of any greens and purples in the image that may be competing with our blue.

All of these approaches have obvious flaws, and it is up to us to decide which is the least evil for the particular picture. In the case you are talking about probably #2 is best, although #1 is certainly reasonable unless the windbreakers are actually in the school colors.

We had a professional prepress house do a sep of the same scan and I pulled a contract proof of that also and then compared it to my on-screen channels in Photoshop. Although I knew there would be a quality difference—wow, WHAT a difference!

They can and apparently did choose some approach other than #1 above. Their scanner can be adjusted to each individual image.

Their magenta plate was totally detailed and much lighter. By playing with my magenta channel there is no way I could come close to matching theirs without maybe blending channels, and I'm not quite ready for that.

Yet.

The main quality advantage that drum scanners have over desktop models is that they capture more detail in the shadows. As far as the magenta plate is concerned, that is a three-quartertone to shadow, so one would expect to see a better-looking magenta from off the drum scanner than from yours. Keep in mind, though, that in defining contrast in a deep blue, yellow and black are the important colors, not magenta.

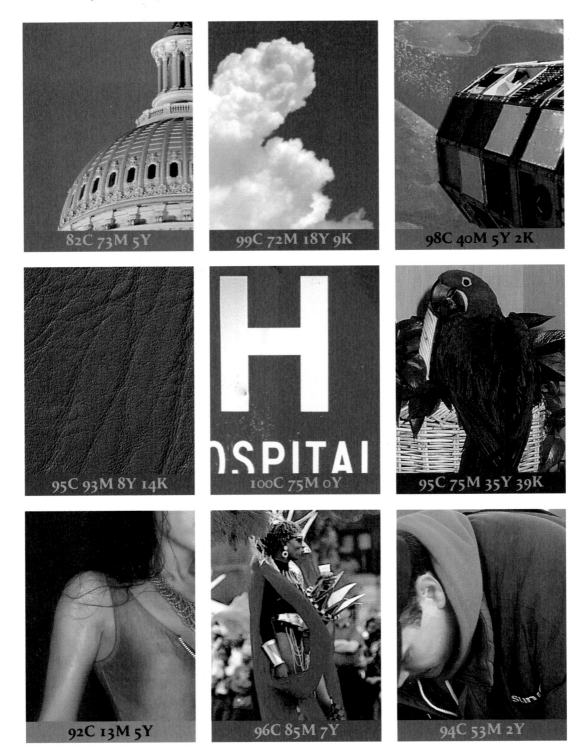

82C 73M 5Y

99C 72M 18Y 9K

98C 40M 5Y 2K

95C 93M 8Y 14K

100C 75M 0Y

95C 75M 35Y 39K

92C 13M 5Y

96C 85M 7Y

94C 53M 2Y

Do you think a desktop scanner can do decent seps...

Yes, understanding that a much more expensive scanner would be somewhat better.

...and why do you think it is seeing so much red in the dark blue parts of the images?

For the reasons discussed above, I think it is seeing the proper amount of magenta, but is being done in by the limitations of CMYK.

Do you think I can correct this at prescan and how would you solve this problem?

Prescan correction is a function of the software you are using so I can't tell you whether there is anything you can do at the time of the scan. Taking a worst case scenario (you can't correct on the scan, and the magenta plate lacks detail because your scanner is poor in the shadow areas, and you are not content with Plan 1 above) then I would consider the following:

1. Make a copy of the image and convert the copy to LAB.

2. Working on the original image, use Select: Color Range to make a soft-edged selection of the blue area.

3. Duplicate this selection into the L channel of your LAB copy.

4. This L channel will have more detail than the magenta channel of your CMYK document. It will also be lighter, but how much lighter we don't know. So, with the blue selected, copy the selected portion of the L channel to the clipboard.

5. Paste the clipboard contents into the selected area of the magenta channel of the CMYK document. Do not deselect once done.

6. Open the Layers palette, and adjust the opacity setting until you think you have a good result. Probably, you'll want something like a 50–50 split between the L and the magenta. This will make your magenta channel lighter, but will also give it much more detail.

Is it necessary for me to invest in a color process book so I know what mixtures give me certain colors? Is this the missing link?

Figure P.1. *In CMYK, deep blues can become purples quite easily, since magenta ink overpowers cyan. Opposite, some ways of handling the problem. In each case, an average value of the blue is shown below the image.*

Not in my opinion.

Is it beneficial to do any correcting in RGB?

RGB and CMYK are similar. If you are going to limit yourself to the by-the-numbers techniques of setting highlight and shadow, one will work about as well as the other. For more complicated stuff, CMYK is definitely better. Personally, therefore, I don't use RGB because CMYK can do everything RGB can and more. I do, however, use LAB as a correction colorspace, because, being entirely different in concept, it does have certain advantages in certain cases.

Am I expecting results in too short a time? I've done about six seps—two were good.

You say you haven't done color before. Sounds like you're doing fine. What do you want, perfection? It won't matter how many years you do this--you'll still be learning, just like I am. ●

Is there any future in this field? Should a student get involved?

I am a student, and am interested in getting more information about some things you mentioned as you talked about your jury.

You mention "color perception, as measured by the industry-standard Munsell test." Do you have any more information on this test? I am particularly interested in possibly taking it myself.

To take it yourself, you would probably have to go to your nearest prepress supplier, most of whom will own a copy. You can't take it at home, since the test has to be taken in a controlled viewing environment such as a graphic arts lighting booth.

The test is in four parts. In each, one is given 20 pegs of closely similar pastel colors. The first set runs from yellowish-pink to aqua, the second from aqua to light blue, and so forth. You have to arrange the pegs in proper order, from pinkest to greenest or whatever. Scoring relates to the number of mistakes you make, thus zero is a perfect score. Each mistake costs at least four points, possibly more depending upon how bad it is. The population as a whole has an average score of just over 30. For graphic arts professionals, a score of 20 or below is highly desirable, and all the people on my jury tested in this range. [Information on where to obtain the Munsell test is in the Notes and Credits section to this book.]

You mention that "every member was a full-time color professional." I have not declared a major yet, and am exploring different fields. I realize it's a broad area but could you expand on who full-time color professionals are?

To me, a color professional is one who 1) spends most of his or her time involved in one way or another in the preparation, dissemination, or other handling of color photography for print or other high-quality application; 2) works in an environment that permits a major impact on the quality of the final product; and 3) does this for a living.

The jury mentioned in the article consisted of retouchers, scanner operators, personnel whose job was to approve the appearance of color, persons whose job was as a liaison to clients for color work, etc. It could also reasonably have included pressmen, photographers, vendors, and the like.

What are the common themes in their background, fields of study, and types of work they do?

In terms of background, they had almost nothing in common. In terms of the type of work, that used to be the case also, but now the industry is becoming less specialized and we are heading for a time when all these people are capable of manipulating color on the computer.

Following that, and even more importantly, how do you see the future of this field as technology advances? What jobs have a limited future and which ones do you see opening up?

I believe that the field will grow because the reproduction of color is getting cheaper and cheaper. Things are somewhat unsettled now because the work is migrating to in-house settings rather than to traditional color separation houses. Any individual with no computer/Photoshop capability has no future. Best positioned of all will be people who are skilled at correcting images. More and more, we are moving to a time when instead of using chromes (professionally shot color film) as the basis for the final product, we will be using a digital file that comes from who knows where, in who knows what colorspace, based on photography of who knows how much technical merit. At least when we get a chrome, we can usually tell very quickly if it is any good. With a digital file of unknown origin, this is not true; a careful on-screen inspection is needed. A skilled operator can get very good results out of what looks like very bad data.

Could you describe what exactly a "computer artist" is?

Your guess at the exact meaning of that nebulous term would be as good as mine, but it sure is a fun profession! ●

PART I

The Curse of Trying Too Hard

*and other ways that people who
should know better go astray*

Trapping and the Split Infinitive
Trapping and the Split Infinitive
Trapping and the Split Infinitive
Trapping and the Split Infinitive

Trapping and the Split Infinitive
Trapping and the Split Infinitive
Trapping and the Split Infinitive
Trapping and the Split Infinitive

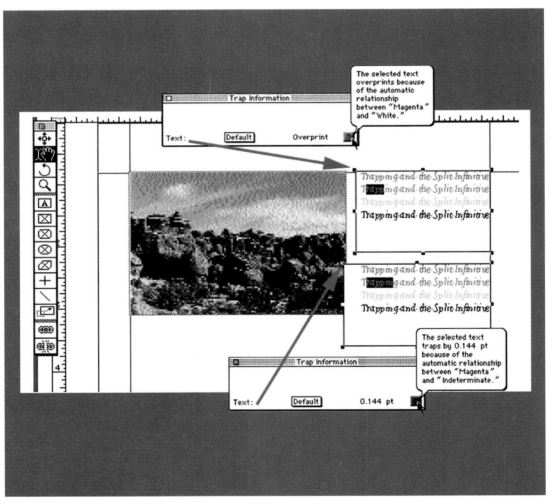

1

Trapping and the Split Infinitive

Proficient graphic artists know when to build in overlap where contrasting colors intersect. Really proficient graphic artists know when it isn't necessary.

ome years ago, my very first article for *Computer Artist,* a discussion of trapping, likened trap to a hyphen. Nobody likes hyphens, I said then; they cause end-of-line hesitations and make text less readable, but doing without them would result in consequences even worse.

That was before desktop publishers began to obsess on trap, and to imagine it some kind of mystic solution to all graphic problems. The resultant misinformation and printing disasters clearly necessitate a better simile today, and I have found one.

Trap is like a split infinitive: an overrated fine point, much fussed over by purists, capable of striking the fear of seeming ignorant into the hearts of the misunderstanding majority.

In reading an essay by the great authority on grammar and usage, H.W. Fowler, I was struck by the exactness of the parallel. Substitute *trap* for *split infinitive*, and save me the trouble of paraphrasing.

"The English-speaking world," he wrote, "may be divided into (1) those who neither know nor care what a split infinitive is; (2) those

Figure 1.1. *Automated trapping can have a sting. The first set of four lines is identical to the second in terms of proximity to the photograph, so why does QuarkXPress fatten up the second four with an ugly attempt to trap? Answer, below, a slightly misplaced text box. A tiny overlap between text and picture boxes is enough to persuade QXP that the background is "Indeterminate." By default, no doubt programmed in by someone who should have read this column, the program causes the colored type to spread.*

27

who do not know, but care very much; (3) those who know & condemn; (4) those who know & approve; & (5) those who know & distinguish."

A Happy Folk, To Be Envied

Although readers of this magazine may be presumed to have more of an interest in trap than does the graphic arts community at large, overall Fowler is right again: "Those who neither know nor care are the vast majority, & are a happy folk, to be envied by most of the minority classes."

Indeed, despite all the palaver about how mastery of trap is the distinguishing mark of the professional, there is a case to be made for neither knowing nor caring what it is. If you are determined to ignore trap, here is all you need to know to be able to defend your decision:

- Trap is a means of disguising problems of press registration, but in real life, most jobs do not have such problems.
- If your job is nonetheless misregistered, knowledgeable observers will see the misregistration easily whether you employ trap or not. On the other hand, a layperson may very well ignore the ugly white lines that expose a failure to trap. So, exactly who benefits here?
- The page layout programs that most professionals use take care of most simple trapping situations by default, without the operator knowing or caring what is going on.
- As discussed below, trap merely substitutes one kind of defect for another. Often enough, that kind of trade doesn't help much.

The Deliberate Defect

Before opening fire on those who do not know what it is, but who care very much, I ask your patience while we define trap and briefly discuss when it should be used.

Trap is the willful introduction of a defect into a job, as an insurance policy against the possibility that an even worse kind of defect may occur.

In printing, each ink is laid down separately, each by a different press unit. At press speeds, it is quite difficult to keep the inks perfectly aligned with respect to one another, although good operators can keep the misregistration down to a twentieth of a millimeter or so.

Figure 1.2. Spreads, shrinks, and other trapping options (highly exaggerated) aimed at avoiding the white line in the "T."

Figure 1.3. *Trap should be subtle enough not to call attention to itself. Here, the same techniques shown in the last three letters of Figure 1.2 are in use, but using normal trapping widths for the overlaps.*

When the design of a job calls for two colors that don't have much in common to touch each other, such misregistration can be very offensive. If a cyan object is butting something magenta, and they have no undercolor in common, then if the plates are misaligned the objects will miss.

The result is shown in Figure 1.2. In the T, the cyan plate is deliberately misregistered, causing an unsightly white line on one side, and a less noticeable dark one on the other.

If we are afraid that something like this will occur on press (and we should be) there is an elegant solution. If we make the cyan T slightly larger than the hole in the magenta background, there should be an area of overlap everywhere. Even if the job is misregistered there will be enough safety margin that the white line will not appear.

That is a nifty dodge, a skillful way of eliminating a bad problem in favor of a much smaller one—in an isolated case. It is not an excuse for prostrating oneself before the altar of trap. Pure cyan and pure magenta don't hit each other that often. Before deciding that trap is needed, ask yourself what defect you are trying to insure yourself against. Then ask if doing so is really worth building in a different defect. It will be only if one of the potential defects is far worse than the other, as it was in the T.

The R is defined as 70C60M25Y. As the background is solid magenta, a white line is impossible: there is at least 60 percent magenta everywhere. The worst possible case, obviously, would be a line of 60M falling between the blue foreground and the magenta background. Such a prospect does not seem sufficiently fearsome to me to make matters worse by trapping.

The A is even clearer. It is now 100C100M. There is no hole in the magenta plate at all. One of the plates could be a quarter of a mile out of register for all we care. Wherever the cyan ink falls on the background, there we will get a perfect A, no white lines, no dark lines, no problem, unless, of course, we are using some kind of automated trapping program that decides to take action against this phantom foe.

The two Ps are prepared once with trap, once without. Which looks better? This is a challenge for the printer of this book. Will the dreaded white line appear?

The final three letters of Figure 1.2 show, in exaggerated form, our three trapping options; in Figure 1.3 they are shown with the slight trap (.2 point in this case) we would normally use.

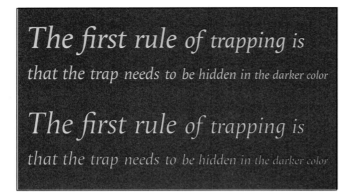

The first rule of trapping is

that the trap needs to be hidden in the darker color

The first rule of trapping is

that the trap needs to be hidden in the darker color

Figure 1.4. *One book on QuarkXPress, using purple and yellow as its example colors, gets fouled up and hides the trap in the lighter of the two colors, rather than the darker. Here, an illustration of why that approach is disastrously wrong. At top above and at left below, the overlap is properly put into the purple; at bottom above and right below, it goes, as this author would have it, into the yellow.*

This is in addition to the two obvious alternatives: no trap at all (a *knockout*) or the brute-force method of ignoring the background and printing the foreground color right on top of it (an *overprint*, generally used when the foreground color is black or something else very dark.)

The I shows a *spread*. That is, the letter expands so that the overlap is in the background. This is the correct approach when, as here, the background is darker than the letter. We'd like to hide the overlap, so we conceal it in the darker of the two colors.

The N is a *shrink* (or choke); the hole in the background gets smaller as the letter stays the same. This should be used when the background is the lighter of the two colors, but it is wrong here.

Traditionally, trapping was done in film by strippers, and the options were limited to the above two. The electronic age has given us some others, one of which is shown in G. The trap is divided between the two objects. This can help if neither is much darker than the other. Also, the colors are toned down in the overlap area, making the trapping line seem less obtrusive.

The sad truth is that around half of all professional strippers do not understand when to trap. Considering the amount of verbiage wasted on trapping nowadays, one might think electronic artists would do better. Not so. To verify the level of knowledge on the subject, I selected at random three of the many general books on QuarkXPress, which has a much-ballyhooed automated trapping feature. I reasoned that, in view of all the fuss, the authors would have to try to explain trap, but that, in doing so, they might betray some white holes, as it were, in their own experience.

The Naked Emperors

If you are a novice QXP user, and expect to learn from a book what this trapping stuff is all about, here is what's in store for you.

Book X, of the randomly chosen three, briefly discusses the arguments for trapping. There follows a color section of several pages, showing how trapping allegedly works, using purple and yellow as the two colors, which, since they have nothing in common, are just as good a choice as magenta and cyan.

All of the example traps printed in this book are backwards. Everything that spread should have shrunk, and vice versa. Instead of hiding his traps in the purple, the author "hid" them in the yellow, as in Figure 1.4. This is an example of the cure being worse than the disease. No trap at all would have been better, much better, than putting the overlap in the yellow.

Book Y makes more sense. We're back to magenta and cyan; the reader is invited to create a large magenta headline on a cyan background. The author then explains that, as cyan is the lighter of the two colors, QXP will shrink, rather than spread, the type.

That is certainly what we would *like* it to do, but as QXP is unable to shrink type (it can shrink other objects) it would treat magenta on cyan exactly as it would cyan on magenta: it would, incorrectly, spread the trap equally between them. The author should have advised readers to make the headline in an illustration program, where one can assign an overprinting cyan stroke to the magenta text. Import such a headline into the page-layout program, and the problem goes away.

Figure 1.5. Another QuarkXPress book suggests that trapping is necessary if 0C20M100Y5K meets 30C50M90Y. The graphic below, showing every way that combination can misregister, suggests that the authors should read their Fowler.

Book Z, tired of magenta-cyan and yellow-purple examples, gives us something tricky: a 0C20M100Y5K foreground object against a background of 30C50M90Y.

Such complexity is not easy on the readers. With all four inks in play, QXP does some fancy footwork and comes up with some, shall we say, interesting solutions. The authors try manfully to explain, then give up, saying, "If you don't understand this, read the last few paragraphs over several times. If you still don't understand it, then give up and believe us when we tell you that it's a really good thing."

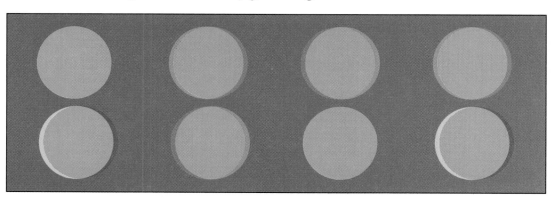

Personally, I could read those paragraphs several *hundred* times before understanding why trapping these two colors is a good thing. Think about it. The lightest color that can possibly appear is 20M90Y. Ergo, nothing terrible can happen, trap or no. An artificial overlap is a Maginot Line erected against a pacific and weaponless enemy.

Figure 1.5 shows why: although misregistration always results in two separate defects, trap will not be a palliative unless one of the defects is far worse than the other. There are seven different ways that this combination can misregister, but none of them meet this test.

> **A**lthough misregistration always results in two separate defects, trap will not be a palliative unless one of the defects is far worse than the other.

Rather than the paragraph quoted above, the authors might have considered the following substitute, from Fowler.

"Those who do not know but do care, who would as soon be caught putting their knives in their mouths as splitting an infinitive, but have hazy notions of what constitutes that deplorable breach of etiquette...betray by their practice that their aversion to the split infinitive springs not from instinctive good taste, but from tame acceptance of the misinterpreted opinion of others; for they will subject their sentences to the queerest distortions, all to escape imaginary split infinitives."

To Know and Approve...

Such is the public appetite for trapping "solutions" that all five of the major DTP programs (QXP, PageMaker, Illustrator, Free-Hand, and Photoshop) now have automated methods. Left to their own devices, all except Photoshop overtrap considerably, yet all have their uses.

Until recently, art generated in one of the illustration programs had to be trapped manually, using strokes on objects. That is still a good way if, unlike the authors cited above, you know what you're doing, since it avoids pointless traps and gives greater control. Automatic trapping filters do, however, make it easier when one object abuts several different backgrounds.

Such multiple backgrounds pose a particular problem for QXP and PageMaker. If one background is darker and one lighter than the foreground, both programs give up, but QXP gives up in a ridiculous way, by spreading the foreground object. Worse,

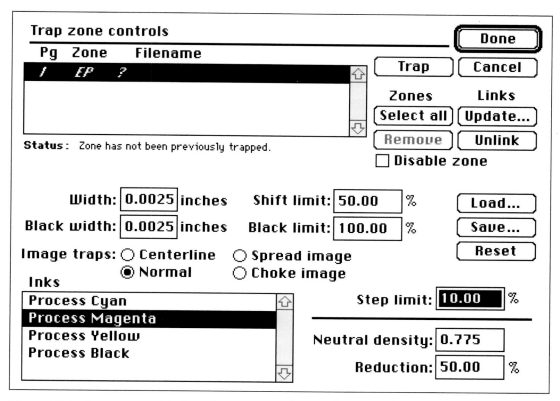

Trap zone controls

Pg	Zone	Filename
1	*EP*	*?*

Status: Zone has not been previously trapped.

Done

Trap　Cancel

Zones　Links
Select all　Update...
Remove　Unlink
☐ Disable zone

Width: 0.0025 inches　Shift limit: 50.00 %
Black width: 0.0025 inches　Black limit: 100.00 %

Load...
Save...
Reset

Image traps: ○ Centerline　○ Spread image
⊙ Normal　○ Choke image

Inks
Process Cyan
Process Magenta
Process Yellow
Process Black

Step limit: **10.00** %

Neutral density: 0.775
Reduction: 50.00 %

Figure 1.6. Dedicated trapping programs, such as Luminous Corp.'s TrapWise (above) cater to most trapping possibilities, but are compute-intensive and cost thousands of dollars apiece.

considering the amount of artwork we need to place, the presence of any graphic behind a QXP object will provoke a spread.

Suppose we want a line of type in some color or another and that we set it in a text box with no background. If we are precise, nothing will go wrong, because QXP ignores white backgrounds. But let the text box drift a little, so that a point or two of it inadvertently overlaps a picture box, as shown in Figure 1.1, and prepare to be punished. Although the background is still white, QXP doesn't know it. It calls it "indeterminate," and spreads the type to compensate. Which is, incidentally, usually wrong. If the type actually were to knock out of the image in Figure 1.1 the yellow type should probably spread to the extent that it intersects the blue sky, but the others should not, and even the yellow is an exceptional case. An intelligent user can and should turn this absurd default feature off.

Three expensive, compute-intensive standalone trapping applications, aimed at service bureaus and other volume users, also have a presence. Luminous Corp.'s TrapWise, Scitex's Full AutoFrame, and DK&A Trapper are currently the only methods by which one can trap to a vignette. They also, as you can see in Figure 1.6, have the controls over thickness of trap, shrinking vs. spreading, weight of the overlap, and minimum difference between the two colors, that a thinking artist might want.

...or Condemn

Some years back, I gave up trapping for Lent. Since I do not appreciate white holes between colors any more than the most doctrinaire of trapping aficionados, this required a certain change in my mindset, but once I began, it turned out not to be onerous at all, and, with the exception of jobs with more than four colors, I have not designed anything that required a trap since then.

Savvy designers already know to avoid certain color choices. On the screen, it seems so easy to make small type cyan on a magenta background. Doing this, however, is a good way to get a printer to refuse your job. There is no way of resolving the trapping problem. If the type gets spread, it will seem too bold; if it gets shrunk, it will become purple rather than cyan. Accordingly, designing in this way is an outright error, as much as a typo or a blown-out highlight.

Figure 1.7. At first blush, this appears to be a trapping problem, since the gray, which is a tint of black, has nothing in common with either the purple or the light blue. But, with proper handling, there is no need for a trap at all.

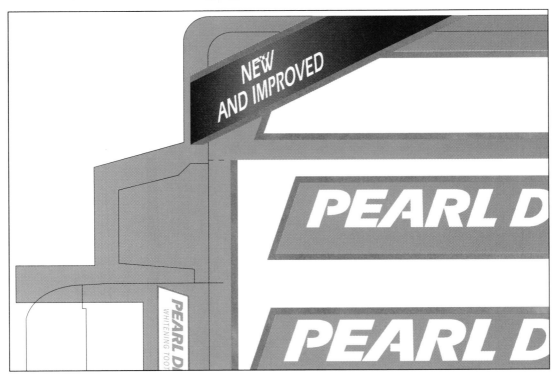

Similarly, unless you or your service bureau has access to TrapWise or one of its competitors, you can't use a gradation that collides with some radically different color.

In Figure 1.7, you will perceive either a major trapping problem, or an opportunity to use common sense.

There are three colors here, including a gradation. The blue color is mostly cyan with a little magenta. The purple is mostly magenta with a little cyan. If these two colors were butting one another, trap would be unnecessary, but, as the devil would have it, each one butts a gray that is almost entirely composed of black.

In accord with the aforementioned religious practice, I have left the thing untrapped here, hoping the printer would get it right. If I had decided to trap, I would have had to face four major problems:

- It is far from obvious whether the gray border should spread into the blue background, or vice versa.
- Because the blue and gray are both so light, any trapping line will seem relatively obvious. I might have to use some sort of semi-trap, making the overlap consist of toned-down versions of both colors.
- Whatever method I use to trap the blue-gray intersections in the larger logos may not work for the smaller one at the bottom left of Figure 1.7: it may make the gray rule around that one seem smaller than it should be.
- The purple gradient needs to spread in some areas where it hits the gray and shrink in others.

With the help of TrapWise and a reasonably powerful computer, these problems can be solved by brute force. If you would rather use finesse (or if you have given up trapping for Lent) the following approach may seem more appealing.

The gray is currently defined as 7C4M0Y30K, accounting for its bluish tinge. In Photoshop, open a small LAB file and fill it with this color. Go to Edit: Preferences>Separation Setup and change Black Generation to None. Set the Info palette to read CMYK, and read the value of the filled color to see how Photoshop would construct it without the use of any black. It's still the same gray—but now the numbers are 35C24M20Y.

Armed with this information, we can now throw the Photoshop file away and substitute the three-color gray values for the predominantly black ones in our art file.

The purple color has more of both cyan and magenta than the gray does, so where the two colors hit, the minimum shared color is 35C24M. The blue color has only 20 percent magenta, so the minimum is a few points lower. Either way, the minimum is so close to the gray that it would make no sense to build in artificial overlaps to guard against its appearance.

The inexperienced artist recoils from a graphic with as many potential problems as this one. This is trap at its most terrifying. And yet, with a little forethought, *this file does not have to be trapped at all.*

To Know and Distinguish

The theme of substituting the CMY colors for black is a recurrent one in trap avoidance. This is especially so when designers specify process equivalents of PMS colors. The Pantone Matching System, as a rule, favors the use of black ink when possible. Often, that will cause trapping problems that can be eliminated with the dodge described above.

Many such maneuvers exist, provided we are not intimidated. As long as we remember that trap is not neat or keen in and of itself, but is instead a dreary desirability in a few isolated situations, we will be safe.

Before burying your artwork under an avalanche of useless traps, look at the minimum values of each color, and ask yourself, what is the worst that can possibly happen if I don't trap? If the worst that can happen is white, or is a color vastly lighter than either of the two colors that are butting, then ask yourself, is there a way of reorganizing the colors? If the answer is no, you may well have found a situation where it pays to accept the technical defect that trapping is.

If you work with QuarkXPress, be careful when large text overprints a picture box, as in Figure 1.1. Ordinarily, QXP will spread such type, and ordinarily, it is wrong to do so, though this will depend on the character of the picture. The offending type can manually be set to overprint or to knock out using QXP's Trap Information dialog box.

Be aware that trap is not the only misregistration problem that can plague unwary designers. Attempting to print small light-colored or white type on a multicolor background is a lot worse than printing without trap: it is too likely that misregistration will result in the type becoming illegible.

It is hard to know whether editors or printers are the more dangerous and unpredictable group. Prudence dictates not handing either one a stick of dynamite in the belief they are unlikely to decide to light the fuse.

As writer, I happen to be one of those who knows and approves of split infinitives. I split them freely in *Computer Artist*. But with an unknown editor, I avoid not only split infinitives but anything that might be mistaken for one. As designers, when dealing with an unknown printer, similar caution is advisable. After all, if we meet someone who doesn't know what trapping is, but cares very much about it, the last thing we need is to tempt that person to start tinkering with our files. ●

Afterword

In one of the Ps in Figure 1.2, I flouted good practice when I left it untrapped. Obviously, I can't predict whether the printer of this book will have such good control of register that no white line will appear. For what it's worth, when it appeared in *Computer Artist* I got away with it, as I would expect to in most professional contexts.

The fact that one normally gets away with it does not, as some service bureaus who make a lot of money running their clients' files through TrapWise think, mean that I am anti-trap. Quite the contrary. If you are the art director of *Wired* magazine, or otherwise are in the habit of having radically different colors butt one another, I certainly advocate trapping them. Furthermore, except in rare instances I advocate doing it yourself, rather than letting an automated program have at it.

Lack of trap alone will not ruin a job. Half-baked measures may. If you "hide" your traps in the wrong half of a yellow-purple combination, as the author did in Figure 1.4, you will be far worse off than if you throw up your hands and ignore trap altogether.

Similarly, if you don't understand why black type should overprint a color background, some day you are going to try to take yellow type and overprint it on a purple background, and then you *will* have a ruined job and a printer who is going to insist on being paid for it.

In addition to the screams from service bureaus, I took grief about this column from those who thought I should have included specific rules for when to trap and how wide to make the overlaps. That might have been nice, but if readers get a basic understanding of the topic, that will eliminate the huge majority of trapping disasters. Like so many of the concepts in this book, the idea of trap is simple, as long as you realize it is neither a panacea nor a bogeyman. ●

Jargon Watch

choke See *shrink.*

gradient See *vignette.*

knockout Where a foreground object meets its background exactly, without any overlap. Used when trap is considered unnecessary, as in the initial *S* on page 27. The brown letter *knocks out* of the two background colors.

misregistration The reason trap is desirable. Since each ink is laid down by a different part of the press, it is conceivable, nay likely, that all the cyan, say, may come down slightly to the left of where it is supposed to.

overprint Where an object prints over a background without knocking any of it out, ordinarily used when the object is black or very dark and will not be altered by the underlying color. In the Dialog Box text opposite, the black type *overprints* the light brown background.

Pantone Matching System Industry standard color specification method, used by printers to give formulations for inks and by designers to indicate what colors they want: PMS 186 would, for example, be a rose red.

shrink Where the size of the hole in the background object is slightly reduced, so that an area of overlap occurs inside the foreground object. Used when trap is needed and the foreground object is darker than the background.

split infinitive In English, basic verbs are defined to include the word *to;* thus, the infinitive form of the most common verb is *to be.* Certain grammarians insist that no third word should ever be suffered to be inserted between the *to* and the verb, although it has been standard English to do just that for several hundred years. Nevertheless, split infinitives are frowned on by most publishers, much to the annoyance of the present author. Fowler describes those who neither know nor care what a split infinitive is to be a "happy folk" because "'to really understand' comes readier to their lips & pens than 'really to understand,' they see no reason why they should not say it (small blame to them, since reasons are not their critics' strong point), & they do say it, to the discomfort of some among us, but not to their own."

spread Where the size of the foreground object is slightly increased, without increasing the hole in the background that accommodates it. Therefore, an overlap will occur in the background, but not in the original foreground object. This technique is used when trap is desired and the background is darker than the foreground object.

vignette Also known as a gradation, fountain, gradient, or blend, a gradual, continuous transition from one color to another, as in the purple in Figure 1.7.

Dialog Box

For a concept as simple as trapping is, it certainly has been able to delude a lot of people, including some of my fellow authors, into thinking that it is unfathomably deep. Accordingly, this column's revelation that trapping *can* be understood by the intelligent layperson, and in fact is frequently unnecessary, was treated by many readers as a revelation. This piece generated more positive response than any I have ever written, save the one on correcting a Photo CD image, Column 4 in this book.

The more one gets into trapping, though, the more sticky a subject it can become. To balance things a bit, let's visit with a couple of users who deal with scenarios more troublesome than those mentioned in the column.

First, a look at a trapping problem that has become more and more common. Nowadays we frequently print with fifth and/or sixth inks in addition to the normal CMYK on press. Often this is because the extra color is that of a corporate logo or some other known color. But more and more, art directors are using the extra spot colors in significant design elements, creating screen angling and trapping problems, among others.

As the column points out, CMYK images, at least photographic ones, are normally self-trapping, in that the picture will have enough in common with whatever touches it that no artificial overlap will be needed. But what if it has nothing whatsoever in common with the thing that touches it? The following correspondent is wrestling with a silhouetted CMYK image that has to rest on a fifth-color background.

If you are sophisticated enough to take in all that follows, you may well be capable of raising a different objection. If I am that good, you may sneer, why can't I avoid trap altogether by seamlessly incorporating the fifth ink into the CMYK image, using color replacement principles?

Well, as a matter of fact, I *can*, and have, done so, but it isn't always possible. So, let's assume that, in the following case, the writer has twelve different versions of his job, and has to paste his silhouetted photo on top of twelve different spot colors. So there! Now, down to business.

Trapping headaches: a silhouetted photograph that butts a fifth color

I have a small scan of a pizza. It is a CMYK Photoshop EPS file. It imports into Quark with a clipping path and sits on a spot color background. Obviously if I do nothing, it won't trap to the background, it will simply butt the fifth color, and will cause problems on press.

You should be concerning yourself with a general solution to this problem. The fact that you have a simple shape, the pizza, is deluding you into thinking that a clipping path is going to help you. If instead, you had a person's head, with an irregular hairline, a clipping path approach would be out of the question.

My solution was to open the scan of the pizza, convert to grayscale, then resample the image to 1200 dpi, select the clipping path, convert the path to a selection, and stroke the selection with an 8-pixel stroke. (I calculated 8 pixels at 1200 dpi would give me exactly double the final trap amount I needed, and used this doubled amount since half the stroke will sit on the same colored background and is lost anyways, only half sits on the image.) Then I killed the path, converted this grayscale image to a bitmap (with 50% threshold, keeping at 1200 dpi) image, and saved it as a TIFF. Then I took the pizza picture box in Quark, duplicated it in the same spot, imported the stroked path image into exactly the same coordinates, and colored it the same color as the spot color and manually made it overprint. Whew!!!

This sounds like a fun way to spend an afternoon. I hope somebody is paying you for all this time.

Bottom line is that it almost works, but not exactly. If I make the stroke really big, it seems to work, but the fatness of the stroke only masks that it doesn't REALLY work at the fineness that it needs to for a proper trap.

I also tried duplicating the effort above without resampling to 1200 dpi, leaving it at 300, and using only a 2-pixel stroke. Same problem.

Figure 1.8. *When a color photo butts another colored object, trap is rarely necessary. The pizza's crust has more of every ink than the tan background does. It is therefore impossible for a white line to occur between the two. If, on the other hand, the background were not a CMYK mixture but rather a true fifth color, then the pizza would have nothing in common with it, and some means of trapping would have to be devised.*

What appears on film is a nicely stroked path which seems to fit the image, but isn't in registration. If I line up the films by eye and ignore the registration marks, I can pretty much make it fit. But if I line up the register marks, or (since our imagesetter punches the film) I lay it on the pins, it winds up being out by about a point.

When dealing with photographic images, we rarely have to worry about trap. Figure 1.8 illustrates why. The background box behind the type is 0C8M10Y2K. The crust of the pizza varies but it always has around twice as much yellow and magenta as the background. Therefore, no matter how far out of register this gets, the absolutely lightest color that can possibly appear is the color of the background. There are people in this world who'd look at it and panic and send it to their service bureau to run through Trap-Wise. We will leave them to their phobia and their checkwriting.

If the background is *not* composed of CMYK inks and instead is a true fifth color—and that is happening more and more these days—then we indeed have a trapping problem, a white line waiting to arise and bite us.

The following is the method I have used and if it is cumbersome (though not as much so as the method you are now using without success) at least it works. It relies on replacing part of the fifth-color background with a new Photoshop file. As long as Photoshop names the color exactly the same as the page layout program, this will be seamless and invisible to the viewer. This also eliminates the need for a clipping path.

The best way by far to handle this is with a plug-in, such as PlateMaker, ICISS, or Co-Co, that allows Photoshop to save a five-channel file. Then, all one need do is create a fifth plate in the manner described below, and place the file.

In the absence of such a plug-in, you can still make it work with the following kludgy technique, illustrated in Figure 1.9. This will cause the background to shrink into the image, which is normally correct. It can, however, easily be adjusted to make the image spread into the background, if that is desired.

1. Save a copy of the silhouetted file. Select the entire yellow channel and delete it. You should now have a picture of a blue pizza (top left of Figure 1.9).

2. Load the path and select the pizza. Apply a curve to it that

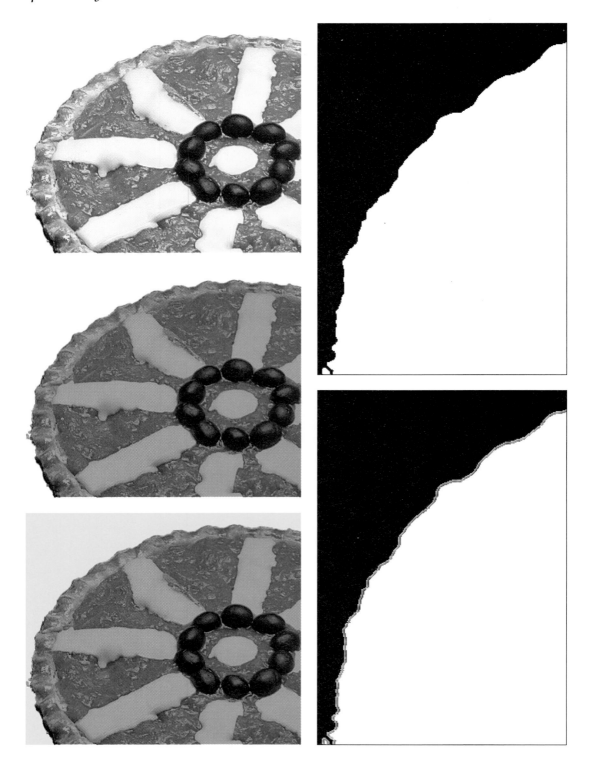

Figure 1.9. *Opposite, procedure for trapping a silhouetted image to a lighter fifth color. Starting with the pizza of Figure 1.8, Top left: all yellow is deleted from the image. Center left: cyan and magenta are increased throughout, so as to make a harder edge on the pizza. Bottom left: the white background is selected and replaced with solid yellow. Top right, an enlarged look at the new yellow channel, with a hard edge where it hits the pizza. At this point, the bottom left image is run through Photoshop's Trap filter. This creates a soft-edged overlap in the yellow channel, shown bottom right. The ridiculous-looking blue pizza at bottom left can now be discarded, except for its yellow channel, which will eventually become the fifth color.*

forces the minimum value of magenta and cyan to 25 percent, so that the edges of the silhouette become very hard and pronounced. (Center of Figure 1.9.)

3. Deselect the foreground. Set the magic wand tool to a tolerance of 32, and click into the background. This should result in a selection that is a perfect butt to the hard silhouette edges, yet also hits any stray light pixels on the edge.

4. Replace the selected area with solid yellow, so that the pizza is a muddy blue and the background is yellow.

5. Run this document through Photoshop's Trap filter. This will give a nice, soft trap that will vary in darkness with the darkness of the pizza's crust—not that objectionable stroking path.

6. The resulting yellow channel is now a perfect rendition of what you want your fifth-color plate to look like. If you have one of the plug-ins that allows a fifth Photoshop plate, simply copy this channel into your fifth channel of the original CMYK document, place and print. If not, the kludgy workaround continues as follows.

7. Take the trapped yellow channel and paste it into a new grayscale document of the same size. You can now throw away the CMYK file with the blue pizza.

8. Change the document from Mode: Grayscale to Mode: Duotone. Whatever the two colors are that come up as defaults, change the names of one of them to Black and the other to Background Color or whatever the name of the color in your page layout document is. Change the curve for the black plate to null, i.e. all values become zero. Change the curve for the Background Color plate to default, so that this plate will be identical to the original grayscale channel. Save this duotone document as EPS.

9. Take the original CMYK document and paste it, without a clipping path, in your page layout document in whatever position you have chosen for it. Note the exact parameters, and now place the duotone document, again without a clipping path in exactly those same parameters.

10. Bring the CMYK file to the front, hiding the duotone, and save.

11. Print the CMYK plates only, without the fifth color.

12. Delete the CMYK image (but do not save the file) and print the Background Color plate only. ●

Concepts are fine, but how about giving us some hard numbers?

I LOVE your articles— BUUUUT...When you did the article on trapping you didn't take the final step and give a couple of suggested, ballpark, trap amounts. I know it's a can of worms, but people want hard NUMBERS.

Well, I can hardly have done that without explaining *how* to trap in the various programs, which I wasn't inclined to do. I saw it as more of a basic-concept article. The problem I've been seeing so much of recently is not people like yourself who have good ideas of what to do, but people who are so buffaloed by the whole concept that they assume that *any* multicolor job has to go to a service bureau and be run through TrapWise.

Yes, I design so there are screens in common. Yes, I send it through the Scitex [for Full AutoFrame trapping] if it's complex. But yes, I still need manual trapping when I send simple 2- and 3-color jobs straight through the imagesetter.

Here are various suggestions I've gathered over the years:

The amount of trap needed for a funky quick print shop working on offset paper is .4 point.

The amount needed for your basic 2 color press is .23 point.

(I took the difference between a service bureau that says their standard default on the Scitex is .22 point. or .08 mm, and a good 2-color printer who told me .25 point.)

For coated stock on a great press with good operators, I suggest .15 point.

(This is the difference between the .16 point that my color house normally uses and several magazines that use .144 point.)

Flexographic printers and silk screeners may want as much as 1 point trap.

These are basically very reasonable numbers. Personally I like to use slightly smaller traps than what you are indicating, but both of us favor values slightly lower than the figures that are most frequently recommended.

And don't forget to double all amounts if you're doing overprinting strokes in Illustrator.

Correct. Vector-art programs such as Illustrator and FreeHand center their strokes on the outside border of the object, so only half of the stroke will fall in the area where we are trying to create overlaps.

Some advice I got from a service bureau about trapping in Quark years ago is still good: Turn trapping OFF in your Quark preferences, and trap only the items you really need to through the dialog box. That way there are no accidentally fat letters.

There is a case to be made for that, though in a complicated job I find it easier to just go in and correct the few things that are wrong.

A magazine I read recommended varying trap thickness with line screen as follows:

Line screen	Trap Amount
85 line	.5 point
100	.35 point
133	.3 point
150	.25 point
200	.2 point

There is no technical reason to vary thickness with screen ruling, except the inferential one that a higher line screen implies better printing conditions and better printing conditions imply less misregistration. Therefore, I am rather skeptical (for a change) of incorporating this complication. ●

2

The Curse of Trying Too Hard

Beginners make beginner mistakes. The mistakes that experienced artists make can be so sophisticated that a beginner would easily avoid them.

wo professional sports leagues are currently shut down by labor strife, and talk has already started about starting seasons with "replacement players," whose primary appeal can be expected to be their hilarious ineptitude, when compared to their professional predecessors.

In the graphic arts, the replacement players have already taken over, and the results are no longer so funny. Up until very recently—less than five years ago—substantially all professional prepress work was done by *real* professionals. That is, typesetting was done by a person who had done nothing but set type for a living for many years. Color scanning and correction was a highly skilled, highly paid craft that required years of full-time apprenticeship. None of these individuals had to worry about design, copywriting, salesmanship, or any of the thousand other problems that eat away at the time of today's computer artist.

Considering that we now have to master several crafts instead of one, do it on a part-time rather than full-time basis, have many more artistic possibilities, and use tools that are not, by and large, designed

Figure 2.1. *Conventional wisdom equates higher resolution with higher quality. The bottom image opposite indeed demonstrates the perils of proceeding without sufficient resolution. Note the jagged appearance, particularly in the diagonal lines of the flags and in the face of the woman wearing the green blouse. But does this prove that the top scan is better in all conceivable circumstances? Figure 2.2 offers an answer.*

with the professional in mind, there is no way that we are going to be as accurate as yesterday's professionals. Our work may be better in many ways, but there will be more mistakes. The only question is, how *many* more?

Among serious artists, the screwup rate seems to be much lower than it used to be. I know this from practical experience: for several years I have managed production departments in New York City prepress firms that cater to high-end users.

At least in this atypical world, the level of sophistication of the desktop artist has improved greatly over the last three years.

> **A file can be loved to death by artists who go to such lengths to improve it that it actually becomes worse than it was in the first place.**

To be sure, one still finds clients who are outraged because their film proofs didn't produce colors as vivid as they got when they output the same file on a color copier, or because their 6-point Baskerville Italic reversed out of three colors looked great on their screen but became illegible in real life. On the whole, though, desktop jobs are much better thought-out and executed. Also, there is a welcome trend away from needless complexity in files.

A more novel species of error is, regrettably, on the rise. This is the error caused by too much sophistication, rather than too little. A file can be loved to death by knowledgeable artists who go to such lengths to improve it that it becomes worse than it was in the first place. This type of problem, where a user just goes too far, will be the focus of this column.

When Bigger Doesn't Equal Better

The jagged-looking mess at the bottom of Figure 2.1 shows what happens when an image is scanned with insufficient resolution. The extra data in the top version certainly helps—up to a point. Too many artists assume that the more resolution, the higher the quality. This is not so.

Having extra resolution in a scan is a big pain from the standpoint of file management. File size increases with the square of the resolution, meaning that things get very big very fast. If an image is scanned at 300 samples per inch as opposed to 200, you might expect it to be half again as large. In fact, it will be more than twice as big as at the lower resolution, clogging up our hard disks, decreasing system performance, taking longer to image, etc.

Nevertheless, if quality is the main consideration, we may have to make this sacrifice—as long as we don't go overboard.

These two images were scanned on the same scanner, by the same operator, to the same color settings. The top version has three times as much resolution as the bottom, making it nine times larger on disk.

The general rattiness of the flags in the bottom version is but one of many indications of insufficient resolution. Every significant detail seems coarse and exaggerated.

When the images shrink to the size of Figure 2.2, however, those who think the more resolution the better are in for a rude

Figure 2.2. The same two scans as in Figure 2.1, but this time output at a much smaller size. Now, the weaknesses of the bottom version have become strengths. The upper version now appears too soft, in addition to taking up about 20 needless megabytes.

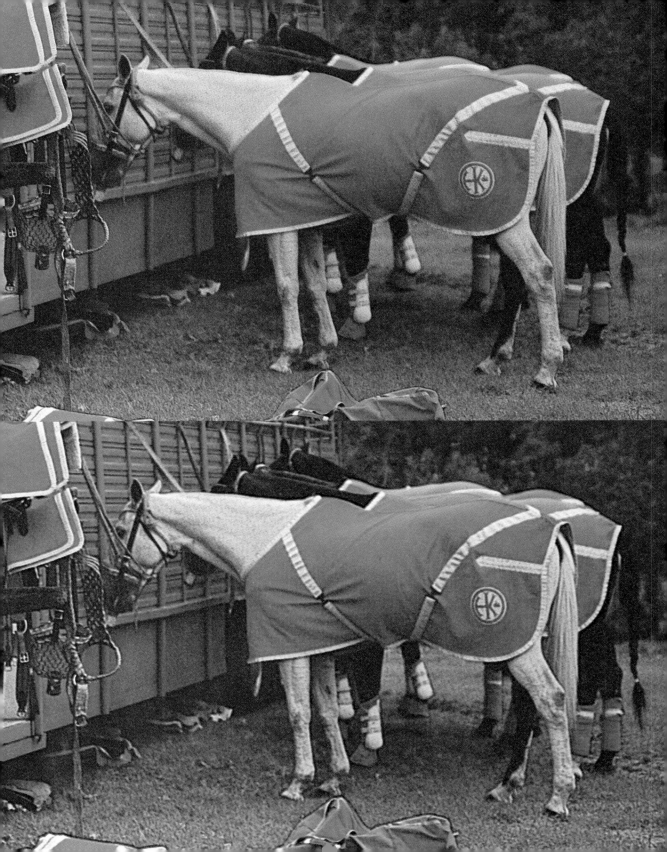

awakening. The same factors that damaged the smaller scan in Figure 2.1 give it an overwhelming quality advantage at this size.

Often, what we take for added detail in an image is actually only color variations that give us the feeling of action. In such a case, scanning at a high resolution will *hurt* detail, not enhance it. Figure 2.3 repeats the experiment of Figures 2.1 and 2.2, but this time with a much softer image.

At the large size, the lack of resolution in the bottom version is not nearly as noticeable as it was in Figure 2.1. You can see the

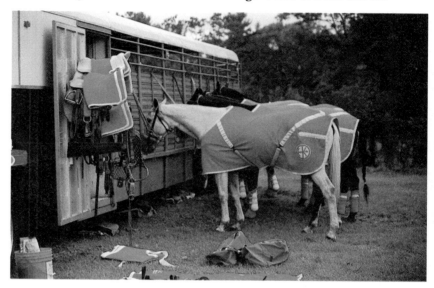

Figure 2.3. *As in Figures 2.1 and 2.2, these two scans are at radically different resolutions, and shown at two different sizes. This time, the image subject is somewhat softer. The result, however, is the same: the one with lower resolution is better at the smaller size. In each case, the top one has three times the resolution of the one at bottom, meaning it takes up nine times the disk space.*

problems in the horse's bridle among other places if you look for them. Yet we could almost get away with printing this picture, whereas the bottom half of Figure 2.1 is out of the question, unconditionally unacceptable.

Moving to the smaller size, ask yourself this question: assuming we want the grass to look like grass, and not a green carpet, will higher or lower resolution be better?

The printed evidence speaks for itself. The more resolution, the more pixels will be averaged together to make the final halftone dot. Therefore, a higher-resolution image will be softer, smoother, less prone to variation. In moderation, that can be a good thing. In this example, though, the extra trouble of dealing with a much larger file is worth less than nothing—the low-resolution version is better, period. The reason: the scanner is not going to resolve individual blades of grass no matter how high we ratchet up the resolution. Nor are we actually seeing individual blades of grass on the printed page. What we are seeing is variation in a green area, nothing more. But, logical creatures that we are, our brains are telling us what seems obvious, that we are looking at blades of grass.

> **Two sources you should not trust to tell you what screen ruling will be too high: your contract proof and your printer.**

Almost everyone knows to avoid resolutions of less than about 1.5 times the screen value times magnification percentage. Many do not realize, however, that too much resolution can be as bad as too little, and that anything in excess of two times screen times magnification will probably be counterproductive. The prevalence of overly soft reproduction of images that should be crisp gives away the sad truth: some of us try too hard.

Too Tight a Pair of Jeans

Once a job gets to press, a similar problem can rear its head. If you think that the higher the resolution the better the scan, it is a short step to believe that the higher the screen ruling the better the print quality will be.

The purpose of a halftone screen is to fool the viewer into perceiving shades of colors. We have no pink ink available on press, but if we show some magenta and some white, we should be able to fool the viewer into thinking that we do. We need to put down the magenta in some kind of pattern: it could be lines, crosses or whatever, but nowadays it is almost invariably dots.

It would defeat the purpose to have the dots be too large and obtrusive. We would like to give, if possible, the illusion of continuous color. One might therefore think that the finer the dot pattern the better will be the perceived quality when ink hits paper.

And so it will — provided that the pattern is not too fine for the press to reproduce accurately. Trouble is, when ink, or any other liquid, hits paper, some will be absorbed, and some will smear. The worse the printing conditions, the worse the quality of the paper, and the more inattentive the pressman, the worse the effect will be, but it will be there to some extent no matter what. If the screen ruling is so fine that adjacent dots start to smear and blend together, the whole image will go to pot. The result will be worse even than printing with a screen value that is clearly too low. Yet, again and again, art directors shoot themselves in the foot by calling for unmanageably high screen rulings.

Unfortunately, there are no clear guidelines on what ruling to use. For newspapers, 65, 85 and 100 dots per inch are common. Magazines run from 120 to 150. In commercial printing, values of up to 175 or even 200 are sometimes possible. One thing is for sure, though. If you stay in the lower half of these ranges sometimes you will do well and sometimes not, but on the whole you will absolutely get better reproduction than if you push too hard.

Two sources that you should emphatically *not* believe on this score are your contract proof and, surprisingly, your printer. If you produce 175-line film it will look just splendid on a Matchprint or whatever, since these are immune from the press's inking problems. If you ask a printer whether he can hold the screen on press, his answer is almost certain to be yes, at least if the paper is good.

Figure 2.4. *The purpose of trap is to compensate for small misregistrations on press. More trap is not better. People who engineer in one-point traps are trying too hard.*

Figure 2.5. Building in a one-point trap, as in Figure 2.4, assumes that a job can print a point out of register. But if that happens, the job is worthless anyway. Below left, an original image; below right, a version that has been intentionally thrown a point out of register. Would you accept it?

But what would *you* say, if you were the printer? The finer the screen, the more difficult the work, the heavier the dot gain, and the more critical the skill level of the press operator. Chances are, half of your pressmen might be able to do well with it and the other half would make a hash of the job. Can you afford to tell a client this?

If you wish to impress people with how sleek and svelte you are, the best approach is to go on a diet. If, instead, you force yourself into a pair of jeans four inches too tight, you may get away with it for a short while, but when the seam starts to split you will be much worse off than you would have been without all that extra effort.

Snared by a Trap

Since trap is the most overrated and most misunderstood facet of today's production process, people who bend over backwards to try to accommodate it may find they have fallen into a variety of trap quite different from the one they sought to achieve.

For several pages more on the perils of misunderstanding trapping, refer to Column 1.

To hear all the industry discussion of trap, one would think it was the *sine qua non* of fine printing. The fact is that many of our colleagues have never even heard of trap, and live blissfully in their ignorance. Someone who never uses trap has a better than even chance of getting a perfectly acceptable job off press. The cases where lack of trap causes an offensive effect are bad, no doubt about it. On the other hand, they may well be preferable

to the effects achieved by those who fail to recognize trap as the last pinch of spice to add to the printing recipe, and instead pour in a quart of Tabasco sauce.

Trap is a sensible defensive method against misregistration on press. Where two unlike colors butt, if the printing is not perfect a white line may appear between them. No matter how narrow the line, it will be unsightly. To guard against this possibility, the skillful artist engineers in a slight overlap where the two colors meet.

The key word is *slight.* The overlap is supposed to be subtle enough not to commend itself to the casual viewer. In commercial printing, an overlap of a quarter of a point is more than sufficient; a tenth of a point really ought to do. Some artists, a little unsure about this concept, and fearful of being scorned and reviled by the community for the sin of inadequate trap, go to the trouble of building in traps as large as a full point, as shown in Figure 2.4, or even two.

> **The curse of trying too hard usually often up as an excessive reliance on local correction. Nearly every image has some area that of primary importance. The temptation will always be to isolate it.**

All this extra effort yields a product considerably inferior to one with no trap at all. Consider Figure 2.5. I threw the right-hand version a point out of register. Do you think it is acceptable? If your printer gave it to you, wouldn't you complain, and perhaps refuse to pay? Trap is supposed to guard against what may reasonably occur, not against a brain-dead press operator.

The Picture as a Whole

Color correction is the most obvious area where extra effort can turn counterproductive. The very power of the correction tools can seduce us into ignoring the straightforward, simple path.

Even limiting the discussion to the basic tools, however, the person who tries too hard can be more dangerous than one who does not try at all. The three variations of the seal image in Figure 2.6 illustrate this.

The original, top, is plainly too flat. When I used the image in a previous column, I made the major improvement shown at bottom by setting proper highlight and shadow values, and by allocating as much contrast as possible to the lightest third of the image, which is where the animal's fur is.

The image, as frequently occurs when harsh sunlight reflects off something white, has a blue cast. In keeping with the principle of catering to colors that the viewer knows must be neutral, I moved in the direction of whiter snow, by cutting cyan and magenta and increasing yellow throughout the image. Ideally, the shadows in the snow should be gray, but I judged this to be inadvisable—though not, as you can see in the middle version, impossible.

When I presented the raw image to a class on color correction, one of the students refused to concede defeat. He was determined to get rid of the blue cast, by force if necessary. Snow and baby seals should be *white*, after all, and all one needs to make them white is a violent enough set of curves.

When a square peg refuses to fit into a round hole, usually all that is needed is a little finesse and discretion. The middle image is the work of someone who thinks that what is needed is a bigger hammer.

This correction, such as it was, was carefully executed, and required good knowledge of the

Figure 2.6. *The original, top, leaves a lot of room for improvement, but only someone with a good knowledge of curves can do as poor a correction, losing so much detail, as the middle version.*

workings of curves. Neutralizing the snow was a fine idea. In principle, that is. But this artist tried too hard.

In color correction, the curse of trying too hard usually shows up as an excessive reliance on local correction. Nearly every image has some area that we will consider to be of primary importance. The temptation will always be to isolate it, so that we can work on improving its color and contrast, without risking damage to the rest of the picture.

This approach is generally harder than applying a global correction. It is also considerably less effective. Other than this, it can be recommended.

> **If there is something wrong with the color balance of a foreground object, this may be the biggest problem with an image, but it will not be the only one.**

Figure 2.6 is extreme, but it does prove the point. Suppose we were to isolate the seal, then apply curves to it that corrected it as in the bottom image, without changing the background at all. First of all, it would not look natural. It would seem that the seal was cut out from another picture and pasted into this one, regardless of how smooth and well-feathered our selection path was.

More than that, though, even if the background is not high on our priority list, why waste the chance to improve it? If there is something wrong with the color balance of the foreground object(s), this may be the biggest and most important problem with an image, but it will not be the only one. By applying the change globally, we will make subtle improvements in "unimportant" areas, the sort of improvements that are associated with professional work.

What Value Experience?

The errors described in this column are rather sophisticated ones, well beyond the capabilities of the nonprofessional artists of the early days of desktop publishing. Nowadays, computer artists have almost as much proficiency in the basic programs as the professionals do, so their blunders can be far more creative.

Realistically, there are only two major advantages that come with experience. First, there is a whole horde of job-specific techniques. If you are having a problem, a long-time professional may well have run into the exact same thing in 1991 or whenever, and, having been burnt once, know better than to repeat the error that you are about to make for the first time.

More than that, though, professionals understand the virtues of the simple approach. They are rarely guilty of trying too hard. They respect the power of today's tools, but reserve their use for special occasions. Extra effort is admirable. The objective, however, is improvement. If the extra effort doesn't improve things, what in the world is the point? ●

Afterword

The glorious thing about color, and the thing that keeps us in business, is that everybody has an opinion about it. If people don't like the way an image looks, they will not accept the word of an expert that it *does* look good. Annoying.

On the other hand, experts are supposed to be able to predict what people will like, and within two weeks of publication of this column I realized the extent of my failure in this regard. I was assisted in this realization by nearly a hundred e-mail messages and faxes from half a dozen countries, all accusing me of, in my evaluation of Figure 2.6, having failed to see the blizzard for the snow.

Some of these missives expressed puzzlement. "I have to ask, just what is wrong with the more neutrally-balanced version of the seal?" wrote one reader. "It looks cleaner, with better shadow detail. Am I missing something here?"

Then, there was the strident variety: "A baby seal signifies purity. To carry that mood it deserves the most attention. It needs to be *white*. The other images look dirty. Like it's been flopping around in the mud. They destroy the mood of the photograph and are totally unacceptable.

"Here, a little extra effort definitely PAYS OFF. Your student hit a home run. I don't care how big of a bat he used to hit it out of the park."

My notorious color-correction philosophy also took its lumps: "I know plenty of art directors and editors who would reject your version and accept your student's. When doing color work sometimes the correct decisions are not always ones that go by the numbers. All too often one is forced to take into account the aesthetic judgment of those who are uneducated about color and who consider 'what snow really looks like' before they consider issues like contrast and cyan color cast.

"Your effort to get this point across and communicate these issues reminds me very much of a graphic designer trying to explain to the client why the really superior design is better than the uninformed choice the client is making. Invariably every time I'm with designers or artists this kind of issue comes up. Somehow the client just doesn't get it and usually he is the one paying the bill."

Staggered and somewhat shell-shocked, I reconvened the ten-person jury I had used to evaluate images in the

article that appears as the prologue to this book. In the course of a 50-image series of tests, I snuck in the seal. Although I really wanted the jury to choose between the two corrected versions of Figure 2.6, the conditions of contest required a third alternative, and plainly the original would have been ridiculous. I therefore wheeled out a second student version, and presented the jury with Figure 2.7, identified only as, from top to bottom, A, B, and C. The jury was by secret ballot to decide not just which was the best version but which was the worst. There was no definition given of what *best* and *worst* meant.

It was no landslide, but I was a winner. A got five votes as best to four for B and one for C. More tellingly, three contrast hounds agreed with me that B is the worst. The other seven jurors rated C the worst.

I therefore ran a semi-correction in a subsequent issue, under the headline: "Readers to Columnist: If It Isn't White, It Isn't Right." I confessed that, considering the jury's finding, B was clearly a contender, so I shouldn't have trashed my student in the column.

Figure 2.7. *These three images went to a professional jury, with the instruction to choose which version was the best and which the worst. How would you have voted?*

Whoever coined the expression "once bitten, twice shy" obviously had never met me, for my apology provoked what might be called a white backlash, of readers infuriated that anyone could see anything meritorious in B.

A European professional photographer represented this group with the following statement:

"I must agree with A. When I first looked at the three pictures, immediately C was too much cyan and magenta, and it had better detail than B. B was very washed without contrasts. Since I have shot (and done much trickery to the automated exposure computer) much in very bright conditions, there are always reflections and ambient colors in the white. Even if I had used a polarizing filter, the white would be purer and more contrast be seen, but I would need to stop down and more details would be seen of foreground and background. (Unless I override with exposure, but that's another subject.)."

Amen, say I.

Not willing to leave well enough alone, my prophetic last phrase in the correction box was, "You haven't seen the last of this seal."

By this, I meant that I later intended to discuss superior methods of correcting the image. My version, A, was done in CMYK, and in real life I believe better results can be obtained with a picture as flat as this by starting in LAB. If you fast-forward to Figure 7.4, you can see why.

My experience with this column is all the more annoying and less forgiveable because I had just seen the same mistake made in print by someone else. In a magazine article, another author presented the images shown in the prologue to this book as D, E, and F and stated that it was obvious F was the best. It certainly wasn't obvious to my jury, which picked D by a narrow margin.

And yet, in spite of that, the seal.

Since I am so busy quoting everybody, I may as well give the final word to William Faulkner. His favorite misanthrope, I.O. Snopes, would have been able to warn me away, "since as the feller says even a fool wont tread where he jest got through watching somebody else get bit. Again, good night, all." ●

Jargon Watch

contract proof A color proof of sufficient quality that a printer is willing to use it as guidance as to how the printed job should look. As opposed to, say, something off a color copier.

feathered A selection that has had its edges softened so that whatever correction is applied will affect the edges only partially. The point is to avoid an obvious transition between the corrected and uncorrected area.

global correction Any correction that is applied to the image as a whole, without a selection.

halftone dot In printing, all colors are simulated by laying down a less than solid amount of each ink. Although there are many ways of achieving this, the most common by far is by a series of dots that are the same distance from one another but that vary in size.

highlight Used generally to indicate the lightest areas of an image; sometimes used (*the* highlight) to refer to the area the scanner operator or image technician uses as a base point for setting range and color balance. *Specular* highlights—depictions of actual light sources or reflections—are excluded from consideration under this second definition. The highlight must not only be the lightest area of the image, but also an area that the operator is prepared to represent as *white*. If both prongs of the definition are not met (which happens in about 25 percent of all photography) then the image has no highlight.

local correction Any correction that applies only to a selected area of an image, and not to the image as a whole.

out of register On press, where one or more color plates are misaligned with respect to another. This inaccuracy, which is usually measured in fractions of a millimeter, is adjusted by hand by the pressman.

pixel Short for "picture element," the smallest addressable element in a digital image file; one scanning sample.

resolution The number of pixels contained in an image. Resolution is generally, and sloppily, stated in terms of *dots per inch*. This leads to confusion with the term used in printing (see *screen value*). The term *pixels per inch* or *samples per inch* would be more appropriate to specify resolution. It is generally considered that, once a digital image has the same dimensions it will on the printed page, optimal resolution is 1.5 to 2 times the screen value.

screen value Also known as *screen ruling,* the frequency of halftone dots, expressed as dots per inch in the United States. The higher the screen value, the more difficult to print, but also the smoother the appearance. Higher screen values are therefore associated with better quality printing; anything 175 dpi or over is considered boutique. 133 or 150 dpi is typical for magazines and general commercial work. Newspapers generally use 65 or 85 dpi.

selection In image processing, the

isolation of an area prior to altering it. When portions of the image are selected, other areas are locked and cannot be changed.

   selection path An efficient means of storing certain types of selection outlines. A selection path may be saved and edited for later use, or converted into a mask for sophisticated image maneuvers.

   shadow The darkest neutral areas of an image. Sometimes also used to refer specifically to *the* darkest such area, which is the point that a scanner operator or image technician uses to set range and color balance.

6-point Baskerville Italic Baskerville, a late 18th century face, is rather tricky to print, and its fine-lined italic is even worse. 6-point type is roughly half the size of what we customarily read; this clause is set in 6-point type. Hence, printers use *6-point Baskerville Italic* as a derisive equivalent for any type that is going to be a pain in the neck to print.

   trap An artificial, intentional overlap of two touching colors, used to prevent an unwanted white line from appearing between them in the event the job prints out of register. See Column 1.

3

The Case of the Counterfeit Color

We all know that color separators dislike computer artists. But would they actually stoop to sabotage? Don the deerstalker, get down the glass, scope out the clues...

The mysterious words scrolled up the screen, having emerged from the electronic ether on a foreboding night, full of thunderclaps. *Can you help me flesh out a conspiracy theory I'm working on?*

What a promising start to a message! Everyone loves a conspiracy theory, and everyone loves a good detective story. I would gladly give up all my color knowledge for a few months of being Dalgliesh, Poirot, Wolfe. Did the stranger who sent the message know this? Let's get back to his recital of facts.

The Theory: "traditional" color separators, threatened by encroachment of desktop systems, purposefully screw up my data when I give them a separation file made in Photoshop.

The Evidence: Almost without exception, files I generate look great when output at a service bureau. Bright, lively, punchy. Exactly what I expect. The same files, when run through a traditional system, look flat, drab, and washed out.

I do retouching for ad agency clients, and I've never had a job bounce when run at a service bureau (the plates seem to run fine at the pubs as well).

Figure 3.1. *Gray component replacement (GCR) alters the balance between black and the other three inks. For each of the two color images at left, either of the black plates shown can theoretically work; if you want a heavier black, you simply reduce the other three colors in more or less equal quantities. As a practical matter, though, one of these images should take the heavier black and the other one not. Do you know which?*

Send the file to a separator, and they invariably come back with a flat proof and an explanation that the separation is inferior. Everyone feels that the "flat" proof is a poor separation, and typically the separator wants to punch up the color on the Scitex, or the client asks me to output to chrome (I work in RGB) so he can have the separator scan the chrome conventionally. Usually THIS sep looks like the one I get from the service bureau from my CMYK file (bright and punchy). Then the separator makes a few smug remarks about "artists doing seps,"and my customer thinks I don't know what I'm doing. Any idea what gives here?

> A press does not behave like a computer. It behaves like what it is: a powerful, fast, and dangerous combination of machines, not conducive to great precision.

That is a fairly complete statement of the case, containing critical clues surrounded by a morass of irrelevant detail. Ellery Queen, at this point, would issue his Challenge to the Reader, saying, "by the exercise of strict logic and irrefutable deductions from given data, it should be simple…the deductions are natural, but they require sharp and unflagging thought."

With that in mind, gentle reader, can you now solve the case of the correspondent's counterfeit color?

Starting off with a puzzle is a time-tested way of suckering the reader into paying attention to a boring topic. Seldom has the device been used more shamelessly than here, since the subject of this column is dot gain. So, let us temporarily set aside the question of whether the separators of this world are engaging in sharp practices against computer artists, and move to a consideration of some of the grim realities of the printing process, and how to take advantage of them for best results.

Getting good printing largely depends on understanding that a press does not behave like a computer. Rather, it behaves like what it is: a large, powerful, and dangerous combination of machines, full of cylinders, fountains, bolts, and rapidly moving gears and parts of all descriptions, all dedicated to smearing large quantities of several varieties of ink and water–alcohol solution at great speed under less than spotless conditions to paper that is flying through it at rates in the five figures of sheets per hour.

Such a beast is not conducive to great precision.

Despite continuing quality improvements, the press is still, by far, the source of the most variability in our entire production process. Worse yet, it comes at a point where we don't want much variation. Consider, in the context of getting a photo into print, where we want precision and where there is a little leeway.

It is not at all necessary, to start with, for a photographer to be able to shoot exactly the same exposure tomorrow as today. Creativity is part of the process here, and we understand and accept that there will be individual differences of approach on similar shots.

The photo lab that processes the chromes, on the other hand, is not a place where we would like creativity to creep in. Instead, we want consistent, repeatable results. By and large we get them, but as with any process that involves film and chemicals, there will be some day-to-day variation.

We now proceed to scan and correct the photo, and here again some human variation is acceptable. There is a huge difference between the color range of photograph and press. If we do not compensate at this point by methods such as unsharp masking, our reproduction is going to look flat and blurry— much like what my correspondent thinks the separators are doing to him on purpose. Some tonal correction is almost always desirable, and how much this is will be decided by a human being whose judgment may vary from day to day.

At this point the finished scans are placed in a page makeup program and sent off to a RIP. These digital steps are conceptually perfect. Tomorrow's repetition of today's work ought to yield exactly and precisely the same results, unless some brain-dead user runs the photos through EfiColor one day and not the other.

The last steps before the pressroom are pulling and processing film, and then making a contract proof such as a Matchprint or Cromalin, or sometimes a digital proof such as an Iris. As with the photo lab's work, this is a place where we don't want variation. It occurs to some extent nevertheless. Cromalins made from the same film on successive days will look slightly different, and they will surely look different from Matchprints.

We call these *contract* proofs because they actually serve as the contract between client and printer as to how the finished job is supposed to look. All these proofing methods aim at duplicating what is likely to happen when ink hits paper. To lapse into lingo for a moment, they have their dot gain built in.

In principle, we would like to be able to replace the pressman with a monkey. Unlike the scanner operator, who must visualize how to take a vivid photograph into a smaller, drabber

The incompatibility
between proofing
systems is getting
worse, with the intro-
duction of dye-
sublimation printers
that are accurate and
controllable enough
to be used for con-
tract proofs. Croma-
lins and Matchprints
are both film-based
proofs, and they still
don't match one
another. Iris is a
different kind of
proofer still, a high-
quality ink jet printer.

colorspace, a pressman has a perfect map of what is expected, in the form of a proof carefully prepared to his requirements, so that he can match it without any artistic interpretation.

And yet, this whole brilliant system can fall to pieces because of the vagaries of the pressroom. Film changes with age and storage conditions; chemistry, despite the automatic replenishment systems found in graphic arts processors, also varies in potency from hour to hour. But a press? Forget about it! The type of press, the paper, the temperature; the humidity; who manufactured and who mixed the inks; what rotation they are being printed in that day; how well the units were washed, if at all, prior to running our job; how fast the press is being run; the brand of imagesetter and whether it was imaging positive or negative film; the state of the fountains and the dampening system; and, most important of all, the skill of the pressman and whether he is in a good mood that day—these are just some of the variables.

Calibrationists are wont to say that the job of the proof is to predict the press conditions. That is about as achievable as knowing what the weather will be like three weeks from next Friday. No, the job of the proof is to give the printer something to try to adjust the press to.

Asking the printer to match the unmatchable, however, is unreasonable. We cannot give him output from a color copier—which is capable of more intense colors than can be attained on press—and ask him to match it. And, if the press is as unpredictable as the weather, well, the weather is not *totally* unpredictable. I live in New Jersey, where it frequently reaches 80 degrees. I am nevertheless confident, extremely confident, that it will not do so three weeks from Friday. It never has, in February.

The Mystery of Dot Gain

To say that dot gain is one of the most misunderstood topics in our industry is to indulge in a cosmic understatement. Few *printers*, let alone computer artists, have more than a fuzzy comprehension of what it is and what its ramifications are. I have had more requests from readers to write on dot gain than on any other topic relating to image reproduction, and have up until now avoided doing so for fear of making a highly confusing situation even worse. But, since this is a column of detective work, we may as well wheel out the topic here.

[Time out for a reminder. Have you already come up with a

solution to the bizarre charge of sabotage by the separator? If not, remember what Holmes said: "As a rule, the more bizarre a thing is, the less mysterious it proves to be." Now, back to our regularly scheduled program.]

There is no reasonable way of discussing dot gain except in conjunction with other press phenomena, all of which conspire to make life worse for us when we print our images on lousy paper. Let us, therefore, go over the reasons, of which dot gain is but one, that we should not be surprised when an image printed on, say, newsprint, fails to look like (or as good as) the same one printed on a coated sheet, or the proof, or our monitor.

When ink, or, for that matter, any kind of liquid, hits paper, a certain amount will lie on the surface but a certain amount will be absorbed into the sheet. This absorbed amount will spread away from the area where the liquid originally hit.

Generally speaking, the worse the quality of the paper, the more absorbent it is. If you would like to test this for yourself, you can do so with a cup of coffee, a magazine, and a copy of your local newspaper. Spill one drop of coffee on each periodical, and see how much wider the brown stain gets on the newsprint.

If we are printing halftone dots, with ink instead of coffee, the same thing will happen. We will perceive the dots to be larger if they are printed on poorer paper. This will make the image appear darker overall. Thus, dot gain.

Suppose we have a sample printed on a fine coated paper. What differences should we expect if we go to a lesser sheet? There are four major ones I can think of, each with a different impact—and each, in its own way, a form of dot gain.

1. **Real dot gain in the midtones.** The lesser paper will have more of it. If you are mathematically inclined, you can work out the theory that suggests that it will be most noticeable in dots that originally range between 50 and 70 percent, the midtone and three-quartertone, in other words. On the poor paper, these tones will appear darker than on the good stock.

2. **Counter-dot gain in the shadows.** Dot gain fools the eye into believing the image is darker by removing some of the white space between dots. But what if there is not that much white space to begin with? On a poor paper we may perceive that shadow areas have become solid, with no space at all between dots. You would think that would mean deep shadow areas would seem darker on a poor paper just as the midtones

would be. It isn't true. When a *lot* of ink is hitting the paper—and in shadow areas, it is—what we perceive as darkness is based less on dot diameter than on how much of that nice glossy ink sits on the surface of the sheet instead of being absorbed. And on a fine sheet, that is what most of the ink will do, and the shadows will look *darker* than they would on newsprint, dot gain be damned.

3. **Pseudo-dot gain in the quartertones.** Although, as indicated above, dot gain is theoretically greatest in the midtones, we *see* it as being heavier in the quartertones. This perception is caused by an even more important factor than dot gain: the underlying color of the paper.

A poorer-quality paper usually is not as white as its more expensive counterparts. This has profound implications. Since we can't produce a color in our image lighter than the paper itself, we are stuck with a smaller color range, and will get flatter-looking reproduction.

> **D**ot gain can only be understood in the context of other press phenomena, all of which conspire to make our lives difficult when we print on lousy paper.

Starting with a grayish paper is roughly equivalent to adding, say, 10C10M10Y to whatever colors we happen to be calling for. Adding ink in equal quantities will emphasize the ink that had the lowest value in the first place. Thus, if the color is green, the gray paper will seem to add magenta to it; if the color is blue, it will seem to add yellow.

Professionals and color scientists usually call said lowest-value ink the *unwanted color,* or the *contaminating color.* Those terms sort of sum up its function. What it does, obviously, is make every pure color look muddier.

4. **Human dot gain throughout.** How heavily the ink flows onto the paper is obviously critical. That flow is controlled by the pressman. If it is different from what is anticipated, this will have more of an impact on the image than the other three factors put together.

An inking deviation in one or all colors can be the result of carelessness, or the pressman may be doing it on purpose. Either way, the move will probably be toward more ink, not less.

A pressman adjusts ink flow globally or in selected portions of the sheet to make the job as a whole look better. As an aid in this process, virtually all jobs will have a quality-control bar like that of Figure 3.2, which can then be read by a densitometer.

Densitometers, though, are dull, prosaic machines. They are not to be relied on for sensitive judgments, for they lack that most fundamental of human visual skills: the ability to evaluate color in context. They may be able to measure that the press sheet densities match the densities of the proof—but that doesn't mean the two will *look* alike. For that, one needs a person—and the person will make adjustments.

Whatever adjustments are made cannot isolate an element from whatever happens to be printing above and below it. Design and layout, therefore, may determine ink flow to our image. If, for example, the typeface is Baskerville or Bodoni or anything else that features thin strokes, bet on the pressman increasing black to avoid washing the letters out. The fact that this excess ink may also muddy up an image will seem to him the lesser of two evils.

These interventions by the pressman are as predictable as they are purposeful. We can compensate for them. But what if the change in ink flow is inadvertent, a mistake? If we have no clue what the pressman is going to do, we can't adjust, can we?

Yes. Yes, indeed. With a little forethought, we *can*.

Figure 3.2. *A pressman can use a densitometer on this quality-control swatch to find out if inks are coming down at appropriate levels, but the numbers don't tell the whole story. Many prefer just to make the picture of the young woman look good, assuming that this will compensate for intangibles such as the underlying color of the paper.*

The Photoshop Response

Of these factors, Photoshop's dot gain compensation scheme only addresses the first, which is the least important of the four.

Increasing Photoshop's dot gain setting (through Edit>Preferences>Printing Inks Setup) doesn't change the actual CMYK file, but it does alter the monitor preview. It does so by increasing the displayed midtone value, darkening the image overall.

This crude method does not really do justice to the complex interaction of factors described above. True, in a heavy dot gain

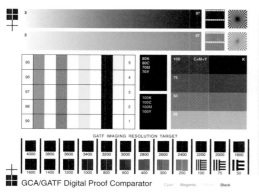

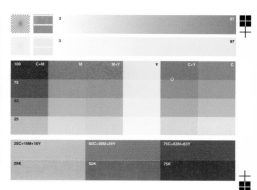

GCA/GATF Digital Proof Comparator   Cyan   Magenta   Yellow   Black

situation, the image *will* look darker overall, but that is not nearly all that will happen. Accordingly, even if you have tweaked your monitor to the point that you trust it slightly for normal commercial jobs, just raising Photoshop's dot gain setting will *not* give you an adequate preview of how a file is going to print on poor paper.

By default, Photoshop uses 20 percent dot gain. This figure is not the amount by which the dots increase in apparent size. Instead, unbelievably, it is the absolute amount that a 50 percent dot in film will appear to increase by on press. (Adobe cannot be blamed for using this absurd method of expressing dot gain; it is in fact the industry standard.) Twenty percent dot gain means, a 50 percent dot will look to the viewer like 70 percent.

> **Most of the time, a poorer-quality paper is not as white as its more expensive counterparts. Starting with a grayish paper will make every pure color look muddier.**

If 20 percent seems extreme, actually it is rather conservative. By this definition, a dot gain of less than 15 or 16 percent is unheard of even under the finest printing conditions, and 20 percent is somewhat low even for commercial sheetfed printing. 25 percent is more like it for magazines, and newspapers will be 30 percent or even higher.

These figures are subject to huge variation on any given day. SWOP, the industry-sponsored organization that suggests technical standards for publication printing and prepress, says dot gain in a magazine is typically 24 percent in cyan and magenta, 22 percent in yellow, and 28 percent in black. More ominous, though, is the uncertainty: plus or minus four points for any or all of them.

For magazine work, therefore, plan for dot gain to be anywhere from about 21 to about 29 percent. That is an enormous range, as Figure 3.3 indicates.

We should not, however, throw up our hands and say it's hopeless. We can't predict the exact temperature in February, but we can state with some certainty what it will *not* be. It will not be in the 80s. Shorts and golf shirt will not be suitable attire.

In exactly the same way that we can select our clothing intelligently for some future date, without knowing precisely what the weather will be, we can take measures in preparing our images that will cater to the likely problems that we will meet on press, without knowing specifically what they will be.

The Artist Strikes Back

If you work for a newspaper, or otherwise have to deal with poor press conditions on a day-to-day basis, you can customize your process to a considerable extent. Here, please assume that you have not done so, and that you have a color image that you believe will print well under high-quality conditions. However, you have to prepare it for a high-dot gain situation, and you have no satisfactory means of proofing.

Given these unfortunate circumstances, here are my recommendations.

1. **Use the best Printing Inks Setup.** Photoshop treats all inks as equals for the purposes of dot gain adjustment. This is notoriously incorrect. Compensate by using the values shown in Figure 3.4, adjusting the overall gain up or down depending on what sort of printing you are doing. If you are in CMYK to begin with, this will affect only the appearance on the monitor, but if you start off in RGB or LAB, it will (favorably) affect the separation to CMYK. If you have ever thought to yourself that Photoshop gives muddy-looking separations, the

Figure 3.3. An industry standards group estimates magazine dot gain at between 21 and 29 percent. That's a huge range, shown top and bottom left. But in high dot gain situations, Photoshop's preview is not accurate: at bottom right, a more plausible version of how an image might look printed in a newspaper—if we don't take the steps needed to save it.

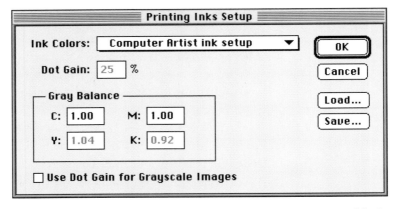

Figure 3.4. *Photoshop's default Printing Inks Setup assumes that dot gain is the same in all colors. It isn't; these values should give better results for magazine work. For higher-quality applications, the overall dot gain percentage should be lower, and for newspaper work, it should be higher.*

main reason is its defaults: a) the GCR setting gives more black than is customary; b) overall dot gain is assumed to be too low; c) no account is taken of the fact that dot gain will be heavier in black than the other three inks. Mix these three ingredients together, and you get mud.

2. **Drop the midtone in CMY.** In a high-dot gain situation, there will be a drastic loss of contrast in the darker ranges of the image, worse than shows up on your screen display. If nothing of importance in the image has detail in the shadows, fine. But if there is significant detail that you wish to save, lower the midtone in all colors except black. This can be done either through the Levels or the Curves command. Of course, if you know of more accurate ways to exaggerate contrast, use them by all means.

3. **Increase saturation.** Open Photoshop's Image>Adjust Hue/Saturation and add 10 to 20 points to general saturation, as in Figure 3.5. This move may be excused for being so crude by the fact that it works. Recall that Photoshop does not compensate for the underlying grayness of the paper. This means that the colors you see on the screen will be cleaner than what you get on press. Compensate by making the screen preview seem lurid.

4. **Use GCR intelligently.** GCR—the substitution of black ink for some of the CMY inks—can be an antidote for human dot gain of the unintentional kind. Although we cannot control what an incompetent pressman will do, we can make damaging our job a lot tougher for him by asking ourselves the following question: Would it be worse for this image if it prints too dark, or if it prints with a color cast?

In the frogman of Figure 3.1, too much black would be a disaster. Everything depends on holding detail in the dark areas of his suit, and if black for whatever reason comes down too heavily quality will go to Davy Jones's locker. Too much of some other color would not be nearly as bad, since we don't have much color perception in objects this dark. The image of the bride, on the other hand, will be badly damaged by a color cast, and not so much by just printing darker. If a bridal gown is not supposed to be *white,* it's hard to know what is.

We take the bomb out of the pressman's hands, therefore, by using GCR in the lighter image, but not in the darker.

5. **When in doubt, assume the worst.** The pressman is more likely to run the inks too heavy than too light. If he sees a washed-out image, he is *sure* to do it, a nice safety belt for us. Cater to it by assuming a dot gain that's on the heavy side. For magazines, use 25 percent.

J'Accuse!

The time has now come to name the culprit. You remember: the correspondent accused separators of sabotage, since his files seemed to look much better when a service bureau handled them.

I will resist the temptation to call this case "elementary," and cut to the chase. The printer did it.

Say *what?*

How can this be? How, and why, did *he* get involved?

"If a thing could only have been done one way, and if only one person could have done it that way," replies Lord Peter Wimsey, "then you've got your criminal, motive or no motive."

Confronted with work from the separator that looks much worse than the service bureau's, the writer suspects the obvious, that somehow the files were the victim of foul play at the separator. Not too likely, in my opinion: in the Scitex workflow,

Figure 3.5. *If the paper is not very white, more than contrast gets lost. If the paper is gray, the impact is similar to adding small, but equal, amounts of all three CMY inks to the image. And if equal amounts are added to all three inks, whichever of the three was weakest to begin with will be helped the most. The weakest ink is the contaminating, or unwanted, color. Therefore, if the paper is gray, every color will appear dirtier overall on paper—but it won't on your monitor, since Photoshop doesn't alter its display to compensate for paper color. Therefore, assume that your monitor is showing you cleaner colors than you will get, and clean them up more. Increasing saturation, right, is a crude but effective way of doing this.*

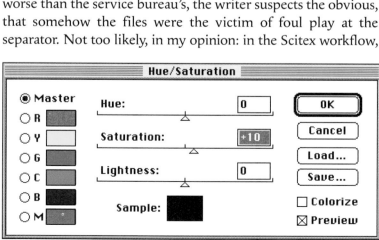

such sabotage would be quite inconvenient, not to mention dangerous as all get-out. Additionally, since the writer appears to use more than one separator, this theory would require a wildly improbable conspiracy. When we hear hoofbeats in the distance, we detectives think horses, not zebras.

The writer said, "*the plates seem to run fine at the pubs as well.*"

"At such moments," says Poirot, "the brain should be working feverishly, not sinking into sluggish repose. The mental activity, it is so interesting, so stimulating. The employment of the little grey cells is a mental pleasure. They and they only can be trusted to lead one through fog to the truth."

When I heard about the pubs, I knew that the printer was guilty. And my proof? Well, the proof is the proof, in this case.

How do you think the writer came to his conclusion that the separator's work was worse, by consulting a crystal ball, or what? Of course not! He believed the evidence of his own eyes, examining the contract proofs from both sources. His mistake was in believing that the two proofs were in any way comparable, and that is how the color-killer got away.

Contract proofs have to behave like presses if printers are to be able to match them. Manufacturers therefore build in a compensation for dot gain, so that the color in their proofs becomes heavier than in the film, just as happens on press.

By default, though, the proof is calibrated to commercial printing on good paper. The base paper of the proof is a brilliant white. Dot gain, although there, is low.

This is the kind of proof that, I deduce, the printer asked the separator *not* to supply, because it would not be possible to match it under publication conditions.

For magazine and lower-quality work, such a proof leads to overoptimism on the part of the client. The printed result is fated to be flat and disappointing by comparison. One can't ask the printer to achieve a color whiter than the paper.

Accordingly, all of the manufacturers of contract proofs offer other options. The base can be white (commercial), off-white (pub), or gray (newsprint). The dot gain can be established as low, moderate, or heavy. Magazine printing presumptively has off-white paper and moderate to heavy dot gain.

A separator works more closely with the printer than a service bureau does, and often is told by the printer what kind of proof to make. The service bureau may not even know that its client intends to use his color in a magazine. Unless specifically told otherwise, a service bureau will make a commercial proof.

The separator, on the other hand, will keep the printer happy by providing a pub proof for what it knows to be publication work. Compared to the service bureau's, it will indeed look "flat, drab, and washed out"—just as any image on pub paper will, next to one that appears on stock twice as expensive.

The service bureau's proof looks nicer, but the separator's proof is the one that reflects reality.

So, there is no conspiracy among the separators, but we may have to credit the separator's derisive remarks about "artists doing seps." If the separator can "punch the color up on the Scitex" and get better results than what we supplied, well, then, what we supplied must not have been so hot.

The poorer the quality of printing, the more important prepress skill becomes. Compensating for heavy dot gain is an art. The better separators can squeeze every ounce of contrast out of an image. But it isn't because they have a Scitex system; it's because they are doing something similar to what I have suggested here. It is skill, not equipment. If their work is better than ours, let us tip our hats, and resolve to do better next time.

In color correction, each image is its own mystery. The best color detectives find clues, draw the logical conclusions, take the necessary steps. Conspiracy theories are unnecessary, extraneous, pointless. The true solutions are out there, waiting for us to discover them. ●

Afterword

Calibrationists and computer artists alike are very reluctant to accept how much variation there is in offset printing. If you are one of these skeptics who thinks that a press is merely an overgrown version of a composite color printer, and just as easily managed, I have arranged a small demonstration.

Some of the pictures in this book print in more than one place. Imagesetting, processing, and platemaking conditions should be virtually identical, as are the digital files. The press is the only variable. Two of the seal pictures in Figure 2.6 are repeated in Figure 2.7. These figures fall on the same press signature, which means they were printed at the same time by the same press crew. I still expect differences.

The two variants of the little girl in Figure 6.3 also appear in the Epilogue, as images D and F. These *don't* fall on the same signature, and I am betting on even more variation, vastly more than you would get on any any two competing brands of contract proof, or for that matter, than between the alternate versions shown in Figure 6.1, which are *not* identical, yet have the advantage of appearing directly below one another, so that whatever ink settings are in use for one will affect the other.

We'll see what happens. My money, as I say, is on substantial differences. The images look identical on the contract proofs, of course.

Every printer realizes the futility of trying to predict exactly how a given press is going to behave on a given day. Calibrationists do not; they scurry about with densitometers, swatch books, and various other moonbeam-catchers, developing a "profile" of a given press, which promptly changes drastically during the next washup or whenever the next shift takes over.

It is one thing to accept the notion that the pressrun is a crapshoot, and quite another to bet on the shooter rolling a 13. This is why standards like SWOP exist, almost as a least common denominator approach to the process, trying to ensure matchable proofs.

Everybody knows that a toner-based color copier is worthless as a contract proofer, but recent advances in dye-sublimation printers have made it possible for many of us to own devices that are in principle capable of contract-proof kind of quality. With this availability (they are around $15,000, at this writing, plus $5 to $10 materials cost per proof, still much cheaper than a tradi-

tional film proof) comes responsibility. The object is not to make a pretty proof but a realistic one, one the printer can match. That usually requires tweaking.

The column's point that we should expect accuracy and repeatability in the proof and not the press is very old, but well worth repeating. Always shoot for perfection in the agreed-upon proof— but if you can take an educated guess at how the press is likely to *vary* from the proof, so much the better.

The correspondent's point is a good one, too. We have reached a time when a number of parties who never used to compete with one another are now doing so. The correspondent thinks that the separators feel threatened by his work. Well, what does he want them to do, give him a kiss? Independent computer artists *are* competitors to color separators in today's world.

I have known some pretty disreputable dealings by separators and service bureaus in my time, but have never encountered actual sabotage. On the other hand, how much difference is there between sabotage and turning a blind eye to obvious problems? If the service bureau sees a typo in a client-supplied file, chances are it will get fixed. But how many separators will step in when their clients include horrifically bad images?

In this case, I think the correspondent is guilty and the separator not, but the real crime is the lack of trust between vendor and client that allowed the idea of sabotage to germinate. And the development of trust is very much the responsibility of both parties. ●

Jargon Watch

ad agency Advertising agencies are notoriously the most finicky and unreasonable clients for prepress work.

Baskerville Descriptive of certain typefaces designed in the late eighteenth century by John Baskerville. Baskerville types have some thin areas and are rather difficult to print, especially in smaller sizes. Samples are shown in Column 10.

Bodoni Descriptive of certain typefaces designed in the early nineteenth century by Giambatista Bodoni. Bodoni types feature extreme contrast between the thick and thin areas of their strokes. They have traditionally been nightmarish for printers to cope with. See discussion in Columns 10 and 11.

calibrationist One who is more willing to believe a densitometer reading than his eyes.

chrome Photography in positive film form, especially if taken by a professional.

CMYK Cyan, magenta, yellow, and black, the inks used on press, but also a major colorspace used in electronic imaging applications.

contact proof Often confused with *contract proof*, a contact proof is one produced by direct exposure to final film. Contact proofs are normally used to show position only, such as the blue- and brownlines used in book publishing. In black and white work, some types of contact proof are used to show halftone quality as well.

contract proof A color proof of sufficient quality that printers will accept it as a valid predictor of what will happen on press. As the column points out, there are many different flavors of contract proof. They vary in whiteness of paper as well as the amount of dot gain they predict.

Cromalin A major brand name of film-based contract proof, marketed by DuPont.

densitometer Device that measures the amount of reflected or transmitted light. Often used to guarantee that film or similar output is being processed under correct conditions.

EfiColor An ill-fated color management system chiefly known for being included as a default in QuarkXPress 3. Most users delete it as being unnecessary and in many cases damaging.

GCR Gray component replacement, the substitution of black ink for more or less equal values of cyan, magenta, and yellow.

LAB Also known as CIELAB or L*a*b*, Photoshop's native colorspace. Its uses in color correction are explored in Column 7 of this book.

Matchprint Major brand of contract proof, marketed by Imation Corp.

midtone Areas of an image channel that are roughly halfway between light and dark; sometimes used specifically to mean the midpoint of a reproduction curve.

Photo CD Image format developed by Kodak. Although it is possible for images scanned from other sources to appear in Photo CD format, ordinarily Photo CDs have been digitized with a proprietary Kodak scanner. See Column 4 for techniques for working with Photo CD images.

quartertone Areas of an image channel that fall roughly halfway between a highlight and a midtone, that is, at about 25 percent ink coverage on press.

RGB Red, green, and blue, the colors of light to which human vision is principally sensitive; also, a major colorspace for electronic imaging.

RIP Raster Image Processor, hardware or software that drives an imagesetter or other output device by converting incoming image data (usually PostScript) to the pixel-by-pixel structure that is needed.

saturation Measure of a color's purity. Can be visualized as the relative presence or absence of the opposite color. For example, a brick and a fire engine are the same color, red, but the brick is much less saturated. On press, that would mean the brick has a far higher percentage of the opposite color, cyan, than the fire engine does.

Scitex The leading vendor in high-end prepress, manufacturer of workstations, imagesetters and many other professional products; a favorite of many separators. "The Scitex" as used in this column means the separator's Scitex retouching workstation.

separator A company specializing in the production of color separations and related services.

service bureau A company specializing in film output and supporting services for electronic files supplied by its clients. The line between service bureau and separator has become rather murky. A separator probably, but not always, has more expensive equipment, more experienced personnel, a better reputation for quality, and higher prices than a service bureau. Separators often work directly with the printer of a job; service bureaus do this rarely.

shadow The darkest neutral areas of an image, sometimes used in color correction to mean the single darkest such area.

SWOP Specifications for Web Offset Publications, a set of standards and technical rules followed by many printers, web and otherwise.

three-quartertone Areas of an image channel that fall roughly halfway between a midtone and a shadow.

web Descriptive of the presses designed for high-volume printing. Web presses are fed by continuous rolls of paper as opposed to sheets, and can run at vastly faster speeds than sheetfed presses.

Dialog Box

In Photoshop, it seems so *easy* to make a color separation. But, as you are about to see, it is a real minefield. The dot gain adjustments discussed in the preceding column are only one part of the overall equation. Photoshop's defaults are pretty miserable, but still, you might think, how deeply can one plumb these questions of shadow value, black generation, dot gain, and GCR?

Well, prepare to find out, at great length. Some of these separation problems are similar, but each correspondent has a special case, when you get right down to it.

Dry stuff, perhaps, but desperately important to those whose livelihoods depend on getting good color on press—not just on a proof. It was no exaggeration when I stated in the column that this is the topic I've gotten the most requests to cover, and rightly so.

Most of these missives deal with the pivotal role of black ink, and the equally important question of how to get as dark a shadow as possible, without losing detail. This is tough sledding. I do not propose to pretend that this section is anything other than the most technically difficult of the entire book.

With that disclaimer, let's see how the world is coping with the necessity of making the separation meet the press conditions.

Default Photoshop sep setup as a recipe for "the most ghastly scans"

We in South Africa mostly use 5C3M3Y as standard highlight, and 94C89M90Y75K as a standard shadow setting. I have no knowledge of anyone here using undercolour removal to any great degree, and therefore have no experience with it. My question is why is Photoshop's default Separation Setup is so far from both this and the setup you recommend? As we scan to CMYK "on the fly," it doesn't affect us much, but hordes of people scanning on low-end scanners, who do not know of adjusting the Separation setup, produce the most ghastly scans after using Photoshop to convert RGB to CMYK. 100% Black does nothing for Cromalin proofs, let alone a press run where black is usually run heavier for the type. I have found that a 75% Black Ink Limit and a Total Ink Limit of 348%, set on GCR with medium black generation, produces excellent proofs as well as press runs. What part of Adobe's thinking am I not understanding?

Your suggested highlight is fair enough, if conservative, but the shadow value would not be typical of U.S. work.

I would surmise that this is because here, there are so many possible destinations for the work that we cannot be sure who is going to be printing it under what conditions, or on what kind of press. Therefore we must almost assume worst-case conditions and go with a lighter shadow than we would like. If we are certain that the press can handle a shadow as dark as the 95C90M90Y75K you suggest without loss of detail (or if there is no important detail in the shadow that we are worried about losing), then of course we do it.

Absent other instructions, U.S. suppliers produce work to standards suggested by a group known as SWOP, Inc. (stands for: Specifications for Web Offset Publications). SWOP dictates that film is unacceptable if the maximum shadow value exceeds a combined total of 300. Many American magazines go further and insist, for ease of handling on press, that maximum ink value be 280, or even lower. Magazine printers employ film inspectors whose sole joy in life is to reject client advertising that fails to meet these guidelines.

Under these circumstances undercolor removal is mandatory as a practical matter, as to get a realistically dark shadow the black will have to be as heavy, if not more so, than any of the three colored inks.

Conceding this, Adobe's default is quite poor. Allowing 100% black leads to thin-looking shadows, difficulties in color correction, and closure of shadows in many cases. I therefore recommend 85% in the Separation setup dialog box, although your value is certainly reasonable.

Another reason for the muddy-looking seps from Photoshop is not so much that a rather heavy GCR is used as that, in its calculation, Photoshop erroneously assumes that the black behaves like any other ink. As you point out, dot gain will almost certainly be heavier in black—even if the pressman is not doing it intentionally, to compensate for type or something else.

Therefore, Photoshop's black plate tends to be entirely too heavy for practical use. The two ways to avoid this are 1) to use Light GCR and/or 2) change color balance within Printing Inks setup, using a value of .92 or so for black. ●

GCR, UCR, skeleton blacks, shadows without detail, and 3-color seps

I've always suspected that GCR was causing me grief—your column seems to confirm that. I get jobs back from the sep house sometimes with too much black where the original has little—and this seems to get darker still at my printer—so I usually under-expose the black final when I suspect a problem.

Yecch! That's no way to do things.

I have a question: If I tell my sep house no GCR, does that mean a 3-color separation? (or almost a 3-color separation)

No. It means a "skeleton" black, where the black only appears in depth-of-detail areas and not in areas that have a perceptible color, such as a face. Using moderate GCR, a face may have some small amount of black in it, and if the printer is running heavy black (like, for example, if he is trying to compensate for light type on the same page) this may make your image look muddy. With a "skeleton" black, on the other hand, if the printer overinks, you may start to lose detail in the deep shadows, but that's it.

Strictly speaking, if you are giving the printer this instruction, you should include a maximum total ink value as well, such as: No GCR, 280 total ink. An equivalent phrase would be: UCR only, 280 total ink.

If your sep house uses "Light GCR" (Photoshop definition), there is a slight technical difference between this and UCR only, but not enough to worry about; this will give you the same kind of skeleton black that you seem to want. ●

Why do the experts recommend Light GCR and 85% maximum black?

I've noticed that you and other authors recommend a Photoshop Separation setup default of (roughly) GCR Light, 85% maximum black, 300 maximum total ink, 0% UCA. One author has mentioned that he believes that PS is optimized for GCR seps and states that he has noticed some unwanted grain produced in Photoshop UCRs.

I and most of the clients I work with are getting most of our scans from service bureaus with high-end drum scanners.

While the service bureau rarely discusses this matter with you, they typically make UCR seps. Many corporate clients (even the ones with desktop drum scanners) don't know the difference between UCR and GCR. The clients are gathering/producing seps from a number of different sources and then combining them in the same brochure, ad, etc. I'm sure you know where this is going—the client can easily develop a library of images that drive the pressman a little nuts.

Is GCR Light close enough to typical UCR seps to keep the pressman happy?

To all intents and purposes they are identical. As long as we get a "skeleton" black plate, meaning no black at all in relatively clean color areas, the image will handle the same on press. GCR Light, as a term, is a Photoshop invention. "Typical UCR seps" vary wildly from scanner to scanner, anyway.

With this type of situation in mind, how do you recommend clients make their "in house" seps?

Generally, in the manner you have described. If scanning into CMYK, choose UCR or whatever the equivalent is on the scanner. If scanning into RGB, use Light 85/300/0 in Separation setup during the conversion to CMYK. There are exceptions, mind you, and some of them are mentioned in the column. However, in the absence of what seems to you a good reason to depart from the general rule, leave the black relatively light. ●

If Photoshop's programmers were pressmen, there'd be no problem

Besides not knowing what is happening, what's wrong with setting the endpoints with the levels eyedroppers like Adobe says?

1. It will zero out your highlight unless you change Photoshop's defaults.

2. It does not control black generation.

3. It does not allow you to shape the curves so as to maximize contrast in the interest areas of the image.

4. Lots of images don't have easily measurable white points or midpoints.

Also, why is their shadow value so different from your 80C70M70Y70K? Theirs is something like 55C55M55Y100K.

If Photoshop's programmers were pressmen the difference would vanish rapidly. This is largely a function of Preferences>Separation setup. If you change yours from 100% to 85% maximum black, the problem will go away and you will get a shadow similar to mine. Allowing 100% black is very inferior.●

Lowering the total ink limit to keep shadows from plugging on press

I recently came under serious criticism by my predecessor because of your book. I would greatly appreciate your opinion.

My predecessor left the drum scanner set for 340% total ink limit. Your book states that 280 is standard for web, and "for sheetfed printing 320 is acceptable. Should you be using very high quality paper, or printing on a waterless press, an even higher limit may be attainable."

Based on this, I decided to start scanning at 280 for work that was to be printed on our sheetfed press. My predecessor, insisting that I had a reading problem and was without a clue to the difference between a web and sheetfed, cited your book as proof of my ignorance. (I'm paraphrasing his words quite generously.)

My reasons for attempting to use SWOP settings on our sheetfed:

1. My pressman has had trouble keeping the shadows from plugging. He had asked for lower ink limits for some time. He felt he had no room for adjustment, particularly at 150 lpi and above.

2. This is a small, price-conscious town, and we are the only 4-color press here. So many jobs are run on second grade paper, or even recycled stocks. Premium coated paper is not the norm.

3. Our press is one finicky beast. The pressman here works miracles. He's the only one here that can balance the water to get decent prints.

Obviously, 280% can and should change from job to job, even image to image. A client wants 200 lpi work next week, and I think it's going to be a big headache.

The problem here is, as in your articles, that your book cannot be simply read and quoted verbatim (please don't take my use of the word "problem" literally). I felt that I was reaching into what you wrote and came away with a better understanding of the purpose of the Total Ink Limit.

My SWOP scans haven't come off the press yet, so I have no concrete results. But, I felt I had to question 340, and will always question my own work. One can get overconfident and complacent if they don't keep asking questions.

The first order of business is to find out what in blazes is going on! You need to know how heavy a shadow you can put down on your press and still hold detail. From what you are saying under your particular conditions 340 sounds way too high. A test run of several versions of an image that has significant shadow detail seems like the indicated first step. Try out several different separation parameters, rather than guessing at the scanner.

Ink density and screen ruling are interrelated. A lot of times if the screen ruling is too fine, shadow detail can be lost. You say that you have a questionable press and are printing on a lot of questionable stocks. If so, 150 line work is *really* questionable. The higher the screen ruling, the more difficult to handle on press. Try a test with 133 or 120 and see if it looks better—it probably will. Or better yet, run 120, 133, 150, and 200 side by side on the same sheet. You may not be able to see a drastic difference from afar but if you take a loupe to them you'll see where the dots are plugging.

SWOP calls for 300 total density, not 280. Most magazines take it down to 280 because of concerns about handling problems on press (ink contamination from unit to unit; drying/smearing problems if sheet is too tacky, etc.) It is not unheard of for 340 to work but from what you are describing it sounds high.

The real issue is, how heavy a dot can your press hold and still portray detail? If 340 is your maximum total ink, shadow should nominally be 90C80M80Y90K. That is indeed quite heavy, and under the conditions you describe I question that it is possible.

It makes sense to me to scan to a maximum shadow of 80C70M70Y70K all the time since that will work for almost any application short of newsprint. Nothing stops you from tweaking it up in Photoshop if you know that the particular press conditions support higher values, or if your shadow is a glass pot of coffee or something else that has no detail to begin with. ●

Reseparation and other sneaky methods to reduce total ink density

After optimizing color and gradation, many times we have pushed total ink beyond the original specs. We always do a final check immediately prior to running the film. If total ink is too high, I convert to LAB mode and change sep setup to UCR and total ink to what we need, before reconverting to CMYK. I've found that method, or selective color correction of the black, to be the most reliable way to do it without screwing up my curves too much.

There are a number of approaches one can take. If you are just off by a little, selective color correction of the black, as you say, is undetectable. On the other hand, converting into LAB gives us the opportunity to do some useful correcting there as well. Don't see why UCR is necessary on the resep, since the total ink will be OK regardless of what black generation you use.

Another interesting use of selective color is that one can perform manual GCR on blacks only. Select blacks, and then subtract the CMY components and then add compensating black ink. We have found that on some pickup jobs where we have to adjust total ink way down, say from 320 to 260, after our usual CMYK to LAB to CMYK scheme, we can close up the black dot giving more visual weight to the shadows without exceeding the total ink spec. It works quite well and it is really amazing the difference closing up the rosette can make. We still don't exceed 95% in the black dot of course.

In a situation like this we are in bad shape no matter what. I don't trust selective color correction of the black to accommodate a 60-point drop gracefully. Whether you use that approach or CMYK>LAB>CMYK, you face a choice of a shadow that is too light or a black that is too heavy, hurting detail. If the printer is asking for only 260 total ink, his paper must be pretty poor, worse than pub grade. And if that's the case there is no way he can hold detail in 95% of any color, let alone black. He would be lucky to hold detail in 80%.

I try to use a combined approach in such cases: I reseparate to get down to 290–300, but then when doing the selective color correction, I really hammer the yellow and only reduce the cyan and magenta a small amount. Yellow doesn't pull its weight in the shadow, so if something has to go that is the first choice. By having an unbalanced shadow that is chiefly CMK we can get both darkness and detail.●

What's wrong with using UCA to guarantee a properly dark shadow?

I've been told that some UCA is usually best to ensure a proper dark shadow. This goes back to my drum scanner training. Why aren't you using it in your suggested separation setup? You say several times that your shadow value of 80C70M70Y70K is conservative (too light?) so why not darken it with UCA? That is a lighter shadow than I've ever dealt with.

It may be lighter, but it isn't thinner than Photoshop's default. People who say they get better results with UCA are generally using it as a form of damage control to compensate for failure to set Black Ink Limit to something sensible.

All UCA does is pour CMY ink willy-nilly into shadow areas.

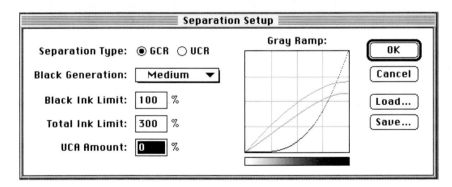

Figure 3.6. Under-color addition (UCA), at least in Photoshop's rendition, forces more cyan, magenta and yellow into the shadows, but as the ends of the curves in the bottom version show, all it adds is depth, not detail. There are better ways to strengthen a shadow.

It does nothing at all to add detail, which is the nominal reason we want deep shadows.

The reason I advocate a shadow value with black set at only 70 percent is not that I believe a press can't handle higher. Rather, I think it is harder to add detail to a picture than it is to subtract it. This lesson has been brought home to me painfully by many of my students. At 80C70M70Y70K I am sure I will not be losing detail under almost any printing condition. The Photoshop default shadow of roughly 65C55M55Y95K, on the other hand, gets you the worst of both worlds. It is *guaranteed* to lose shadow detail because of clotting in the black, and on a bad day it will actually print *lighter* than the one I recommend.

As you know, a lot of the time shadow detail isn't that big of a deal.

Right, because of the characteristics of the individual image. If we have a picture of a black cat we want to hold detail in the fur. If it's a picture of a black squash ball, we probably don't care whether whatever detail can be found in it stands up or not. Accordingly, we can and should go with a darker shadow.

Figure 3.7. *Under-color addition loses shadow contrast, and is generally inferior to steepening the black curve. However, in this image, UCA is right. The less detail in the black areas of the cards, the better; at the same time, we would like to guarantee a dark shadow.*

My method of attaining this would be to lengthen the black curve so that the shadow became, say, 80C70M70Y85K. Because I am using a skeleton black (Light GCR) to begin with, this move is going to be *very* helpful to the image as a whole. It will add snap and life everywhere, not just in the shadows, because contrast is being added to the black plate.

Compare that to the alternative shadow-darkening method of UCA. As Figure 3.6 illustrates, UCA just pours in flat tints of the CMY inks into shadow areas. It does not add detail in any way, and squanders the opportunity to improve the image.

About the only time I would want to use UCA is in separating an image such as Figure 3.7. There, if I lose detail in the shadows, I *like* it. The black paint of the cards is the only thing that's even remotely close to a shadow. Any detail that's there is probably a scratch or a reflection or some other thing that we don't want. So, naturally, the heavier the shadow the better, and UCA will help cover up any imperfections that are in the black plate.●

Bright reds, dark blacks, and lousy transitions: is this a GCR problem?

I had a tough GCR problem the other day. The subject was a red car; the chrome was excellent [Figure 3.8, I trust, is comparable—DM]. The car's ducts and vents made large, solid shadow areas in the striking red paint. These areas were large enough to cause drying problems when separated at a light/skeletal GCR; the areas would be at the total ink limit.

So, naturally, I separated at a fairly medium GCR. Total ink in the shadows added up to just 210 (about 40C35M35Y100K). Just fine for our press, which has trouble with anything over 300 total ink.

The problem came in the transitions. Around some shadow areas, between the red paint and black shadow, the paper showed through like a halo. I know what happened; the car (about 10C95M90Y0K) and shadow (about 40C35M35Y100K) transition caused rapid removal of magenta and yellow, letting paper show.

Already, you have engineered in three major problems:
1. The overall shadow is too light despite the 100% black; if you can get 300 points total ink why are you settling for 210?

2. There is now a big hole in your magenta and yellow plates in the shadow, as Figure 3.9 indicates (you have rightly pointed to this as a major problem in the job).

3. Your black should not be at 100%, as this will make for a very bad transition; at some point detail will be lost (Figure 3.10).

For shadow areas, GCR setting (light, medium, heavy) makes no difference. The only pertinent numbers are total ink and maximum black. Maximum black should be no higher than 85 percent, always. Total ink should be whatever you feel comfortable with. Photoshop will be feeding black ink as necessary to meet these target numbers regardless of what your GCR settings are.

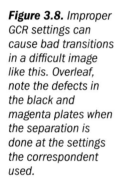

Figure 3.8. *Improper GCR settings can cause bad transitions in a difficult image like this. Overleaf, note the defects in the black and magenta plates when the separation is done at the settings the correspondent used.*

How can I avoid this blemish in an otherwise beautiful job?

If you had separated at a normal 85%–280, your shadow would have been something like 75C65M65Y75K. This would probably have solved your problem right there, since there is now no significant hole in the magenta.

Better way still: separate at 85%–320. Shadow should now be something like 85C75C75M85K. This is too dark, of course, but

Figure 3.9. *The corre-spondent's magenta plate, top, has holes in the black areas in the grillwork at top rear of the car, causing poor transitions. Below, a normally separated magenta.*

we aren't done. Open Adjust: Selective Color and choose Blacks. Move the yellow slider all the way to the left, decrease cyan slightly and increase magenta. Now, your shadow will become something like 80C85M40Y85K. (If there is anything else of significance in the image other than the car, you should select the car and work on it only, since God knows what impact this move may have on other areas.)

Figure 3.10. *Comparing the black plates shows a similar problem. Detail in the tires is lost at top, Furthermore, the shadows in the car are sudden, harsh. Below, a normal black separation.*

This gives you a very dark shadow, but only 280 ink coverage. Also, there is now no hole to speak of in your magenta plate. Yellow is so light that it has little impact in shadow areas. You won't notice the hole that remains in the yellow. And if you are having an ink coverage problem in shadow areas, but you still want them nice and dark, you don't get nearly as much bang for your buck with yellow as with magenta or cyan. ●

The perils of preparing separations for web newsprint reproduction

Dear Mr. Margulis,
I have read your book on correcting in Photoshop and found it to be the BEST resource for production work in Photoshop. I have the utmost respect for your knowledge on correcting and can't begin to tell you how much your book has improved my work. In fact I'm such a novice I am just now reaching "ape" level. Having said that, I have also had many, many frustrations trying to get consistent results on web newsprint "rag" pieces. The following is a help request that I was going to post to one of the Adobe folders when I saw your name helping other people that have asked for help. The following was too large for a simple post, so I thought that you might be so kind as to help me if I e-mailed what I was going to post. Being the guru that you are, I hope you will excuse the novice, stupid questions and comments that some of this will undoubtedly be. [Post follows]

I have some questions regarding proper steps in preparing scanned and Photo CD files for film output to be printed on newsprint on a web press. I don't seem to have much problem getting images to look good on a good sheetfed using a good stock. But I'm having big problems trying to get good, consistent color on a web/newsprint combination. One project will be beautiful, the next has red faces and washed out backgrounds or shadows totally clogged up or something else is wrong with the color.

I've read every book, article, posting or anything else I could get my hands on regarding getting good consistent desktop color. It seems that everyone contradicts everyone else, and I come away scratching my head. One person says that it's all in calibrating the scanner to monitor to output device. Obviously, you should have these things all closely matching so you can get some idea that seeing what's on the monitor is something close to what is going to print. There are lots of software packages on the market that claim that their software will get it all working in sync. Then you have someone like Dan Margulis in his book on color correcting with Photoshop saying to completely ignore what you see on the screen and go by the numbers that you sample with the eyedropper tool. Admittedly, using his techniques have improved my novice color correcting to a semi-comfortable place.

At the risk of completely oversimplifying Margulis' book, basically his approach is that if you get what you know the colors should be *to be the right numbers, the rest of the colors should fall into place. I have found this to be completely true for the most part. I can get things looking great on the screen, and even great looking proofs. Getting them to go on web newsprint is something else.*

I am in a position that I have control over every facet in the process except making the plates and running the press. This brings up the questions about Photoshop's preferences settings:

Re: Monitor setup
1. Does the monitor setup interfere with the settings I have in the Gamma control panel that I have automatically starting at computer bootup?

They work in tandem.

2. I have a 20" Radius Precision Trinitron monitor. The monitor drop-down menu does not list this monitor. What should I select, default?

Any Trinitron setting should do.

3. Do the settings in this dialog box affect the actual file or just they way the screen looks in Photoshop?

If your file is in LAB or CMYK, only the screen display. If the file is in RGB, there will be a slight variation in the actual data when you convert it to either of the other two colorspaces.

Re: Printing Inks setup
1. Does selecting the various ink/paperstock/dot gain settings here affect the image file itself or does it simulate on my monitor what the printed piece would look like, thus enabling me to visually adjust the image for the intended press/paper/dot gain combination?

If you have a CMYK file already, the file itself will be unaffected by a change in these settings, but if you have an RGB or LAB file, two different Printing Inks setups will result in two different files once you convert to CMYK. Changing the Printing Inks setup also alters the monitor display in CMYK, but not in the other two colorspaces.

2. When I calibrate my imagesetter, I can send (have been sending) with the calibration, a compensation for dot gain. If I use the SWOP (Newsprint) setting at 30% dot gain in the Printing Inks setup in

Photoshop, and adjust my image to look good on the monitor, can I assume that dot gain is accounted for at that point, or do I also account for dot gain when I calibrate my imagesetter?

If your printing conditions vary, compensate in Photoshop, not on your imagesetter. Its calibration should be the same regardless of final destination. You need (at least) two different Photoshop Printing Inks setups, one to load for commercial jobs and one for newsprint. While a good monitor can help, keep in mind its limitations in portraying what will happen in high dot gain situations, discussed in the preceding column.

3. What does the gray balance do?

It compensates for unusually heavy dot gain in one specific ink, or a known printing anomaly. Since Photoshop incorrectly assumes that dot gain is the same in all four colors, I recommend using the values of Figure 3.4 instead. Thereafter, if you find a *consistent* color imbalance (everything prints too red, for example), you can make further adjustments.

Be very careful of ad hoc changes in monitor settings, though. It is critically important that you not base such an adjustment on one or two samples only, as you could just be spinning your wheels, adjusting to unusually sloppy presswork.

Re: Separation setup. I have been using GCR/Black Generation Light/80% Black ink Limit/ Total Ink 250%. This gives me a dull, flat image in RGB to CMYK conversions. I then go to curves, start at getting the highlight dot somewhere close to 6C2M2Y, then darkest shadows near 70C60M60Y60K. Most of the images I use are people poses, so next I go to work on the skin tones bringing them to an average of around 20C40M40Y0K (for Caucasians). I don't worry too much about black levels until this point, even though the image is still very dull and flat. Next I go to the black curve and start adding black at the midrange to highlights. This of course brings in all the definition and sharpness.

The fleshtone values you are citing are too high in the cyan and magenta, even for commercial printing, and newsprint would be worse. On newsprint, cyan should be no more than a quarter of magenta and yellow should always be higher than magenta.

Your shadow values are correctly balanced, but they are too light. Your 250 maximum ink density is probably correct, but your final values should be around 65C55M55Y75K, which is much darker than the 70C60M60Y60K you cited.

1. Is my Separation setup correct for going to web/newsprint?

Yes.

2. Are these good separation setup settings for different press/stock combinations?

No, Light/85/300 is more customary.

3. What about all this software I'm seeing advertised that promises to separate to CMYK from RGB scans or Photo CD, color correct, and sharpen, for whatever press/paperstock combination, all flawless and automatic with one small click of the mouse?

If you are willing to spend five to ten minutes correcting manually, you will be able to do much better. If you are not willing to do this these programs will be better than nothing.

With the flood of all the articles, books, software manuals, seminars, calls to vendors, reading on-line postings and all of my own trial and error on the subject, it seems like the answers to consistent color on web/newsprint would be attainable. But I seem to be getting more confused. It seems that decent, consistent color on lower quality "rag" style web/newsprint would be the easiest to attain. I find it much harder than on better quality paper/sheetfed combinations.

It is. Color correction is a compensation for poor conditions. The worse the range of colors available to us, the more important it is to get all the contrast we can. Newsprint is going to give us a flatter picture than fine paper no matter what we do, and our skill level is very important to compensate. Look at it this way: suppose that because your newsprint work is so unsatisfactory, tomorrow your company cuts your pay by 25 percent, and you can't find another job, so you have to accept this. The question is, now that you have less money available in your paycheck, is it *more* important or *less* important that you spend your money wisely? In going from fine paper to newsprint, you take a contrast cut instead of a salary cut, but the principle is exactly the same.●

Is the RIP a good place to apply a curve to compensate for dot gain?

HELP! I'm doing a large job on an unfamiliar and lower quality press than I'm used to, and I've got some ink questions I can't figure out. We're bringing the prepress in house to get better control, quicker turn-around, better quality, etc. The specs I've gotten from the printer include: 45-lb coated paper (similar to the advertising inserts you get in the Sunday paper), 270% max ink coverage, 75% GCR, 133-line screen.

I've done a lot of web work, but never on a press/paper combination with quality this low before. The main thing that strikes me about the previous magazine is the loss of highlight detail; particularly in images of marble statuary, the highlights have been almost completely blown out. I received some of the scans from the previous issue, and have looked at the highlight dots, and am thinking that I might be able to improve on the quality by using different GCR and highlight settings.

The printer uses Matchprints to proof files. They then remake the film and apply a curve on the RIP that takes the 50% dots to 35%. I'm thinking that this might be part of the problem...

I'm thinking it might be *most* of the problem. Such a curve decreases contrast in the lighter half of the image and increases it in the darker half. This would account for the lack of detail in the highlight. Sounds like a big mistake to me.

...and that a carefully constructed curve in Photoshop would give better results.

You bet it would.

A sample highlight number from their drum scanned file is 2C2M3Y3K. Applying their RIP curve in Photoshop, this gets taken down to 2C1M2Y2K.

This is one of the most fouled-up numbers I've ever heard of. There should not be any black in the highlight. The cyan has to be at least two points higher than the yellow. It is unlikely they can hold the 1 percent magenta dot under these printing conditions. I'll bet that they are using some kind of color management system and have somehow been persuaded by a densitometer salesman that what they are doing is right. This almost has to be calibrationism at work—it's virtually impossible for a human to come up with a setup this bad.

I reseparated this file in Photoshop (Heavy GCR, Black Ink Limit 85%, Total Ink Limit 270%, UCA 0%). This gives me a highlight of 5C4M5Y. Applying their RIP curve, this gets taken down to 3C2M3Y.

This is better than what they had, but will result in a red cast. The cyan ink must be higher, otherwise the highlight will not be neutral, and neither will much of the rest of the image.

The GCR in the printer's file seems to continue all the way into the highlights; in fact, the minimum black dot in the original image is 3K.

You should call the police and send them over to the printer. Somebody there should be facing arrest on charges of impersonating a scanner operator.

My Photoshop separations with Heavy GCR don't put any black dot in the highlights at all. Is this an advantage or a disadvantage? It seems to me that having such heavy black in the highlights drops down the values of the other three inks to the point where they break up, possibly leading to the loss of highlight detail.

The GCR setting shouldn't have much of an impact in the highlight—there shouldn't be any black there no matter what. I would be a little chary about using Heavy GCR in this setting because newspaper black dot gain can be absurdly high and Heavy GCR shifts crucial detail into the black plate. If you are going to do this, you definitely need to use the Printing Inks setup adjustment recommended in Figure 3.4.

My first thought is to shoot for a highlight of 9C3M3Y, which would get taken down by their RIP curve to 5C2M2Y. My second thought is to do the curve myself in Photoshop, and engineer a curve that would spare the highlight values, and possibly increase contrast a bit in the highlights.

#2 sounds like a much better plan.

I'd really like to know what kind of highlight I should shoot for in this situation. 5C2M2Y seems low to me.

5C2M2Y is a conservative highlight, appropriate even for newsprint. The question is whether your press can hold a 2% dot on this paper. Most can. Possibly 6C3M3Y might be more prudent, but I doubt it. You use the term "blown out" to describe your complaint about the highlights. Most people use this term to mean that the highlight is missing altogether and you see paper only, not dots. What you are describing sounds like general lack of detail, not lack of dots. ●

When adding undercolors actually makes the shadow seem lighter

I'm working on short-run, large format displays on a new plotter with a number of interesting controls. In running my color tests, I've found that the 400% 4-color black actually appears duller and less intense than the 100%K.

I assume this has to do with the "reverse dot-gain" you mentioned in the column, where the extra saturation causes ink to be absorbed into the paper instead of reflecting light while lying on top of the paper.

No, it doesn't, sorry. The counter-dot gain I was talking about there was where adding ink makes the image darker, just not as fast as one would think. Whereas, when we are in a heavy dot gain situation we are accustomed to color getting darker *faster* than we think. In principle, if you add ink, of no matter what color, you *have* to be making the image darker. Your printer, though, doesn't use conventional ink; it probably uses heat-released dyes.

What you are talking about is an entirely different animal: a situation where you add ink (or equivalent) and yet the image gets *lighter.* This happens typically with dye-sublimation printers, apparently because the heat generated to activate the cyan, magenta, and yellow dyes vaporizes some of the black.

I know the phenomenon exists but haven't had enough experience with it to offer any intelligent suggestions on what to do. My guess would be that UCR only, 100 maximum black, 200 total ink, would be a good start. This would yield an almost totally black shadow, without paying the consequences of that decision in the rest of the image. ●

We're a small design studio in Prague, and since there's no information of any kind about anything, we've had to figure out prepress and lithography ourselves. We have pictures scanned, and color-correct them ourselves, without calibration (except a CMYK color chart). A bit of a joke, but we get better results than local printers and lithographers!

However, I have one question not answered by your article (and 100 more to ask!). When we have traditional drum scans made, delivered as CMYK, we usually have to convert to RGB and reseparate as CMYK using GCR in PhotoShop. We've spotted the following: the scanners use UCR, resulting in flat pictures and flat blacks. We've taken exactly the same picture and prepared it both ways, and confirmed our method. While we understand the losses involved in the conversions, we, too, have wondered about a prepress conspiracy. We also receive the same answers, and one new one! They refer to bright pictures with rich blacks as "American"!

Many older drum scanners have this same problem of giving much too much black in the shadow and not enough elsewhere. Frequently, one cause will be that they have programmed the scanner to give a specific maximum of all four inks in the shadows (usually 300 in the U.S.). If this is the case you can ask them to give you a heavier shadow in the CMY colors; if they do this, you may be able to color-correct the black to something you like better, without converting. If you do have to convert as you are doing now, at least the conversion will be better.

We often do 2- to 4-color spot color photo-realistic images. We can't find what opacity we should set ink colors in Photoshop to preview mixing of spot inks. Am I dreaming, or is it possible?

It is difficult at best and also not particularly accurate, since Photoshop only allows you to set the values for 100% of one ink alone or combinations of 100% of two or more inks. It assumes that a 50–50 blend of two inks, would be based on the 100%-100% values and that is not always true. You can try this if you like but a better way in my opinion is to use specialized software such as that of the Dutch firm, Visu Technologies.

When we print a metallic ink, we're not sure if there's a problem printing on top of it. It should be OK, but we can't get an answer.

This depends on the specific metallic ink. Drying characteristics are different for each one. Ordinarily, you are correct, just as ordinarily, the metallic ink is thought to be darker than black for trapping purposes.

We've experimented with crude stochastics in CMYK and can't get the dot-gain right, especially since we (and the printers) don't have densitometers. They work well in 2-color. We use the Diffusion Dither bitmapping in Photoshop to do it. Any suggestions? After 45%, dot gain becomes dramatic. Black is at 85%.

No one has yet been able to conquer the dot gain problem with stochastic screening, which is why the technique has never caught on, except with newspapers. Its dot gain is much heavier than in normal printing. The smaller the dot, the greater the dot gain, and obviously stochastic dots are *extremely* small. This is the same reason that dot gain increases with a finer screen ruling.

Even if you can predict the dot gain from the imagesetter, if you are having your film contacted or otherwise duplicated by hand this introduces another variable, because normal contacting methods are not sufficiently controlled to guarantee precise reproduction of stochastic dots.

For these reasons I recommend that you not use stochastic except on plates that mostly give color and not detail. There is no problem with having conventional screens on some plates and stochastic screens on others. In fact, if you are doing 5-color printing. a stochastic fifth color is probably better, as it avoids moiré. If you are printing five colors, the fifth color is mostly to add depth. Even if you miscalculate the dot gain, the printer will probably be able to control it on press.●

PART II

L*a*b* Meets
The Matador

colorspaces, curves, and a
consistent correction philosophy

4

The Five-Minute Photo CD Gourmet

Drum-scan quality, but at a fraction of the price? Too good to be true? Certainly, unless you intervene after the scan. Here's how it's done, in four easy steps.

On March 28, 1995, Kodak rocked and shocked the graphic arts community with a surprise announcement that Photo CD will now be an open standard. Anyone will now be able to write images into the PCD format, although they will not be able to call them "Kodak" Photo CDs.

Nothing quite like this has been seen since Adobe abandoned its monopoly of the PostScript Type 1 standard, but Kodak's move makes eminent sense: the company would rather have 60 percent of a large market than 100 percent of a small one.

Already, though, PCD was finding more and more favor among imaging professionals because of its undeniable advantages: low initial cost, ease of use, choice of resolutions, convenience for multimedia, an almost indestructible method of archiving.

The March 28 announcement will no doubt accelerate this process, and make it much more likely that the serious graphic artist will encounter, and have to correct, such images—and for the foreseeable future, most of them will come from a Kodak scanner.

The quality of raw Kodak scans can, however, best be described as GEFSOP—good enough for some purposes. If that isn't good

---

Figure 4.1. *Because the Photo CD scanning process doesn't incorporate certain steps that have always been routine in drum scanning, print quality often seems disappointing. It can, however, be brought up to snuff quickly. Top, an uncorrected Photo CD image. Bottom, the same scan after the quick recipe advocated in this column.*

enough for *your* purposes, you will need some quick and dirty way to bring them up to snuff, using Photoshop.

Some assumptions. First, we need to assume a GEFSOP image to begin with. Largely because of its volatile YCC colorspace, it is a great deal easier to create *really* poor scans with PCD than any competitive approach. If you are presented with something totally flat or with a ridiculous color cast, the following methods won't work well.

> **K**odak prides itself on matching the original art, warts and all, in Photo CD. Unfortunately, the marketplace is not quite ready for this concept.

Second, we assume an original Kodak scan. It is, obviously, impossible to generalize about what sort of corrections may be necessary to images from sources unknown on the new plain-vanilla PCD.

Third, we assume you want to do this quickly. Much of PCD's appeal is cost and convenience. If you can justify spending hours to improve individual images you should probably be thinking of drum scans.

The Obstacles to Success

The following, therefore, is a general recipe for transforming GEFSOP images into ones that are GEFMAP—good enough for most any purpose. It is a recipe of the five-minute gourmet variety. If we wanted to spend more time with these images we could make them better yet.

Generalizations are always a little unfair, but on the whole, if you deal with Kodak PCD images, you will see certain problems again and again.

- Images that are too soft, especially in lighter areas. No unsharp masking is applied during the scan, but the problem appears to be deeper than just this.
- Slight color casts. Kodak prides itself on matching the original art, warts and all. Unfortunately, the marketplace is not quite ready for this concept; in high-end work, such casts are normally eliminated during scanning.
- Overly flat images, for the same reason. If the photographer has not managed to get a full tonal range into the original, there won't be one in the PCD scan, either. This is at variance with professional prepress practice, which is to give virtually everything a full range.

These problems, which stem, somewhat paradoxically, from Kodak's grim determination to match the art as exactly as

Figure 4.2. (Opposite) A better original than Figure 4.1, top, but the same dramatic change in image quality at bottom. On subsequent pages, the quick steps used to improve the originals of this and Figure 4.1 will be shown, side by side.

possible, afflict PCD images even at their best. The picture of children in Figure 4.2, in my opinion, is an excellent PCD original, and it was brought into Photoshop using a Kodak-developed look-up table that was customized to the particular scanner used here. The boating picture of Figure 4.1 is not quite as good, but both show to some extent the undesirable characteristics discussed above.

Fortunately, relatively simple adjustments can help most of these problems, but they require the use of something many of us are not too familiar with—the LAB colorspace.

The L Channel's Power

LAB, the current darling of color scientists, is Photoshop's native colorspace. It is also closely related to Kodak's YCC. There are enough real-life advantages to suggest that whatever your method of acquiring Photo CD images, you open them in LAB.

In LAB, the A and B are opponent-color channels. The A is red vs. green, and the B plays off yellow against blue. The color of any area is determined by a complex

Figure 4.3. *Steps 1 and 2 of the recipe, illustrated at left and right with the originals of Figures 4.1 and 4.2. The image is opened in LAB. Top, the original L channel. Step 2, center, is to apply unsharp masking to the L only. With this new L channel, the color now looks like what's shown at bottom, a big improvement with more to come.*

interplay between the A and B channels, both of which are rather explosive. Unless you are quite adventurous [or have read Column 7 of this book, which hadn't appeared at the time this one was written], color correction using the A and B channels is an experience devoutly to be avoided.

The L channel, however, is extremely valuable in fighting the characteristic softness of the PCD image. As all color information is contained in the A and B channels, the L is brightness only. If you like, consider it a black and white version of the color picture.

A better view would be, the A and B have the color, but the L has the contrast. That makes it a tempting ingredient for our correction recipe.

Step 1. *Acquire the image into LAB.*

If you are preparing for print and have the capability to open directly into CMYK, you can save some time by doing so. That may be a legitimate reason for doing it in certain circumstances, but if your object is quality, you'll do better by following this recipe.

Photoshop 3's implementation of the Kodak Precision Color Management System (if you have installed it correctly) allows you to acquire directly into LAB. If you are using a specialized module that does not permit you to open directly into LAB, open in RGB and convert immediately to LAB.

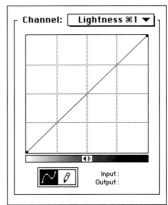

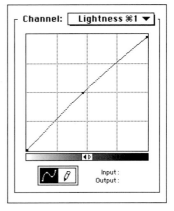

Figure 4.4. *Step 3. Back to the sharpened L channel, to set range. At this point, options should be considered. The top image on each page shows the straightforward method of setting highlight and shadow. (In the image of children on this page, the highlight and shadow in the original were correct, so no change from default was necessary.) The bottom method is for comparison, a move increasing contrast in the lighter half of the image. The curves that accomplish this are shown to the right of each image. Figure 4.5 shows the color images for each of the four; decide which of these L channels seems to do the best job.*

(image degradation is nil when doing this; if you doubt it, look ahead to Figure 6.1.)

With this recipe, unless the scan you are working with is poor, which of the many possible acquisition methods you use shouldn't make a difference in final quality. Be cautious, though, about which of the PCD's five image sizes you decide to use. Since excessive resolution contributes to image softness, you should use the lower of two resolutions whenever a choice is possible. Once the image is correctly sized, you should have a minimum resolution of 1.4 times the screen ruling you anticipate using when the picture is printed.

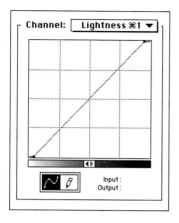

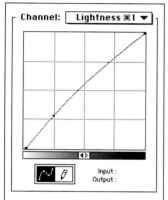

Step 2. *Apply unsharp masking to the L channel alone, not to the image as a whole.*

The general problem with sharpening is that it exaggerates color differences that we may not wish to emphasize, especially in fleshtones. If we have people in our picture, oversharpening can give them what seems to be a skin disease.

That's a strong reason to sharpen the colorless L channel alone—strong enough to consider converting almost *any* soft image, Photo CD or not, into LAB to take advantage of it. But there are actually technical reasons that make it even more effective in a PCD image.

First of all, taking a conventionally scanned image from CMYK to LAB and back again involves a slight quality loss, whereas PCDs are quite happy to be opened in LAB directly. More important, though, is Kodak's data compression scheme, by which enough data for a 24 mb CMYK file gets crammed into

Figure 4.5. *These color versions incorporate the different L channels shown in Figure 4.4. Step 4 is now to choose the one we like best, convert it to CMYK, and make a final adjustment in highlight and shadow.*

4 mb. Kodak's thoughtful and effective compression method preserves the integrity of the L channel. The shortcuts are taken in the color channels, where slight data degradation is not nearly as noticeable.

The translation of this is, the L is more accurate than the other two. The more we sharpen the A and/or B the more apt we are to highlight some relic of compression.

Sharpening the L, as seen in Figure 4.3, therefore accentuates the light-to-dark transition areas of the image, without many of the artifacts usually associated with heavy USM. In fact, the L is so amenable to this technique that much heavier doses than usual are possible. Try it for yourself: open a PCD image and run the USM filter on the L using these values: 250 percent amount, 1.5 pixel radius, 6 level threshold. Once you are satisfied that the L has a chance of handling even this drastic amount, cancel the filter. Rerun it on the entire file—and watch the whole fabric of the image disintegrate.

Step 3. *Adjust for range and contrast in the L channel.*

The L is also a convenient way to keep final CMYK color correction to a minimum. With it, we can make up for PCD's failure to compensate for flat images. Also, we can often arrange a more favorable allocation of contrast, giving more apparent life to the picture.

This involves minor tweaking of input-output curves. Some people shiver at the thought. I will therefore suggest an extremely simple way of making a clear improvement. Curve-proficient readers will understand that even better results come with more precise technique.

Start by going to Photoshop's Edit: Preferences>Separation Setup. If preparing for magazine or catalog work, set the options to GCR, Light black generation, 280% total ink density, and 85% maximum black. If for general commercial work, the total density may be set to 300 or even higher if you know your printer can accommodate it.

Bring Photoshop's Info palette up, and if necessary, set it to show CMYK values, even though the image itself is still in LAB.

With the composite LAB image displayed, now bring up the L channel curve. Position the curve dialog box so that you can see both image and Info palette.

Find what you consider to be the darkest area of the image. Position the cursor there, and read the nominal CMYK value in the Info palette. In most cases, this will be somewhat lighter than the maximum permissible value of 80C70M70Y70K or thereabouts. To compensate, bring the shadow end (upper right) of the L curve up until either the black reaches 70 or it looks to you that you are starting to hurt the picture.

Then, locate the lightest point, if there is in fact any area that you are willing to represent as very light (it is virtually unknown for an image not to have a dark point, but quite a few don't have light points). Bring down the low end of the curve so that the CMY values are in the neighborhood of 5 percent each.

Last, evaluate whether the interest areas of the image are predominantly light, dark or neither one. If light, move the midpoint of the curve up slightly, darkening the picture, but at the same time giving more contrast to the lighter areas and less to the darker.

If dark, move the midpoint down. If neither one applies, grab hold of the curve around a quarter

of the way up from the bottom, and bend it upward slightly. This will increase quartertone value, which is correct in most, but not all, PCD images. (Figures 4.4 and 4.5 show such alternate versions of each of our images, but if you'd like to see a strong example of when this technique really pays off, skip ahead a few columns to Figures 7.6 and 7.7.) Evaluate this last move: if it does not seem to you to have improved things, delete your quartertone point and content yourself with having set your light and dark points. Then click OK to apply the curve to the image.

Step 4. *Convert the image to CMYK, and readjust the white and dark points.*

After verifying that Separation setup is as described under #3, convert the image to CMYK, in preparation not just for printing but for the final correction.

PCD, being calibrationist by nature, does not correct for color casts in the original photograph. This is a major difference from high-end practice. It also differs from what we humans would see, if we were in the place of the camera.

The human visual system, unlike a camera, is adept at rejecting imbalances in the ambient lighting. Shots taken outdoors are very prone to color casts that a human observer would ignore. The original of the sailing picture in Figure 4.1 has a cyan cast. The original of Figure 4.2 has a yellow cast in light areas, but is deficient in yellow elsewhere. These casts in both images are very minor, to be sure, both almost unnoticeable. Enough, though, to warrant correcting.

There is no consensus among high-end trade shops as to how far to go in reducing such casts. A slight majority, of which I am a member, favor eviscerating all color casts, absent some indication that the photographer wanted one.

Even those who think their company's standard is "match the art," however, reduce the cast, whether

Figure 4.6. *The recipe in review. Top to bottom: the raw image; after the L channel has been sharpened; after range has been set in the L channel; after conversion to CMYK and final adjustment.*

they know it or not. Their scanner operators presumably set and balance highlight. That involves a judgment as to what parts of the picture *ought* to be white, whether the original has them that way or not. And that, class, is cast reduction in its most pristine form.

The boat in one of our example images, and the children's shirts in the second, are things that the scanner operator will interpret as being white. He will therefore set the lightest point of each to be approximately 5C2M2Y, a classical white highlight. That will wipe out the color cast in the lighter areas of the image at least, and possibly in other parts as well.

Setting highlight in this way really works. That is why virtually all professionals do it. Since PCD omits this desirable step, it is up to us to do it in Photoshop. Fortunately, because of the curve we previously applied to the L channel, we should be pretty close to our target CMYK values already.

So, we find the lightest area, and *if we think it should be white,* we adjust the point with curves until it is 5C2M2Y. The simplest way of doing this is to add a point to anchor the bottom of each curve. Having the rest of the curve be a straight line is acceptable. In the children image, I found the highlight point to be 2C2M7Y. Therefore, leaving the magenta curve alone, I put a point in the yellow curve reducing 7 percent to 2, and in the cyan I increased 2 percent to 5.

If you are asking, why did we bother to apply curves in LAB first, considering that we are going to reset highlight and shadow in CMYK anyway, you can test your skill if you like by omitting that step. The LAB maneuver got us into the right neighborhood. Anybody can make the three-point changes in CMYK that are called for to establish a proper highlight. If it were a 20-point change, that would be an entirely different story. A 20-point move without destroying the color balance of the picture *can* be done, mind you, but it isn't easy. Been there, done that.

Before applying these final CMYK curves, we should also correct the shadow, or darkest, value. In the image of the children, recall that the original shadow value was slightly deficient in yellow. The corrected version appears to have more realistic hair color for those children who are blond. The rather more golden fleshtones seem to me more appropriate as well: the powerful shadow patterns on the children's faces suggest the picture was taken in strong sunlight.

> **E**ven those who think their company standard is "match the art" reduce color casts, however unknowingly, when they balance the highlight and shadow.

If you are uncomfortable balancing a shadow with curves in this manner, a satisfactory, if not optimal, alternative is to find the darkest point, and if it contains less than 75 percent black, open the black curve and force it up.

Apply, save—and serve.

Living Up to Photo CD's Potential

This recipe may seem daunting at first, but with practice, it can be executed very quickly. If you wish to spend more than five minutes per image, there are a number of ways to make further improvements.

But the bottom line is, would you rather have GEFSOP or GEFMAP? Review the progress of the corrections in Figure 4.6. Photo CD images may not be the best of all possible originals, but they do capture a lot of data, enough for a skillful artist-chef to whip up some pretty tasty dishes.

As a drum scanner operator myself, I am naturally prejudiced against the quality of PCD, but I have to admit that the two originals shown here were pretty good to begin with, GEFMAP already, perhaps.

Even by high-end standards, however, the corrected versions can only be described as EGEFMAP—*Entirely* Good Enough for Most Any Purpose. And if you can get to EGEFMAP, you are well on the way to reaping the huge benefits that the newly open Photo CD process can offer. ●

Afterword

That Photo CD would become an open standard was just one of several startling announcements Kodak made at an extraordinary public session in March 1995. The new Kodak CEO, George Fisher, wanted to reverse a perception that his company was bucking the technological trend. In this, he succeeded, rattling off a series of splashy digital alliances with industry stars.

Since that heady time for Photo CD, however, Kodak has been sending out more conflicting signals than a semaphorist with the hives.

As advertised, the company made available, for less than $1,000, software that would write image data from non-Kodak sources onto CDs in the attractive and flexible PCD format. The honeymoon was brief, however. Even though the software package, Build-It, is still available and still supported by Kodak, there is a small catch.

Build-It, you see, only works in conjunction with one variety of CD-ROM burner—which Kodak has discontinued.

That's some catch, that Catch-22.

To be sure, you can find people who own that burner, and pay *them* to make the CD for you. Kodak also continues to assert that, any day now, other vendors will step in with Photo CD-savvy products that will replace Build-It. The best news, of course, would be if some major image-processing application, preferably Photoshop, incorporated the ability to save in PCD format.

If that happens, fine, but the situation has persisted for several months now, as of press time, and those of us who fear the resurgence of Big Yellow's film dinosaurs are getting antsy.

Meanwhile, the core Photo CD business hums along briskly: photo labs with the efficient Kodak PCD package, churning out low-cost, GEFSOP scans by the ton, waiting for someone to come along and apply the recipe to them.

This was, incidentally, by audience reaction the most successful column I've ever written. I suspect that's because it was the simplest, requiring almost no judgment or understanding of arcane concepts. There is, as the next column will indicate, a phobia about color correction, an assumption that some impossibly nice sense of aesthetics is needed to be effective.

A large number of PCD users, blissfully making corrections in LAB by a follow-the-numbers recipe, now disprove this, I'm happy to report. Those murky-looking originals really *can* look like drum scans, and you don't need to be an expert to do it.

The recipe works. There is no particular need to know why, if EGEFMAP is good enough for you. But if you can make it through the next three columns, and particularly Column 7, you *will* know why LAB corrections work, and you'll know that while this recipe may be a great place to start, your best corrections are yet to come. ●

Jargon Watch

calibrationist As used here, the concept of finding one optimal setting for a scanner and scanning all originals in the same way, as opposed to the traditional method of adjusting scanner settings depending on the characteristics of the original art.

Kodak Precision Color Management System Software that controls the acquisition process from scan to digital file. It is included with Photoshop 3 and higher, as the default method of opening Photo CD images.

LAB Properly known as CIELAB or L*a*b*, a three-channel colorspace propounded by an international standards organization. LAB is Photoshop's native colorspace. Its uses are fully explored in Column 7 of this book.

PostScript Type 1 The standard method of encoding typefaces now, but not in the past. In the early days of DTP, the Type 1 specification was an Adobe trade secret. Other font vendors had to make do with a spec known as PostScript Type 3, which yielded inferior results on laser printers. The possession of the Type 1 standard was a major competitive advantage, but eventually, like Kodak with Photo CD, Adobe relented and made the spec public in 1989. They were at the time faced with the threat of competition from the TrueType standard proposed by an Apple–Microsoft partnership. In retrospect, Adobe's move

cemented Type 1 in as the standard in the graphic arts.

resolution The number of pixels contained in an image. Resolution is generally, and sloppily, stated in terms of *dots per inch*. This leads to confusion with the term used in printing (see *screen value*). The term *pixels per inch* or *samples per inch* would be more appropriate to specify resolution. It is generally considered that, once a digital image has the same dimensions it will on the printed page, optimal resolution is 1.5 to 2 times the screen value.

screen value Also known as *screen ruling,* the frequency of halftone dots, expressed as dots per inch in the United States. The higher the screen value, the more difficult to print, but also the smoother the appearance. Higher screen values are therefore associated with better quality printing; anything 175 dpi or over is considered boutique. 133 or 150 dpi is typical for magazines and general commercial work. Newspapers generally use 65 or 85 dpi.

unsharp masking An artificial method of making images appear better focused. Works by exaggerating transition areas. LAB is the best colorspace for unsharp masking, for reasons developed in Column 7.

YCC Kodak's native Photo CD colorspace. It uses the same lightness plus opponent-color structure as LAB.

Dialog Box

I would appreciate if you could explain further in Step 2, if one is supposed to UNsharpen, why do you call it sharpen?

Believe it or not, unsharp masking *means* to sharpen. The confusing term dates from the time when separations were made on a conventional camera rather than on a scanner. In those days, to sharpen a picture was a several-step process. Among other things, the cameraman had to shoot the image once in focus and once out-of-focus.

If the idea is to sharpen, why do people call it "unsharp" masking?

The out-of-focus ("unsharp") version was used on the stripping table to modify the original version. The term "unsharp masking" has persisted for this maneuver. It is not too surprising that it bewilders those who don't know its history. ●

Is the LAB correction technique good for anything but PCD images?

I read, with great interest, your article and was intrigued by your suggestion to acquire Photo CD images using the LAB mode.

I am working on a promotional brochure for a printer. I would like to try your technique, and I have some questions I hope you can answer.

Does the technique you described work with Kodak's ProPhoto CD images?

Yes, there is no difference in the process.

I usually use the Kodak Acquire plugin v2.2 because it seems to work better than using the Open command in Photoshop even with the newest version of Kodak Photo CD CMS v3.1.1 and KPCP Precision startup v2.5.3.

If you are planning to use the column's recipe, the method of acquisition won't make a significant difference.

I usually keep my images in RGB to do all my retouching and special effects while watching the CMYK values in the Info palette. I then convert them to CMYK to do the final color correction, cleanup and unsharp masking.

Can I still use your technique using this method; i.e., When do I do the unsharp masking?

There is extensive coverage of the benefits of working in LAB in Column 7.

To use my recipe you will have to go to LAB at some point.

You can either do your retouching in LAB, which has a lot of benefits, or continue to do it in RGB and convert to LAB afterwards. The retouching should take place before sharpening. A major point of going to LAB is that sharpening is more effective. So is a preliminary range correction, particularly if the image is flat to begin with.

There is no quality loss associated with going RGB to LAB, so other than the additional time, there is no disadvantage to using this technique.

I was always told to use unsharp masking as the final step.

There is some merit in doing so, since otherwise you risk emphasizing a relic of sharpening by a careless correction later. However, if you are in control of the situation that shouldn't happen. In view of the great advantage of sharpening in LAB, that's where you ought to do it, in my opinion, notwithstanding that you will be correcting in CMYK later. ●

The impact of a scanner that captures more than eight bits per channel

I just finished reading your recipe. I've opened up a few Kodak files from CD and tried your recommendations. Using the LAB format sure made things easy. Thanks for the great advice.

However, I was wondering if I could do the same kind of color correction with images I scan myself. I own a scanner that can capture 30-bit RGB color. I was wondering if a 30-bit file would convert well from RGB to LAB just after scanning and before correction.

Yes, the method would still work. You would convert to 24-bit in LAB after applying a correction curve. You conceivably could see as much improvement as you would for Photo CD, since 30-bit scans tend to be a little soft themselves.

My procedure currently is as follows:

    1. Open Levels

        •adjust white point to near right side of histogram data

        •adjust black point the same way

        •adjust gamma point if necessary

    2. Adjust color channels via curves as necessary

You should forget Step 1 and try to incorporate it in with Step 2. If, as I suspect, you are using the master Levels dialog box for your white and dark point setting, you are running the risk of exacerbating a color cast (see Figure 7.4 and related discussion.) All this work can be done in one application of curves.

    3. Convert to 24-bit color

    4. Bump up the contrast slightly (contrast won't work in 30-bit mode)

Yeah, but curves *will*. I wouldn't ever use the Brightness/Contrast tool. It is strictly for dilettantes; not nearly as strong even as the Levels command. If you are going into LAB, running a curve on the L channel will give much better and more accurate contrast.

    5. Run Unsharp mask. I use the setting found in a magazine: 150%, pixel width 1.5 for 300-ppi images, threshold 3 or 4

    6. Convert to CMYK

Canned settings may be useful as a starting point, but each image has its own special characteristics. The larger it is, the more it will pay off for you to try other things. If you work in LAB, you will have a lot more freedom to use USM. Experiment a little! You have nothing to lose but a blurry-looking print job.●

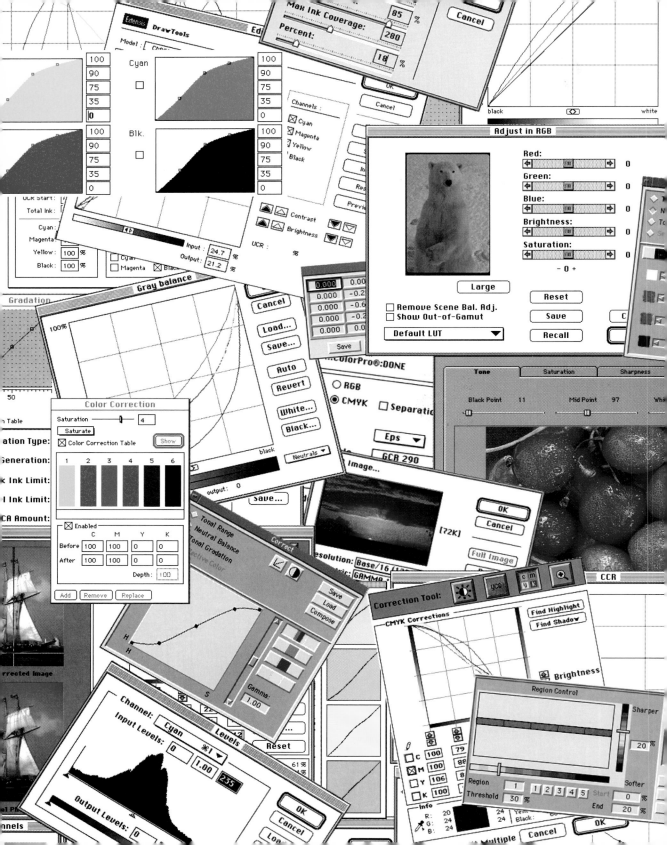

5

Defanging the Curves Vampire

Curves are the key to effective color correction. Everyone knows this, yet some are terrorized into using cruder methods. This phobia can be cured!

Serious graphic artists, as a rule, are not buffaloed by complexity, and try to get full value from the most powerful features of the programs they use. Only the rankest novice, for example, will neglect to make use of style sheets in a long document. In illustration programs, we all manufacture named custom colors when many objects share one color, and few of us will fail to group objects that belong together.

The glaring exception to this rule, the obvious case where many of us fail, from sheer terror, to adopt a method that the entire world knows to be superior, is the use of curves in color correction.

As the first to document this particular disease, I get to name it, and I believe it should be called kampyliaphobia: the irrational fear of mathematical curves. Like the fear of other bogeymen, its elimination is highly desirable, and this is what I will try to accomplish here.

A distinguishing feature of the syndrome is the patients' ability to rationalize their fear, which they do in one of two ways. They may say,

Figure 5.1. *Input–output curves take original image data and rearrange it for another purpose: to take advantage of the shape of a new colorspace, to compensate for dot gain, to emphasize a certain color, or simply to make the image look better. Far from being an esoteric and difficult proprietary feature of Photoshop, as some believe, curves are ubiquitous in the color world. The facing page shows a host of color-altering routines from many vendors. They may not all look like curves, but maybe that is to avoid the fear factor: there's at least one curve in every one.*

123

first, "My color is just fine already, thank you very much,"—and they're right, too, because they are missing the point of curves, which is *not* so much to establish color, as to enhance detail.

Every image-manipulation program has ample tools to change overall color. Color at any rate is highly subjective. You and I may differ on what color is right. We will definitely agree, however, on the desirability of something known variously as bite, snap, life, crispness, sharpness, good detail. It's hard to put into words, but we know it when we see it. And you want it; I want it, our clients want it—and we won't get all we need of it without using curves effectively.

The true kampyliaphobic will now resort to the second rationalization: "This may all be true, but I have no experience with curves at all, and who knows what damage this inexperience may lead to if I tackle such a fearsome unknown."

The unknown is *always* fearsome; but here the patient in fact knows the monster well. If you own a sound system, and you ever twiddle any dial other than the volume, you are undoubtedly applying some kind of curve to digital data. If you ever attempt to adjust color or contrast on your TV, you are already heavily into curves. If you ever use Photoshop's Levels command; if you have a color management system; if you ever convert images into CMYK, use an imagesetter, make digital contract proofs, or attempt to calibrate your monitor; there is no need to fear the vampire of curves: you have already survived its kiss.

Let me be the first to admit that getting the hang of applying a set of curves to a color image isn't easy. We will therefore start with black and white, and with a question that *is* easy, yet critical to the later application of curves: in the four monochrome images that constitute the top halves of Figure 5.2, are there certain objects, certain shades, that are more important than others?

In A, there really are not. The little girl's collar is light; her dress is dark; and her hair and skin fall somewhere in the middle. All are important; none can be shortchanged.

The other three images aren't like that. In B, the rabbit is clearly the most important object, and the rabbit is light. C's kitten is dark, and the lettuce in D falls in the middle. You would presumably agree with me that if we can engineer an improvement in the rabbit, or the kitten, or the lettuce, we should do it, even if that improvement happens to hurt the background.

The next two paragraphs offer a technical explanation of

what a correction curve does. If you do not care why vampires can't be seen in mirrors so much as the fact that they can't, you can skip over them.

A curve remaps every pixel of the parts of an image it is applied to. The interface's horizontal axis represents tonal values as they currently are; the vertical axis what they will become. The default curve is a straight line at a 45° angle, since every horizontal value is the same as every vertical one. Photoshop allows the user to define whether the upper right point of the curve represents lightness or darkness; most professionals prefer that it be darkness, and this is the way it is shown throughout this book, although there is no harm in doing it the other way around.

As anchor points are added and moved away from the default line, the entire curve changes shape, affecting every tonal value, but particularly those that are close to the changed anchor points. Those areas of the image covered by parts of the curve that now fall above the default line will become darker; those covered by areas falling below the default line will get lighter.

The Steeper the Curve, the More the Contrast

Back to plain English. The whole secret is this: *the steeper the curve, the more the contrast.*

Now, the bad news. If you make the curve steeper in a certain area, you have to make it flatter somewhere else to compensate. Objects that fall in the steeper areas of the curve gain contrast. Objects that fall in the flatter areas lose contrast. If you manage to corral all important objects of the image into steeper areas, you have a winner.

The simplest application of this simple concept is found in A of Figure 5.2. The original at top is flat. The white areas of the little girl's collar are too dark and the shadow areas in the background are too light. The conventional wisdom is to change this to a proper range by measuring highlight and shadow values and correcting them, either with levels or curves. The conventional wisdom is quite correct, but *why?*

Moving the lower left point of the curve to the right lightens the highlights, and moving the upper right point to the left darkens the shadows. Everything between these two points now falls in an area of the curve that is steeper than the default 45°. Since we have made one area of the curve steeper certain other areas must be made flatter, and here, those areas are *totally* flat.

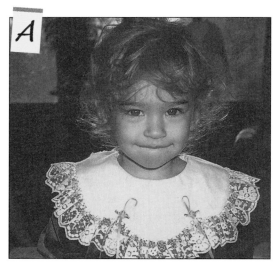

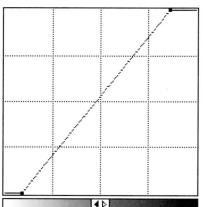

Figure 5.2. *One empha-sizes objects of interest by steepening the curve in the regions that affect them. In A, the image is flat. By shortening both ends of the curve, the middle gets steepened. In B, the light half of the image is clearly more important than the dark half. Raising the curve's midpoint, as at right, accounts for the added life in the bottom version.*

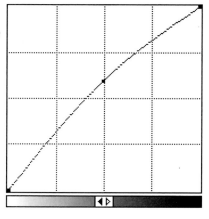

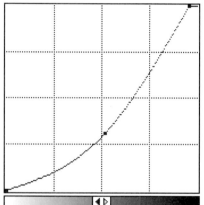

C, being primarily dark, is handled exactly the opposite of B. As B and C are both midtone moves, they could have been done with Photoshop's Levels command. D, however, cannot. Its important area is in the middle, and to steepen the middle the curve must downplay both the light and dark ranges, without blowing them out altogether.

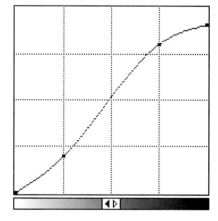

Everything that falls in the steeper part of the curve—the entire picture, in this case—gains contrast. Everything in the flatter areas—namely, everything either lighter than the lightest area of the image or darker than the darkest, in other words, nada, nothing, nichevo, niente—loses out.

> **It's obvious that when we have a chance to help everything and hurt nothing, we should do it. From there, it's a short step to start improving important things at the expense of lesser ones.**

It's pretty obvious that when we have a chance to improve everything and hurt nothing, as in A, we should do it. It is a short step from that realization to B, where we can improve the important things at the expense of the unimportant ones.

The original in B already has a full range. The whitest areas of the rabbit can't be made whiter, and the darkest areas of the background are already at around 85 percent, which is as high as our press can probably handle. A correction like that of A will therefore not work, but there is still room for improvement.

Instead of (or perhaps in addition to) moving the endpoints, we should consider grabbing a point in the middle of the curve and raising it. Let us assume that we use the exact midpoint, although this is not a requirement.

As we raise the midpoint, the picture gets darker. But what is more pertinent is that the lower half of the curve becomes steeper. The upper half, therefore, gets flatter. The lower half is the lighter half of the image. The rabbit falls in the lighter half. Since steepness equals contrast, the rabbit gains contrast. Small parts of the background lose, but we, as image technicians, win.

The kitten in C is the opposite case. If we *drop* the midtone, the curve will become steeper in its upper half and everything darker than a midtone will gain contrast. Everything in the light half of the picture will lose contrast. Few tears need be shed over that particular development.

The Limitations of Levels

Color professionals can do wonderful things in making images come to life, but far and away the most important is what we have just described: moving the endpoints of the image to eliminate contrast in areas that do not exist in favor of giving it to areas that do; plus, some kind of maneuver to allow lightening or darkening the middle of the image.

Photoshop's Image: Adjust>Levels command lets us do exactly those things, which explains why such effective corrections are possible with it. For fear of kampyliaphobic users draping ropes of garlic around their necks, Adobe does not advertise levels as being a curve approach, but a curve it is nonetheless: a curve with only three adjustable points.

The Levels command is definitely more intuitive, and for this reason most Photoshop books and instructors teach people to correct with it. Vampires, vampires! Personally, I favor charging directly into the darkened castle. Levels is a subset of the curves function and has no independent worth. Take ResEdit and hack it off your system. If you are too frightened to use curves for the simple corrections that *can* be done with levels, what on earth will you do when faced with fangs that only curves can conquer?

Before considering D, which is exactly such a case, let's review the other three. A can be corrected with levels just as accurately as with a curve. B and C can be improved with levels, but not with the same precision. The problem is, when we say that, for example, the light half of the image is more important, we don't ordinarily mean exactly the lightest 50 percent. The interest area is more likely to be centered in the lightest 58 or 37 percent, or somewhere else just as inconvenient. If it's 58 percent, then a move of the midpoint, which is what levels does, will help most of the interest area, but it will actually hurt some of it, because everything above 50 percent loses contrast.

If it's 37 percent, then a move of the midpoint has two drawbacks: first, it exaggerates contrast in some of the less important areas of the image, which may look unnatural; and, more importantly, we may not be able to make the curve as steep as if we put the point at 37 percent where it belongs. The improvement in the important areas will be great, but there will come a time when the damage we are doing to the rest of the image will be unacceptable. That time will come a lot sooner if our curve anchor point is 13 points too high.

D, with the interest concentrated in the middle range of the image, can't be fixed effectively unless you take stake, crucifix, and curves in hand and prepare to do battle. In A, only two control points were needed, and in B and C we needed three, but D really needs *four,* knocking levels into the ranks of the undead. To steepen the middle range of the curve, we have to lower the lightest point of the lettuce, and raise its upper point.

We cannot, however, afford to use the endpoints of the curve to do this. In the upper left of the background, some objects of significance are lighter than the lettuce and others are darker. We are willing to lose detail in them to a certain extent, or at least I am. I am not, however, willing to blow them out completely, which would be the only choice with levels.

You may be thinking that if three out of four images can be improved nearly as well with levels as with curves, is it really necessary to go to the trouble of mastering them? Perhaps not—if your practice is limited to black and white. In a color image, any object that has a color other than white, light gray, or black will have at least one channel that behaves like D. So, having established that the reputation of curves is somewhat worse than their bite, let's consider what happens when the lettuce becomes green rather than gray.

> **The one-size-fits-all approach of the master curve sometimes is correct in RGB, but never in CMYK.**

Forget the Master Curve!

Color images differ from B/W in having not one but three channels to correct, plus a black if we are in CMYK. Nevertheless, the same goals are there: full range in each channel, and in each channel as much range as reasonable allocated to the important areas of the image, if these are identifiable. Plus, there is now a third goal, color fidelity, that was not applicable before.

A temptation now appears, in the form of the inclusion of a master curve in both RGB and CMYK modes. The simplicity is seductive, the apparent improvement palpable, and the sinister nature almost undetectable.

The master curve is a one-size-fits-all approach, affecting each channel in the same way. Occasionally, that is right in RGB. In CMYK it is *never* right, since black will always behave differently than the color channels.

If we are dealing with an RGB version of the image of the black kitten, a lightening of midtone value via the master curve will actually be acceptable. The kitten will be just about as dark in one channel as any other.

But when the main subject is not neutral, not black, but rather the green head of lettuce in Figure 5.3, this approach will fail. The channels in such an RGB image look no more like one another than Bela Lugosi looks like Tom Cruise. The green obviously is strongest, and red nearly as heavy, since red plus green equals yellow. The blue channel will be weak. The lettuce falls in different ranges in each one. Only a separate curve for each can be successful.

Writing them requires a little preliminary investigation, for which I will switch to CMYK. A quick look indicates that the strength order of the channels is yellow, cyan, magenta, black. We need, however, more specific values in four areas: the light and dark point for the image as a whole, and also, assuming that we will have a go at the foreground lettuce, the lightest and darkest point of that.

The lightest point anywhere is plainly the bowl. It starts at 5C4M14Y. In my opinion, this bowl should be white (we aren't always lucky enough to find a white object), so a standard highlight value for this will do. I generally like 5C2M2Y.

The darkest point, just to the right of the bowl, measures 81C56M82Y56K. An appropriate shadow value for magazine work is 80C70M70Y70K.

Within the lettuce itself, the lightest point other than a reflection reads 45C11M95Y1K, and the darkest that still seems green is 75C47M100Y31K. That's roughly 30 points of range for all colors except yellow.

The Three Big Objectives

Armed with this information, we proceed to create four curves, simultaneously trying for the three big objectives:

- To extend the range of the entire image as much as possible, consistent with retaining detail
- To get colors that we like, particularly in neutral colors and fleshtones, if any
- Given the constraints of the first two, to allocate as much contrast to the most important areas of the image as possible

In the context of the values we have just discovered, the first objective is not too far off to begin with. The highlight is almost right, and the shadow is only slightly too light.

To achieve the second objective we need to do some work. The plate should be white, and the deepest shadow should be neutral also. Neither one is at present. Both are too yellow. The shadow also is deficient in magenta. We will be trying to extend the range of the lettuce in each channel, but in doing so, we will have to make sure that these problems are also solved.

The four curves that do this appear in Figure 5.3. You could approximate the yellow and the black corrections using levels, but not the magenta and cyan, both of which, like D, absolutely need four points.

The additional life in the lettuce is all the more striking when compared to what went on elsewhere. If anything, the salad in the upper left of the background is worse than the original. That is the work of the curves. The price for the steepness that added contrast to the foreground lettuce was a flatter curve elsewhere. That's a very fair price to pay, I'd say.

The fadeout of the background illustrates, oddly, one of the reasons curve corrections are so effective. The curves emulate what our eyes would have done were we looking at the lettuce in person. The human visual system, in effect, applies curves to whatever it sees. If we are focusing on a green object, we become more sensitive to variations in green, and less to other colors. We emphasize differences in both color and brightness in closely similar colors, and we do so at the expense of detail in whatever is in the background. Cameras and scanners do not do this.

This is therefore a much more natural, not to mention easier, way to correct images than isolating the lettuce by making a selection and then working on it alone. Even if the selection can't be detected, there always seems to be something just a little bogus about such work, and the skilled eye rebels at it.

The Best Curving Tool

I hate to proselytize, but if you become comfortable with curves, you will make your life in the graphic arts ever so much easier, and not just in Photoshop.

Curves are, as Figure 5.1 shows, to be found throughout the graphic arts. If you are proficient with them you will understand

Figure 5.3. *Effective correction of a color image can best be done by assuming it is four grayscale images. In the lettuce opposite, the yellow plate is heaviest, and should be treated as C was in Figure 5.2. The cyan has its lettuce values in the middle and thus behaves like D; the black is light in the lettuce and should therefore be treated like B; and the magenta, being both light and flat in the original, behaves like a combination of A and B. The composite curves, below, transform the picture at top opposite to the much better one at bottom.*

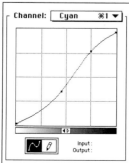 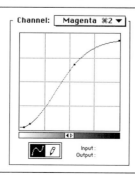 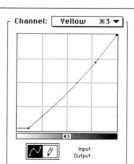 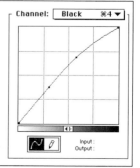

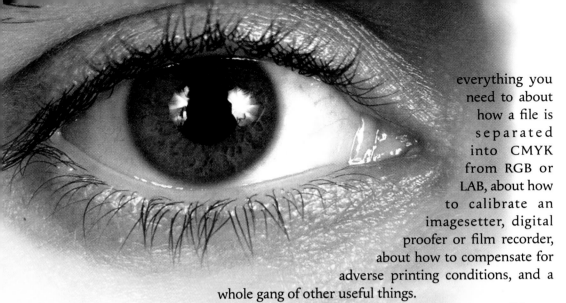

everything you need to about how a file is separated into CMYK from RGB or LAB, about how to calibrate an imagesetter, digital proofer or film recorder, about how to compensate for adverse printing conditions, and a whole gang of other useful things.

If you first began to use a computer as an adult, as I did, you will probably recall the frustrating experience of learning to use the mouse. Remember how it always kept sliding off the pad? Remember how we could never get the hang of clicking vs. double-clicking? How at first we weren't sure which direction to hold it in, and how we kept wrapping the wire around our wrists?

When you look back on that aggravating time, you will probably agree that that blasted mouse was a major obstacle to actually learning useful things about the programs. Now that we have presumably reached the point where the mouse feels just like an extension of our hand, we can get down to business.

The same thing can happen with curves. Some propeller-heads spend hours trying to get the color right in a file that could be fixed up in seconds with a single set of curves. They ordinarily end up with 14 or so supplementary channels and five or six layers, each with a mask, not to mention a file size of a hundred megabytes. Each time I watch it happen I am reminded, in a way, of someone who has not yet grown comfortable with the mouse.

When you do get comfortable with curves, you will realize that all the previous terror was unnecessary. It will be as though a scar has vanished from your forehead.

If you can learn the mouse, you can learn curves. They are both easy once you get past the initial, er, learning curve. Reproduction curves become particularly intuitive when you consider that Figure 5.4 portrays the most powerful densitometer, the most powerful colorimeter, the most powerful curving tool in existence. Lucky you, to happen to own a pair of them. ●

Figure 5.4. *The ultimate curving tool.*

Figure 5.5. *A curve emulation of what happens to an image when it is printed on poor-quality paper, discussed in the Afterword.*

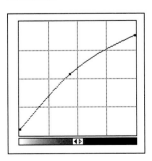

Afterword

In real life in the magazine, one can't easily refer readers back to graphics in previous columns. Books, happily, are another story. I would like to suggest a reconsideration of Column 3, which discusses dot gain and its ramifications. Analyzing the problem in terms of curves is a useful illustration of the points just covered. In Figure 5.5, let's try to draw a curve of what happens when we expect high dot gain.

In Photoshop's simple-minded view of the world, dot gain is heaviest in the midtone, less apparent elsewhere, and nil in the highlights and shadows. If we expect higher than usual dot gain, it reasons, we should be able to simulate it by raising the midpoint of our hypothetical curve. Entering a higher dot gain value in Printing Inks setup does exactly this.

In reality, though, things are not nearly so straightforward, for two important reasons ignored by Photoshop. First, heavy dot gain implies poor paper, and poor papers are usually not as white as good ones. If the paper is grayish, this is more or less the equivalent of printing on white paper but adding five percentage points to each ink throughout the picture. That means we should revise our theoretical curve, raising the zero point at bottom left.

Second, poor papers have higher dot gains because they are usually more absorbent. But in deep shadows, darkness depends more on how much ink lives on the *surface* of the sheet, rather than on the apparent diameter of the halftone dot. Translation: shadows are darker on good paper. Curve translation: drop the top right point. Also, because this effect starts to show up in the three-quartertone as well as the shadow, push the previously drawn midtone point to the left.

Now, remembering that Photoshop's screen display only compensates for one of the three points we have drawn so far, let's consider to what extent the monitor is going to deceive us, even if we enter a properly high dot gain value in Printing Inks setup.

That adjustment will set the overall darkness of the image and probably do a pretty good job of it. It will not, however, compensate for the grayness of the paper. Therefore, all colors will seem to be cleaner and purer than they actually are, and we should compensate by increasing saturation generally.

More importantly, look at how flat the upper right of Figure 5.5 is. That flatness, of course, is a contrast-killer in the darker half of the image. In images such as the frogman of Figure 3.1, which depends on shadow detail, the monitor will give a hideously overoptimistic view of how much of it there will be on press.

You can drive a stake right through the heart of this, by *dropping* the midtone in the original image to steepen the upper half and thus regain some of the lost contrast. If you blithely, blindly trust the monitor, it probably won't occur to you to do so. If you remember the implications of curves, it *will*. ●

Jargon Watch

CMYK Cyan, magenta, yellow, black, the inks used in printing color images, but also a major storage space for digital images.

color management A much overhyped concept: the use of third-party hardware and/or software to attempt to make colors more or less match between two, and frequently more, different kinds of devices.

curves A remap of the tonal values of an image, for color correction, range extension, or enhancement of detail. Normally used to refer specifically to Photoshop's Curves command or the equivalent in other programs; however, many simpler routines, such as levels, or the remap applied during the separation process, use an approach that is technically one of applying curves.

digital contract proof A high-quality color proof suitable for use as press guidance, but produced on a ink-jet, dye-sublimation, or other digital printer, without the use of any film. This differentiates it from traditional contract proofs such as Cromalin or Matchprint. Digital contract proofers, such as Kodak's Signature or Scitex's Iris, have been available for some time but have been extremely expensive. In 1995, several vendors introduced dye-sublimation digital contract proofers for less than $20,000, a considerable price break.

highlight value The lightest value that a given process can accommodate, consistent with retaining detail.

levels A Photoshop tonal-correction tool, simpler and somewhat friendlier than its curves function.

mask A means of confining an image correction to a single area without the possibility of altering the remainder. It is in principle the same as a selection except that *mask* tends to suggest a more complicated correction. Masks are frequently saved in separate channels.

ResEdit A powerful but dangerous Macintosh system utility that allows users to mess around with things like data and resource forks. It has some practical uses in font management among other things. I don't actually recommend that you use it to hack levels off your system, but you could if you wanted to.

RGB Red, green, and blue, the colors of light to which human eyes are most sensitive. Digital image files are frequently kept in files represented by RGB channels; these, however, must be converted to CMYK before printing.

selection In digital retouching, the isolation of a certain area for local correction. The software will not permit nonselected areas to be altered.

shadow value The darkest value that a given process can accommodate, consistent with retaining detail.

Dialog Box

Please excuse an amateur's question, but what exactly do you mean by "balancing highlight and shadow?"

In printing parlance, the "shadow" does not mean what it does in standard English. It means the darkest significant area of an image where the viewer is not supposed to notice color. In other words, something that is navy blue is not the shadow even if it is the darkest area of the image.

The "highlight" is an area that is *both* the lightest significant area and one that we want the viewer to perceive as being white. In evaluating whether an area is the lightest one in the image, we ignore areas that have to do with the actual transmission of light, such as a light bulb or a reflection of light off a mirror.

By the above definitions virtually every image has a shadow. The majority have a highlight as well, but plenty do not.

Balancing the highlight and shadow means setting these areas to neutral whites and grays, not favoring any color. This standard is universal in the prepress industry, as is extending the range of the image so that the highlight and shadow are in fact as light and dark as the process will allow, consistent with holding detail.

Highlight and shadow defined, and why professionals balance them

One of the major consequences of this is to bring the whole picture, not just the highlight and shadow, closer to what the viewer expects to see, reducing or eliminating any color cast. If the original picture contains a slightly green horse, balancing the highlights and shadows will make it less green, whether or not it ever occurred to us that we wanted it that way. There would be some debate in the industry as to whether, after balancing the highlight, we should go in and evaluate the horse to see if it was still somewhat green, and if so take action. But there is no debate at all as to the propriety of balancing highlight and shadow.

When you're making this correction, are you adjusting the highlights and shadows to neutral via some sort of quasi-colorimetry technique (scanning the highlight and shadow areas and looking at the relative values of R, G, & B)...

Well, in C, M, & Y, in my case, although you can do it either way. Yes. Whether doing this during a scan or in Photoshop afterwards, one checks what the values of the highlight/shadow currently are and changes them to what one would like them to be.

...or are you just twiddling the (virtual) knobs and looking at the screen in PhotoShop?

Leaping lizards, no!!!!! The screen cannot be trusted for this purpose, unless you happen to be a spectrophotometer, not a human being. If you are a human, you have been gifted (handicapped?) with self-calibrating vision. That is, whatever light is hitting your eye is simultaneously adjusting your color perception for you. This is not so bad when you are looking at something with a pronounced color, such as a face or a leaf, but if what you are looking at is a highlight or shadow, it's a disaster. Your visual system moves in the direction of neutralizing any color imbalance. Therefore, the longer you look at a light source, such as a monitor, the grayer it will seem to you. This is highly awkward if you are trying to figure out whether the object is *actually* gray. You *must* trust the numbers and not the screen in evaluating highlights, shadows, and neutral colors. Trust the screen for overall appearance, perhaps, but for these three items, a "calibrated" monitor is a contradiction in terms.

And am I understanding correctly that your usual practice is to "stretch" the contrast range of the image to create "true" highlights and shadows where the original had no highlights? (I've shot one or two of those.)

Yes. Prepress differs from photography in that regard, an unhappy necessity in view of how little colorspace we have to play with. This is yet another reason that scans perfectly calibrated to an original piece of film make little difference: we have to change the range in virtually every case regardless.

There is a very interesting consequence of all this. Once they go through this process, amateur photographs that have been printed at the local quick photo booth look very much like professional chromes. Most people suppose that the better and more quality-conscious the photographer, the more he or she needs a drum scan. Just the opposite is true. If you have a technically excellent photograph, just about any old scanner will be good enough. Where the high-end equipment really blows away its competition is where it has to get first-rate results out of third-rate photography.

Your term "where the original had no highlights" is a little ambiguous. Virtually every image has a shadow, but some don't have a highlight. If what you mean is, there is a highlight but you shot it too dark, yes, we stretch it. If what you mean is, there is no natural highlight, no, we don't force it to happen. Highlight must be *both* white and the lightest non-reflecting area in the image. If a man is wearing business attire, including a white shirt, somewhere in that shirt will be the highlight. Change the shirt to light blue (assuming he's not wearing anything else white) and we do *not* set the highlight to be the whites of his eyes.

In such a case one can figure out what the highlight would logically have to be if it were there, and set the image accordingly. This is, of course, easier said than done, but we prepress types have to justify our salaries somehow. ●

6

The Natural Superiority of CMYK

CMYK is the traditional way of doing things in print production. Is there a reason for its success? RGB is more intuitive, but easier isn't always better.

1 n an industry like ours, racked with change, "do it because it's always been done that way" doesn't cut it any more. Traditional methods have been eclipsed in too many cases by the relentless advance of technology. Just because professionals have always used certain techniques does not make them right for the 1990s.

In high-end print work, dot etchers and retouchers have traditionally worked in CMYK. Perhaps this is because CMYK has inherent advantages in color correction (it does), but perhaps it is because up until quite recently any other option was very difficult (it was).

Today, though, it is a simple matter to make our corrections in some other colorspace, converting to CMYK only at the last minute. There are certainly advantages in doing this—for one thing, file size is significantly smaller—but there is always the nagging suspicion that if all these prepress professionals do it a certain way there may be a good reason for it.

As a matter of fact, there are several. We will explore them while

Figure 6.1. *Fear of what will happen during conversions should not be a factor in deciding what colorspace to work in. The bottom right version has been brought in and out of CMYK five times, four times more than ever would be done in real life. The damage is very slight. Conversions between RGB and LAB are to all practical purposes lossless; the top left version is an original while the bottom left has been converted 50 times into LAB and 50 times back into RGB.*

answering this question: in today's world, should we color-correct in RGB or CMYK?

Before beginning this inquiry, we should limit it to those cases where the final result needs to be CMYK and we at least have the option of beginning with an RGB scan. There are certain scanners that can *only* deliver their data in CMYK. There are many times when our final file needs to be RGB. We exclude both of these possibilities.

> **Cyan is a very inadequate ink. CMYK therefore can't generate good blues. This is not neat, not logical, not scientific, not conceptually perfect in the sense RGB is.**

We will also assume that once a file has been separated and printed, if a minor correction or tweak is needed, it should be done in CMYK. Some fanatics consider RGB so sacred that even such corrections should be done there, but this is a fringe view.

Finally, I must point out that the initial question ignores the possibility of correcting in LAB or HSB. These colorspaces offer certain advantages not to be found in either CMYK or RGB, and moves in these spaces should be part of the arsenal of the serious retoucher. However, considerable expertise is required, and the matter deserves a full column in its own right. [And in Column 7, you'll find it.]

A Dose of Castor Oil

There are zealots on both sides of the RGB-CMYK issue, and many of them succumb to a pointless phobia about the colorspace they dislike. Certain Kodak scientists at one time felt that CMYK was so inherently repulsive that no one should be allowed to use it. They designed an expensive retouching station, aimed at high-end users, that could operate in just about every colorspace *except* CMYK. In its initial incarnation it could not even access a CMYK file, this being explained as a means of steering the user away from temptation. This politically correct workstation flew in the face of the conventional wisdom of the time, so the scientists wistfully named it Prophecy. It flopped.

Yet the horror that CMYK arouses in the scientific mind is not totally unwarranted. It is truly an ugly colorspace. Alone among its competitors, it is weirdly shaped. By that, I mean that it produces some colors better than others. Cyan ink is at present quite inadequate, so CMYK can't generate good blues. Reds and oranges, on the other hand, are fine. This is not neat, not logical, not scientific; certainly not conceptually perfect in the sense that RGB is.

Worse still, from this point of view, is the presence of black. What could be crazier, what more maddening, than an ink which, like a doomsday machine, obliterates everything? If you want to make a bull crazy, wave a red flag at him. With a color scientist, try a black one.

This phobia about the limitations of CMYK engenders another set of knee-jerk responses concerning the accuracy of the inevitable RGB-CMYK conversion. Because RGB has a much wider gamut of colors available and is shaped differently from CMYK as well, some see the conversion as the equivalent of running the image through a meat grinder.

Consequently, it can be argued, although not intelligently, that one should always correct in RGB, since the image will be too badly damaged during separation for many corrections to work.

CMYK extremists start with the same premise and come up with a conclusion just as fallacious. They say that the conversion is such a cataclysmic event that one always needs to make adjustments afterwards regardless of the quality of anything that may have been done in RGB. If this were only true, it would surely make sense to swallow the castor oil immediately and get it over with, avoiding the middleman and doing all correction in CMYK.

Figure 6.2. *The CMY colors are lighter and subtler, on the whole, than their RGB counterparts, as can be seen when all six colors are converted to grayscale.*

The truth is that the RGB-CMYK conversion is not all that horrible. Absent operator intervention, there is some quality loss, to be sure. It is by no means the end of the world. A CMYK image will *theoretically* look worse if you convert it to RGB and then back, but on the printed page even an expert won't be able to tell them apart. It's true that a press has a much smaller color gamut than a monitor or other RGB device does, but that doesn't affect the integrity of the CMYK digital file.

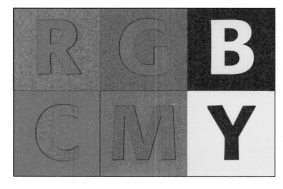 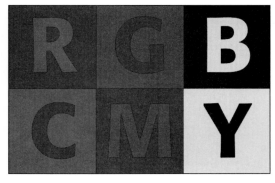

We should not, obviously, just convert and reconvert for the fun of it. The more times an image gets converted, the more severe the deterioration: the range will be constricted; there may be some posterization; and the colors will not seem as pure.

To reemphasize, though: these losses are not as significant as various partisans think. The sailboat image in Figure 6.1 is about as challenging a conversion candidate as one can find, full of bright colors at the extremes of what CMYK can accommodate. As a torture test, I converted one version from CMYK to RGB and back again five times. If the conversion were such a fearsome thing, this should have destroyed the image. Yet the two versions are strikingly close. The wounded version can be brought undetectably close to the original with a minimum of effort.

> **I**f you use the Levels command to correct color, RGB will probably work as well for you as CMYK. If you have figured out the nuances of curves, it's a different story.

The conversion between RGB and LAB, if we decide to make use of it, is lossless for all practical purposes. You can convert back and forth all day if you like. The picture of roses in Figure 6.1 went in and out of LAB 50 times. For any conceivable professional use the original and the megaconverted one are identical.

Of course, in real life we would not convert a file back and forth 50 times, or even five. There are at least three important ramifications of these findings.

- If you like to correct in RGB, don't be buffaloed out of your position by fear of what will happen during conversion.
- If you like to work in CMYK, but come across an image that can be better corrected in, say, LAB, or more commonly, that needs a different-looking black plate, don't be afraid to take it out of CMYK and bring it back again later.
- If you need final output in RGB for Web, video or other multi-media uses, there is no compelling reason to avoid doing preliminary work in LAB or CMYK.

Inserting the Fine Print

These three statements are generally accurate and should satisfy most readers. If, however, you are the sort of reader who sees the holes in them, who says, well, what if there is critical detail in the deep blues that CMYK doesn't reproduce adequately, what then, will an RGB correction still suffice?—if you ask those sorts of questions, the remainder of this column may be of interest. And if you ask those sorts of questions, you eventually will come around to doing your color corrections in CMYK.

It is all a matter of how persnickity you are. If you are accustomed to using Photoshop's Levels command to correct color, RGB will work just as well for you as CMYK. But if you have figured out the nuances of curves, you will need the precision of CMYK to take full advantage of them.

To demonstrate, let us plan a curve-based attack on a generalized unknown image, with particular attention to whether there is an advantage to working in one colorspace or the other.

1. **Set the highlight and shadow.** The most important factor in color correction is forcing the image to have a full tonal range. That means whites should be as white as possible and blacks as dark as possible, consistent with retaining detail. This is done by writing curves that clip off values that are not in use. Example: if the darkest value in our image is 70 percent, but we know our press can support 85 percent, we steepen the curve so that what was 70 becomes 85, theoretically losing definition in the nonexistent areas that were originally darker than 70.

This correction is simple and it will make no difference whether it is executed in CMYK or RGB.

2. **Adjust the known colors.** Once the endpoints are set, we may have to refine the curves if there happen to be any colors that would give us away if we get them wrong. Almost invariably, these are neutral colors — grays and whites — and fleshtones.

In ease of use, there is a vote for RGB as being more intuitive in setting neutral colors. In RGB, all you have to do to get a gray is make sure that all three colors have equal values. In CMYK, it is not so easy. Cyan has to be set higher than magenta and yellow, due to the aforementioned inadequacy of cyan ink.

But, as shown in Figure 6.2, cyan, magenta, and yellow are subtler and less obtrusive colors than red, green, and blue. CMY moves, therefore, can be a little more substantial than they would be in RGB, where we would have a greater chance of throwing a monkeywrench into the color balance of the image. If this were a perfect world we would not have to resort to a lot of twisting and turning in our curvewriting to achieve proper neutrals and fleshtones. As matters stand, however, RGB can be a hindrance in this kind of maneuver.

The more delicate and intricate the correction, the worse

Figure 6.3. Correcting this image is difficult because it has so many different impor-tant colors. It's hard to increase detail in any one without doing harm to another, and even harder when working in RGB.

this RGB handicap will become. At the highest level it can be something like trying to perform brain surgery while wearing boxing gloves.

3. **Target the main interest area.** Adjusting highlight and shadow values to get the maximum color range in the image is critical, but the best prepress operators take the concept one step farther. They are able to provide more apparent snap by making their curves focus in on the dominant areas of the image, even if that hurts areas that are less important.

Suppose that we have a high key original, which means one where most items of importance are relatively light. A profes-sional scanner operator will unthinkingly compensate by making the midtone value darker. There will thus be more range than usual between the lightest value and the midtone, and hence more contrast in the important areas. As against that, there will be less contrast in darker areas, but presumably this will be a very reasonable price to pay for the overall improvement we expect in the image.

More difficult corrections are possible through the use of curves. Suppose we have a person's face that we would like to give more life to, and we find that the magenta component varies from 40 percent in the lightest area to 50 percent in the darkest.

If we now write a curve that takes 40 percent magenta down to 35 percent, and 50 percent magenta up to 55 percent, we will literally double the contrast. Instead of being spread over ten points, the face will now have twenty points worth of variation.

Going farther, if we had taken 50 down to 40, and 60 up to 70, we would have a 30-point magenta range, tripling contrast.

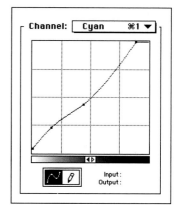

Nice in principle, but in real life other parts of the image can get in the way. If we take 40 down to 30, everything light in the image will get stiffed. Perhaps that's no problem; perhaps this is a dark-haired, bareshouldered model photographed against a dark background.

If, however, there are interesting parts of the image lighter than 40 percent

Figure 6.4 Steepening curves in the interest areas is the way to add snap, but other interest areas can't go flatter. Near right, the measured values for each of the five interest areas, given in both CMYK and RGB. Note in the charts at far right how much longer the ranges are in RGB. In the blue channel, there is almost no room for maneuver. Contrast this to CMY, where all channels have significant holes. Nothing of importance in this image has between 19 and 46 percent cyan. This suggests the shape of the curve shown above right, where that range is flattened, allowing all other areas to get steeper.

HAIR
50C 49M 56Y 9K
125R 107G 92B
to
66C 62M 71Y 38K
64R 56G 46B

SKIN
0C 35M 35Y 0K
243R 181G 192B
to
18C 45M 46Y 1K
202R 143 G 117B

DRESS
79C 50M 6Y 5K
63R 85G 150B
to
91C 69M 24Y 40K
27R 41G 71B

LACE
0C 8M 8Y 0K
254R 238G 230B
to
13C 24M 16Y 0K
221R 192G 189B

WOOD
47C 51M 60Y 10K
142R 116G 93B
to
67C 61M 72Y 56K
45R 41G 33B

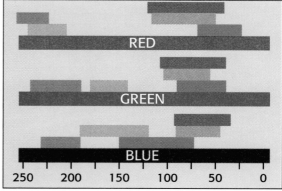

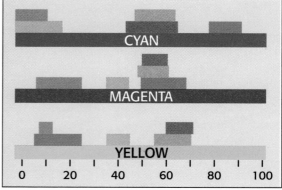

magenta, our correction may cost more than it gains. It is largely a matter of finding ranges that have nothing of importance in them, so that we can extend other ranges to fill them.

In the image of the little girl in Figure 6.3, there is enough happening to make this targeted approach problematic. I see no less than five areas of interest in this image: the girl's face, her hair, her blue dress, the white collar, and the wood of the table she is sitting on. You would think that this is enough complexity to ensure that any effort to improve one thing will hurt another. Not true—provided you work in CMYK.

Charting the ranges of the five interest areas shows some underutilized areas. Nothing is darker than 70 percent in either magenta or yellow, opening up a range for us at the top of the curve. In cyan, there is a large hole at around the quartertone, because none of the interest areas fall between 18 and 47 percent cyan. Raising the 18 percent point and lowering the 47 percent will therefore be highly effective: it will increase contrast in important areas while hurting an area that exists only in theory.

> **Targeted corrections are not nearly as potent in RGB, where color ranges are longer. Each RGB channel is burdened by having to define darkness as well as color.**

Such targeted corrections are not nearly as potent in RGB, where color ranges are much longer, because each channel defines darkness, as well as color. In CMYK, this darkness component is largely transferred to the black channel.

This effect shows up particularly in the girl's dress, where one might expect the red (RGB) and cyan (CMYK) channels to be nearly identical. Instead, the red channel is nearly twice as long in the dress, because it plays an important role in defining the dark folds, where the cyan does not.

A longer range means a less effective correction. To go back to an earlier example: if we are working on something with a range of 40 to 50 percent, and we make it instead 35 to 55, we have doubled range. If the original range is three times as long, our ten-point correction won't be nearly as emphatic.

Moreover, in a complex picture like the one of the girl in Figure 6.3, the longer ranges kill chances for the sort of targeted correction discussed above. In CMYK, there were big, exploitable holes in every channel. In RGB, the blue channel has no hole at all. Every range impacts some important object. If we attempt to

Figure 6.5. Contrast and detail are created by weak color plates, not by the colors that dominate. This leaf image is heavily yellow and cyan, making magenta and black tempting targets for correction. At bottom, the new version has changed in these two channels only—the yellow and cyan are identical to those in the original, top.

improve the face, for example, we have no choice but to damage something else.

    4. **Exploit the unwanted color.** In areas where two channels are heavy and one is light, the weak one—the unwanted color—plays a disproportionate role. Big improvements can be engineered into an image by heavy sharpening and other moves

in the unwanted color—moves that would be unthinkable in the dominant channels.

Furthermore, one can go hog-wild with it. In the greenery picture of Figure 6.5, cyan and yellow are roughly equal, making magenta the unwanted color. Regardless of how much we twist the magenta, this image is going to stay *green*. It will not matter, either, how much we sharpen the magenta plate. It can look terribly harsh by itself but the harshness will be covered up by the dominants, and what the viewer will perceive is superior focus.

The unwanted color has a naturally short range, making it an especially good target for extension with curves.

Flesh is a species of red. Magenta and yellow are about equal, making cyan the unwanted color. The cyan plate is the key to putting life into faces. If faces are an important part of your repertoire, you really should correct in CMYK, to take advantage of all the opportunities that the cyan plate offers.

An objection to this might be, these examples are all well and good when two CMYK inks are dominant and one weak, but what happens when one is dominant and *two* are weak? In that case, the true unwanted color will be red, green, or blue rather than cyan, magenta, or yellow.

For example, certain cactus flowers are basically magenta—no unwanted color in CMYK, because the weak inks, cyan and yellow, are roughly equal. There is a technical advantage, therefore, to working on these flowers in RGB, since green would be the unwanted color.

Where yellow is the dominant, there's not much advantage to an unwanted-color approach, because the unwanted color is blue, which would overpower the yellow too easily. However, if the important objects of an image are cyan or magenta, there is a clear case to be made for correcting in RGB. If they are red, green, or blue, there is a strong argument for CMYK.

A face, a leaf, a cactus flower. One of these, obviously, is a far less common object than the other two. Quick: name something else that is either magenta or cyan. Don't say a sky: most skies are midway between blue and cyan, no advantage to either colorspace. Yet, if I had asked, name some things that are red, green, or blue, you could have come up with hundreds of answers.

Nature and man do not make this an equal competition. The overwhelming predominance of red, green, and blue objects in life casts a decisive vote in favor of color-correcting in CMYK.

Figure 6.6. *A weak plate, such as the magenta in the leaf image, can often be made quite harsh-looking, because it is covered up by so much dominating color. Here, the original magenta from Figure 6.5 is at top; the corrected magenta at bottom.*

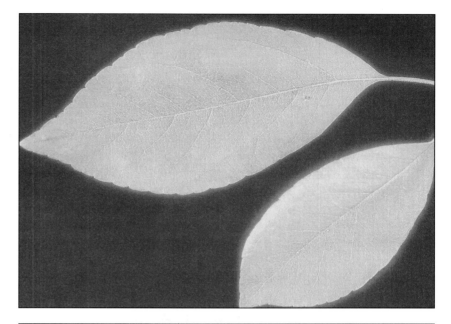

5. The Key Is the K. As we have noted, one disadvantage to correcting in RGB is that the channels are somewhat heavier, and therefore more difficult to control, than are cyan, magenta and yellow.

There is, however, a time for finesse and a time for brute force. If CMYK has three channels that are subtler than the ones in RGB, it also has one that is far, far stronger. Control of that channel is the most powerful tool we have in color correction.

There is no better way to add apparent snap to a picture than to create a sharp black channel. It is also much more amenable to curve-based corrections than CMY or RGB, because black moves generally don't alter color balance.

Curving up the black plate is the simplest way to beef up shadow areas.

The black plate can be treated almost as a second unwanted color. It can be sharpened more than the rest of the image; curves that increase the black quartertone are frequently very effective.

Dead-looking images frequently have a listless black channel to thank. In many cases it can be revivified with an infusion of detail from another channel. It is occasionally possible to blend something into a weak *color* channel, but this often causes some disagreeable change in the overall color balance. Blending extra detail into the black, on the other hand, is usually undetectable.

Furthermore, we can customize the black plate depending on the kind of correction we anticipate doing. Using gray component replacement (GCR) principles, we can generate a black plate that's light, heavy, or in between, and there are images (see Figure 3.1) where each one is right.

Four of a Kind Beats Three

The varied uses of the black channel would be a compelling reason to use CMYK, even if all the other ones I have mentioned did not exist.

If you don't plan to go much further than Step 1 with your images—and Step 1 is the most important—use RGB by all means if you are more comfortable with it. However, the better you get, the more the colorspace will become a handicap. You should use whatever colorspace works best for the particular image, of course, but eventually you will wind up using both LAB and HSB more than RGB.

It is not that pleasing corrections can't be done in RGB, but rather that they can be done more accurately in a colorspace that has four channels rather than three. The more such variables, the more precise one can be in finding areas to fix up. If somebody comes up with a five-variable colorspace, that will probably be better still. Until then, the best corrections will be done in CMYK. ●

Afterword

I am often struck by the thought that spouses of graphic artists must laugh themselves sick at how seriously we take certain parts of our profession. To be sure, I have not gotten any death threats as a result of this column, but it would not particularly surprise me if it eventually happens. To some, the quest to persuade everyone else to use a certain colorspace exclusively resembles a jihad.

The most common reaction to this column, outside of the hisses and boos of the calibrationist community, was, yes, this all seems very logical, but, why do so many people work in RGB nonetheless?

Well, why not? It works, doesn't it? You can get good results with it, just as you can get good results with Photoshop's Levels (or even Brightness/Contrast) command if you are afraid of curves, just as you can get good results with Photoshop's Sharpen command if you are afraid of the Unsharp Masking filter. Depending on how much time you have available and what your quality needs are, these tools can be just what you need.

At a certain skill level, however, the more powerful tools become a necessity. Attractive, pleasing color is possible without working in CMYK, or without curves for that matter. Color as good as leading separators could produce, that's another story. Similarly, is a drum scanner better than a desktop scanner? Surely. That doesn't mean that very respectable, professionally acceptable color isn't possible from quite inexpensive scans.

Whether the benefits of working in the theoretically superior CMYK space are worth the extra effort it may take you to become comfortable with it is, of course, your affair. But just the fact that you have acquired this volume suggests what your answer will be.

The best way, it seems to me, is to adopt the traditional CMYK approach but temper it with an infusion of a radical innovation, namely, correction in LAB. That may be a little tougher than working in RGB, but it gives the best of two different worlds. This endeavor will occupy our next thirty pages. ●

Jargon Watch

CMYK Cyan, magenta, yellow, and black, the inks used on press, but also a major colorspace used in electronic imaging applications.

colorspace Any reasonable means of defining all available colors in a consistent fashion. Photoshop supports CMYK, RGB, LAB, and, to a lesser extent, HSB, but these are by no means the only colorspaces one may come across.

drum scanner The traditional highest-quality device for digitizing a photograph. The original is mounted on a drum which spins rapidly during scanning. Colors are evaluated with the aid of photomultiplier tubes (PMTs).

GCR Gray component replacement, the substitution of black ink for more or less equal values of cyan, magenta, and yellow. Photoshop characterizes its customary GCR settings as Light, Medium, or Heavy. Choosing the proper alternative avoids many press problems and can also aid in digital color correction.

HSB Hue, saturation, and brightness, a colorspace. A Photoshop document cannot be stored in this format, but the program contains several features that in effect work in it, notably the sponge tool.

LAB Photoshop's native colorspace. Its uses in image manipulation are explored in Column 7 of this book.

levels A Photoshop tonal-adjustment command, having fewer capabilities than curves (see Column 5).

RGB Red, green, and blue, the colors of light to which human vision is principally sensitive; also, a major colorspace for electronic image storage.

separated converted into CMYK for printing.

targeted correction A global color correction that aims at bringing out contrast in a particular item or area.

unsharp masking Artificial method of making images seem more in focus, by means of exaggerating transition areas.

unwanted color The weak ink, where the other two colors are dominant. The unwanted color is responsible for much of the contrast that we see in objects such as leaves and faces.

Dialog Box

Care to suggest why it's CMYK, not CMYB? I've heard old hands say that K stands for "key."

Two reasons.

1. In the pressroom the traditional way of referring to magenta is "red" and to cyan is "blue." This was much more the case in the old days than it is today, incidentally. When I got into the industry the normal way of indicating on a Cromalin that one wanted more magenta was to write "+R." and similarly "+B" to mean more cyan. Hence, B for black is highly ambiguous.

Last time I looked, "black" doesn't begin with a K. Why not CMYB?

2. In the pressroom, black is the key for purposes of registration. However, the term has eased its way into prepress, particularly in the midwest, where they may say "up the quarter in the key" the way others would say "up the quarter in cyan." ●

What are appropriate fleshtone inking values for various ethnicities?

My biggest problem in CMYK has always been skintones. In the newspaper I work for they either come out too red or too gray. I certainly agree with your reasoning on CMYK vs. RGB, and I'm using the suggested skin values in your book, but the results are inconsistent.

The fleshtone values I used in *Professional Photoshop*, like all the other numbers therein, assumed magazine printing conditions. If you use them for newsprint, they may be too gray, for reasons discussed in Column 3.

Also, do you have suggested fleshtone values for other ethnicities besides Caucasians?

There is no easy demarcation between racial and ethnic groups; they all overlap to some extent. The following numbers all assume magazine printing conditions or better; if in newspapers, one would have to reduce cyan and increase yellow.

13C 56M 71Y 2K

6C 29M 30Y

14C 50M 60Y 1K

11C 33M 52Y

26C 40M 50Y 1K

35C 44M 55Y 4K

15C 65M 70Y 2K

5C 19M 26Y

13C 43M 69Y

Figure 6.7. (Opposite)
What's a "normal"
fleshtone? The color
of human skin varies
sharply even across
the same ethnic
group. Lighting condi-
tions also have a
major impact. Below
each image is its
average CMYK flesh-
tone value, super-
imposed on a band
of that color.

The general formula I use starts with the magenta channel. There is a wide range of acceptable darknesses, so I just choose a magenta that looks about right for darkness, without worrying about color balance.

The yellow must be at least as high as the magenta across all ethnic groups, sometimes as much as 25 percent higher, in rare cases even more. In cases where the yellow and magenta are equal, this implies a light-complexioned person: a blonde, perhaps, or a baby. A dark-haired person, regardless of ethnicity, will have significantly more yellow than magenta. Don't be faked out, incidentally, by the wiles of the beautician. If you are wondering why the blonde at the bottom right of Figure 6.7 has fleshtones more characteristic of someone with black hair, check out her roots.

Cyan should be not less than a fifth of the magenta value and not more than a third, for all racial groups except blacks. A cyan value as low as a fifth of magenta again implies a very light-skinned individual. Since cyan pushes the dominant red of skintones toward brown, it is the suntan color: the more of it one has, the more bronze the skin. Some persons of Southern European descent are said to have "olive" complexions, which gives a clue as to why such people need more cyan in their fleshtones than others.

Orientals have very slightly higher yellow values in flesh than do dark-haired Caucasians. There is no difference in the cyan.

There is an enormous range of skin colors among black people. Those who are extremely dark are the easiest group of all to get right, because we lose color perception as colors get darker. On the other hand, persons who would be described as "coffee-colored" are very difficult, because the color is so complex. In all other ethnicities the dominating color is red. It's not easy to get that wrong. But with a light-skinned black person, the prevailing color is more neutral. Make a mistake, and you risk portraying a Martian, rather than a human. That skin color gets green easily.

Figure 6.7 shows fleshtone values for a variety of individuals under a variety of lighting conditions. Note that these are the actual values for these particular images, not necessarily the ones I would recommend. The woman at lower left is badly sunburnt, not suntanned, but if you want that look, the numbers are there for you.●

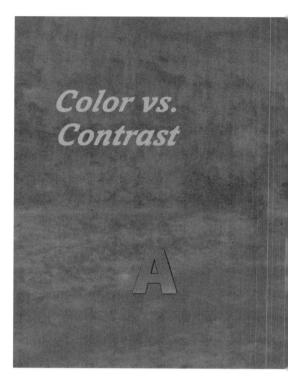

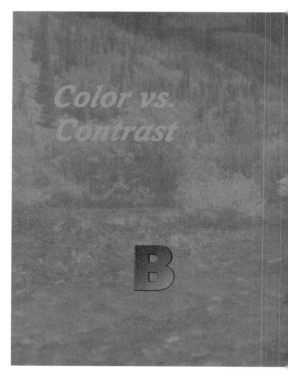

7

L*a*b* Meets
The Matador

Wild and wooly, the most complicated colorspace separates color from contrast. That allows several techniques that aren't possible in either RGB or CMYK.

hen the lion tamer sticks his head into the very mouth of the beast, when the toreador brings the horns of the charging bull to within inches of his heart, we clutch our chests; we gasp at the sheer bravado almost as much as at the daredevil ability to tame the most potent forces of animal nature.

Because this column is devoted to practical production and not frivolous vendor hype, it usually draws a fair response from readers. But of all the pieces appearing in this space over the years, the most popular by far, to judge by an overwhelming favorable reaction, was one that I did almost as a throwaway a year ago, giving a quick and dirty method of improving almost any Photo CD image. That successful recipe [Column 4 in this book] largely depended on a technique that, as far as I know, had never been addressed elsewhere.

That technique involved the partial domestication of the most terrifying beast in the color arsenal, a powerful, brutish creature known to cognoscenti as CIELAB, L*a*b*, or just plain LAB.

Figure 7.1. *The peculiar character of the LAB colorspace, illustrated by a quick look at its channels. Clockwise from upper right, the original color image; the A channel, the B, and the L. The A and B channels carry color information only and consequently have no contrast to speak of. All detail in the image, therefore, resides in the L. This dichotomy can be exploited. LAB has many advantages over either RGB or CMYK, neither of which separate color from contrast in this way.*

The recipe featured two things LAB does extraordinarily well—sharpening and setting overall range—but these are merely the beginning of the LAB story.

Many people, dismissing LAB as impossibly difficult, work themselves into a dither over the question of which one of the two "major" colorspaces, RGB and CMYK, to work in. A safe view, this, but a narrow one. RGB and CMYK are two similar species. Techniques for dealing with one are adaptable, after a fashion, to the other.

LAB, however, is radically different. Like many radical approaches, it is very good in certain ways and very bad in others. We will now explore the good part, starting with straightforward retouching and range-setting. Having navigated that comparatively simple topic, we will then steam straight into the uncharted waters of curve-based correction in LAB.

Color and Contrast

Tradeoffs, tradeoffs. Our life is full of them. Tradeoffs between style and substance, between price and performance, safety and practicality. In the presentation and handling of photographic images, the most haunting tradeoff is the one between color and contrast, two concepts that are so tightly intertwined that it seems impossible to alter one and not the other.

> *LAB can be exploited precisely because it separates contrast from detail, thus solving many problems that are difficult in either RGB or CMYK.*

LAB can be exploited precisely because it *separates* color from detail, solving many problems that would be extremely difficult in either RGB or CMYK. If you customarily work in RGB, you can move in and out of LAB freely to do these things, because, recalling Figure 6.1, there is no quality loss associated with the transition. If you are already in CMYK, there is a minor quality hit in going to LAB, but this may well be outweighed by the benefits of being there.

LAB has three channels, but, as Figure 7.1 demonstrates, the A and B are scarcely recognizable. They define color only, not shape, and are thus unlike anything found in RGB or CMYK. Not only are they blobs, they are *gray* blobs. The LAB color gamut is far wider than anything we are accustomed to. As a result, only about half of the possible tones in these two channels are in use. There are no whites and blacks—only grays, grays, grays.

The two can nevertheless be understood with a little effort. They are, as a scientist would put it, interactive opponent-color channels. The English translation is as follows. In the A, lightness represents an area that is more red than it is green, darkness something that is more green than red. The lighter (or darker), the more intense the color. A pure gray represents, well, a pure gray. The B works in the same way, except lightness means more yellow than blue and darkness more blue than yellow. This explains why, whereas the A in our sample image is appallingly flat, the B is bloodcurdlingly so. At least in the red-green A there is a little variation, because the type is emphatically red and the trees are emphatically green. The B is a blur because both type and trees are slightly more yellow than blue.

The L is far more mundane. It can be seen as a crisp black and white version of the image.

How completely does LAB separate color and contrast? Well, consider Figure 7.2. The original cat is flat and lifeless, so a correction is in order. Suppose that, by whatever technique you choose, using either RGB or CMYK, you come up with a version that is far better, except for one little thing. As often happens, you seem to have lost color fidelity. The main issue here is the gray and white fur. These colors should be neutral, and in the original, they are. The fact that they may be lighter or darker than we would like is not important. The simple way to let this feline have its cat food and eat it too is to convert both images to LAB, and use the L channel from the corrected version along with the A and B from the original.

An extreme case? Perhaps. But if you think it never happens, turn back for a moment to Figure 2.6. That acrimonious controversy was all about color vs. contrast, was it not? If you were now faced with a choice between images A and B there, would you not know how to proceed?

Now let's consider a few more specific instances, not involving the color of the entire image. A recurring theme is this: without LAB, whenever you apply a filter, a curve, or a tool, there is a good chance that the weakest channel will take it on the chin. Eviscerating the weak color, as it happens, is a general recipe for making whatever happens to be the dominant color more brilliant, more vivid.

That is frequently the very last thing we want to have happen. If we work in the colorless L channel only, it won't.

To start with, unsharp masking is more effective when applied to the L than to any combination of channels in RGB or CMYK. In Figure 7.3, you can see why. USM exaggerates transition areas to make the image seem more in focus. It does so by placing dramatic-looking borders around objects that are butting: the darker one gets an even darker border, and the lighter one gets a light border, so that instead of going light to dark, we go light-lighter-darker-dark, in most convincing fashion.

If USM is applied to an entire document, this is equivalent to applying it separately to each channel. In the examples in Figure 7.3, I sharpened in RGB, but the results would have been very much the same in CMYK.

> **W**e can blur the A and B to our heart's content for exactly the same reason we sharpen the L. If there is detail in the A and B, it's probably detail we don't want.

Sharpening the yellow wine label in this way darkens the type as it should, but yields a revolting white halo around it, the result of an exaggerated transition in the blue channel. A different disaster takes place in the second image, where two contrasting, complex colors meet at the edge of the red uniform. In the RGB file, there is not much transition to exaggerate in the blue channel. The red and green channels have transitions, but they go from light to dark in opposite directions.

Vivid colors are wonderful things, no doubt, but they are not exactly what we want from USM. Notice how the woman's neck has become green where it touches the red uniform, and how the edge of the uniform has become such a brilliant red that it has lost detail. The yellow star on the uniform, and the red logo on the wine label, have also become much more intense.

These color-related problems go away if we sharpen the L instead. On the wine label, the yellow becomes lighter where it butts the type, but it clearly is still *yellow,* not that disgusting white. Where the red uniform hits the background, it is again surrounded by a light halo, but the halo is not the eye-popping green that the RGB sharpening brought about.

Should the AB Stand for Always Blur?

Photoshop's extensive defocusing filters—Despeckle, Median, Dust & Scratches, and the various Blurs—are the digital equivalent of going to the dentist. You do it, I do it, we have to do it sometimes in emergencies, and it almost always hurts.

Barring a purposeful attempt to get an out-of-focus look, these filters always damage detail, and can only be justified on a lesser-of-evils basis, as when an image is extremely noisy. But, certainly, they should be avoided whenever possible.

Is it not a happy thing, then, that LAB, unlike other color-spaces, has two channels that carry no detail at all, but only color? We can blur the A and B to our heart's content in a typical picture, for exactly the same reason that we can apply heavy sharpening to the L. If there *is* detail in the A and B, it is probably detail we don't want, namely, noise or damage. In Figure 7.3, observe that Gaussian Blur settings of as high as 3.0 radius, which

ordinarily would destroy an image, may be acceptable in the A and B.

Quite apart from the noise and graininess introduced by fast films and/or imperfect shooting conditions, anyone who has ever scanned knows that the blue channel in RGB, which becomes the yellow in CMYK, usually is home to more static than might be hoped for. Yellow being a weak printing plate, a lot of us blithely blur it, accepting the modest loss in detail,

Figure 7.2. The original, below left, is flat and defocused. A first attempt at correction, below right, gets better detail at the price of unacceptable color. But with LAB, one can get the best of both by combining the L channel from the corrected version with the A and B of the original, yielding the version at top right.

and never thinking that we could have solved the problem with no detail loss at all by the simple expedient of blurring the B.

Grayish noise is a lot less obtrusive than noise with a color component. Killing noise in the yellow-blue B (and in extreme cases, the red-green A) is therefore highly effective, but there is an even more obvious example of when to use this technique.

Prescreened color originals, such as those shot from a printed page, are notoriously difficult. There is no known way of getting really good results; about the best that can be hoped for

is something south of satisfactory. The traditional best method is to scan slightly out of focus at an extremely high resolution, and then downsample, hoping to lose the dot pattern in the process.

The fact that a pattern is detectable in a file does not mean that there will be a moiré in print. But if the patterns happen to be magenta, yellow and cyan, moiré becomes highly likely. If we blur the A and B, they won't be. The pattern will be strictly monochrome, and on a good day, we may be able to retouch some or all of it out of the L channel.

Figure 7.3. *LAB is the colorspace of choice for sharpening and for noise elimination. Facing page, left to right: image sharpened in RGB; the original unsharpened version; sharpening done in the L only. (All sharpening highly exaggerated.) Note how the RGB sharpening creates unwanted brilliance in the yellow areas, the lips, at the edge of the red shirt, and in the weird greenish halo bordering the shirt. Not to mention the green neck!*

On this page, a demonstration of how much blurring the A and B channels can accept. These two were hit with a Photoshop Gaussian Blur of radius 3.0 pixels. This is an absurd value, far higher than used in real life. The left version, which was blurred in the L channel only, shows why. Yet the right version, blurred to exactly the same settings in the A and B only, does not suffer a fraction as much damage. In the upper image, the variation in the yellows of the label is starting to vanish. In the lower image, however, outside of a slightly defocused transition at the edge of the shirt, there is almost no damage even from so overwhelming a blur.

Another delightful use of this idea is in collaging. When we merge an object into an existing image, usually we have to indulge in some kind of anti-aliasing to avoid jagged edges where the two meet. The unfortunate thing is that, depending on how good our selection was, the backgrounds of the two images and a couple of other things, we may get funky-looking transition colors right at the fringe where the two objects meet.

In such a case, if retouching the weird colors out looks at all difficult, save the effort. Go into LAB and blur the A and B.

The Best Space for Retouching and Repairs

Returning for the moment to Figure 7.1, please make the following irritating assumption. Suppose that some knucklehead has merged and saved the red type into the image, without doing so in layers, and that we now find out we have to delete the type and restore whatever was beneath it. Knuckleheads, as you know, do not have backups.

> **R**epairing damage by cloning has a serious limitation in CMYK or RGB: one has to clone every channel simultaneously. In LAB, that isn't necessary.

At such a time, the last thing you probably want to hear is some other knucklehead suggesting that you might try to repair the damage not by cloning, but with Photoshop's smudge tool.

That seems absurd—unless you happen to be in LAB.

However you propose to make this repair, you will surely concede that it is much easier to fix the L channel shown here than the entire color document.

All you have to do to exchange the tough assignment for the easy one is hire a four-year-old to erase the type from the A and B. Doing so is a snap. Most four-year-olds will have no trouble once you explain to them how the smudge tool works. If you care to do the work yourself using a more sophisticated method, so much the better. The resulting color variation will be quite sufficient to hide the repairs needed in the L.

Forgetting the silliness about the smudge tool, consider why the assignment is difficult without LAB. The culprit is the same old refrain: we can't separate color from contrast in RGB or CMYK. To fill the holes, whether we use the clone tool or not, we clearly have to do some kind of duplication of other areas. And that duplication perforce will be of all four (or all three) channels *simultaneously.* It would have to be, to retain any realism.

In LAB, on the other hand, we can usually fill such a hole with *three independent clones.* Once the corrected L is in place we need not clone from the same areas of the A and B. Any other areas that are approximately the same color as what we are cloning will do, and do nicely. Half the problem in selling a clone is that it is an exact duplicate of something else, presumably something else nearby. If the clone is made of of one pass of L and one of AB, or of A and B done independently, there will be variation, but a mild enough variation to be believable.

About ten years ago, I disappointed a client when I was unable to do what she wanted, which was to remove the spots from a leopard. There were just too many spots, and too few areas of the appropriate lighting to clone from. I could erase a few of the spots convincingly but the total job would have taken days and not have been believable.

Since then, I have been brooding over that leopard. Today, I know how the thing could have been done. Without LAB, I was derailed by needing to find fur of a specific color to fill each spot. But working in the L channel alone, any old fur would have done the trick. Getting the color right afterward in the A and B would not have been hard.

There's more. The sharpen tool works better in the L for the same reason that the unsharp masking filter does. Dodging and burning is more effective in the L as well, since it lightens or darkens the image without introducing a new basic color.

I suggest, therefore, that when someone asks you whether the best colorspace for general retouching, repair and collaging is CMYK or RGB, that you answer, "none of the above."

The Best Way to Set Range

The theme of unwanted brilliance also pops up in that most important of color-correction techniques, setting the highlight and shadow. It can once again be avoided neatly by employing the colorless L.

If you do not have a full tonal range, regardless of your creative abilities, channel-maneuvering cognition, etc., you will never be able to beat even a modestly talented person who does no more than set a proper highlight and shadow.

Scans ordinarily fall somewhat short of the ideal, so it is up to us to fix them up. This can be done in RGB or CMYK with curves or, for the timorous, levels. To do it right, unfortunately,

you have to do it separately in each channel. Photoshop tempts us to fall from grace by including a wicked master-curve function that seems ever so much easier.

Setting range with a CMYK master curve will be a disaster, because even if it gets the three color plates correct, it will ruin the black. An RGB master curve move doesn't have this drawback, but it does have the nasty habit of taking little problems and making big ones out of them.

Although in principle the master RGB curve treats all three channels equally, in practice it only works that way if the three were equal to begin with. If we are trying to lighten the highlight with it, whatever color was weakest to begin with will be hurt the most. That, as we have seen, guarantees a cleaner, more vivid dominant color, exactly what we don't want in a highlight, and exactly what we get in the bottom two versions of Figure 7.4.

If you are dead set and determined to apply only one curve and not three, the answer is neither of the master curves of Figure 7.5 but rather the L of LAB, which can set range without altering the prevailing color.

This is easy enough even for the curve-hater. To do it as simply as possible, convert to LAB, and locate both the lightest and darkest significant areas of the image. Set Photoshop's Info palette to read LAB color. The L channel will be defined as

Figure 7.4. *LAB is the sensible way to correct range in an image that's too flat, since working with the L channel cannot introduce a color cast. Top to bottom: the atrocious original; a range correction using the L only; correction using the RGB master curve; and correction using the CMYK master curve. Note the offensive colors creeping into the bottom two versions.*

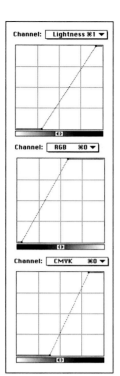

Figure 7.5. *The three curves that generated the alternate versions of Figure 7.4.*

100 (white) to 0 (black). The extreme numbers will not show detail on the printed page. For average printing, the minimum and maximum values should be, roughly, 95 and 10. Move the endpoints of the curve in toward the center until the known light and dark points reach these values.

And Now, the Hard Stuff

A lion tamer may begin his career by scratching a kitten behind the ears to make it purr. The primitive method of setting range described above can be seen as much the same thing.

Inspired, perhaps, by the brazen tactics of the lion tamer and the matador, let us now ignore all intermediate-level stuff in favor of the most dangerous of color game: going full-tilt after an image using LAB curves.

To understand how to tame this creature, you must first completely clear your mind of all color preconceptions. LAB defines colors in a way only a scientist could love, based on cube roots, imaginary light-sources, and hypothetical observers. It is not easy to understand, and Photoshop makes matters worse with a bug: the normal method of finding values on a curve does not work properly in LAB. But if we keep in mind that, unlike RGB and CMYK, where correction techniques often involve a compromise between more detail and accurate color, LAB keeps the two separate, we will stay on course.

Curvewriting in LAB is just like navigating any other minefield, except that in this particular one our maps and compasses are taken away and we must sail by dead reckoning; and that the mines are more sensitive and more powerful than we have ever seen before.

If that stern warning has not deterred you, you will need to study the next four paragraphs at some length. They contain information not documented anywhere else.

In normal curvewriting, we have three sources of numerical guidance: the readings in the Info palette; the input/output numbers in the lower right of the curves dialog box; and the moving circle on the curve itself that appears when we click and hold on any part of the image. In LAB, the last two exist, *but they are completely inaccurate.* If you wish to write curves in LAB, the *only* guidance to be relied upon is the Info palette.

If you have set curves up in the normal way, with light to the left and dark to the right, the L channel ranges from 100 (totally white) to 0 (complete darkness). Moving the curve up yields a darker image and moving it down a lighter one.

The A goes from +128 (laughably luminous red, lower left) to −128 (impossibly iridescent green, upper right), with the midpoint, zero, signifying gray. Moving the curve down makes the image more red and moving it up makes it more green. The B works the same way, except yellow replaces red in the positive (lower) half and blue replaces green in the negative.

The L channel has a normal-looking kind of range, and the curve corrections we make in it, though difficult to control, make sense to anyone who has previously worked in CMYK or RGB. The A and B have neither of these characteristics. Instead, half of their range consists of colors that are unprintable, out of the CMYK gamut. A value of plus or minus 60 is about as high as we can meaningfully get in either channel. A ten-point move in the A or B is absolutely huge.

If colorspaces were tools, CMYK would be a jeweler's screwdriver and LAB a sledgehammer. There is a place for each one. LAB is much too volatile for delicate maneuvering, but there is no such thing as a color cast so violent that it cannot be removed with curves in the A and B channels.

Figure 7.6. When an image's color range is way off, as in the original, below left, LAB is the best space to correct in. The right-hand version has had only one application of LAB curves (see Figure 7.7). It still needs to be fine-tuned in CMYK, but that isn't a big deal.

LAB, therefore, is for really *big* corrections, such as are needed in the flesh of the redheaded model of Figure 7.6. The original, flat as a board, is not particularly close to being acceptable. Furthermore, at 22C36M25Y7K, the skintone is simultaneously too neutral, too pinkish, and lacking in contrast.

Correcting something this far out of whack is a real chore in either RGB or CMYK.

By the Numbers in LAB

The contrast problem, which is causing the model to seem to have no nose, can be attacked in the normal way, by finding the range the face occupies and expanding it. [See Column 5.] The color problem is a big one, since in this kind of image the yellow value should be about four times the sum of the cyan and the black, whereas here it is, incredibly, less.

This calls for LAB, so, whatever space we are working in, we must convert, and, with great trepidation, learn that the typical fleshtone value here is 73L12A5B. In Photoshop's higher-equals-lighter definition, the flesh value in the L is a quartertone.

The A and B are both positive, so red and yellow are favored over green and blue. This is what we might expect, but both numbers should be higher. The image is too gray now, and gray would be a zero. Also, contrary to what we have, the B should be higher than the A, on the theory that a fleshtone should be slightly less blue than green, slightly more yellow than red.

We begin in the L by establishing overall range. We do not have enough precision to fine-tune the highlight and shadow, but we can certainly get into the proper neighborhood.

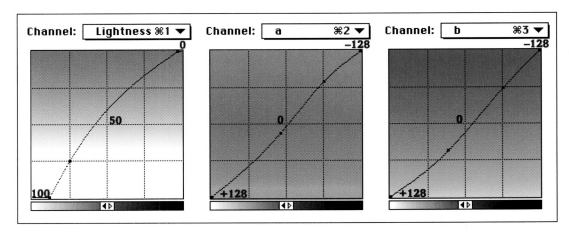

Figure 7.7. *The Info palette, above, is the only way to evaluate values in LAB. Below, the curves that made the change in Figure 7.6, along with some added numerical reference points.*

Happily, one need not worry about color balance in high-light and shadow here, since the L is colorless. So, a simple and effective way to set range is to locate the lightest and darkest areas of the image, and move the lower endpoint of the L curve to the right, and the upper one to the left, as needed to change the range to at least 95 to 10.

This move yields a straight line, not a curve, but we now place a third point, approximately a third of the way up (looking for a value of around 65), and raise it as shown in Figure 7.7. The idea of this is to steepen the range in the lightest area of the picture, which is how we will get extra contrast into the face. This is an extremely common LAB maneuver and it is one that you should consider in almost every image, especially those scanned via Kodak's Photo CD process.

The A and B curves are like a pet porcupine. You can play with them, as long as you are very, very careful. Here, we need to take positive values and make them even more positive. The positive direction is down. The relevant fleshtone points in both A and B are slightly lower and to the left of the midpoint, and we need to force them lower yet, especially the B. The curves shown in Figure 7.7 do this, but LAB offers some fascinating alternatives.

Hypothetically, therefore, let's consider some other possible approaches to this AB correction. The minimalist method, for example, would place a series of locking points along the negative (top) half of the curve. We would then put a point at the current fleshtone value, and bring it down. This would pretty much prevent anything blue or green from changing color.

The redhead image has no neutral grays, but if it did, another option would be to arrange to have their values fall as close to zero as possible in both A and B. Remember, unlike any other colorspace you've ever worked with, zero is the midpoint of the A and B curves.

A more common, and more useful, question is what to do with the opponent color. Forget the A channel for a moment and concentrate on the B, where we need to make a major move downward so as to get more yellow. We have been assuming that the lower half of the curve will get steeper whereas the upper half will be locked into position. Now, suppose that instead, we do *not* anchor the upper half, but rather let it slide upwards, so that in effect we are

Figure 7.8. *Because LAB separates contrast from detail, it is the best space to use when trying for realistic effects that are wildly different from the original, as the change in the model's eye and lip color below.*

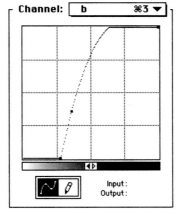

taking the entire curve, and pivoting it counterclockwise around the midpoint.

The result of this is a real mouthful. All colors that are more yellow than they are blue will become even more yellow. All colors that are more blue than they are yellow will get bluer still. Note the important distinction between the words *blue* and *more blue than yellow*. The model's sweater is certainly not blue. It is, however, more blue than it is yellow. It will consequently be affected by the move, going from a burgundy to more of a pure purple.

There may be an artistic reason to prefer this sort of move, one that can only be addressed with LAB. When the object is to increase the prominence of one color, increasing the strength of its opposite number can help. Blue sets off yellow. Red and green, as neighboring colors, compete with yellow.

Figure 7.9. *Soft-edged masks, like the inset above, are often easiest to achieve in LAB. Here, the model's hair is far more yellow than it is blue, meaning it will have a high positive value in the B channel. A steep curve (right) can therefore isolate the hair, from which point the mask can be generated without difficulty.*

Suppose that what we are after here is to emphasize the model's orangish hair. If so, a bluer sweater is *better*, as is an increase in the intensity of the blue area above her right shoulder. Furthermore, a supplementary move in the A channel makes sense: *flatten* the curve by pivoting it clockwise around the midpoint, thus muting all reds and greens.

I chose here a combination approach, with a downward bulge in the curve at the point of the fleshtone. The resulting image still needs some CMYK fine-tuning, but it is hugely closer now to what we need than before the LAB move. The fleshtone is now 80L15A21B, translating to a highly acceptable 9C36M40Y.

A Powerful Masking Tool

So far, everything we have done has been aimed at a more or less faithful rendition of the original photograph. Since LAB is the colorspace for big moves, however, it is also where we want to be when the job involves any major move away from reality.

Suppose that we are asked to make this woman's eyes blue rather than brown, and also to apply a heavier lipstick. Moves this drastic are hard in RGB or CMYK, because each channel contains both contrast and color, and it is not always possible to change one without harming the other. LAB, which rams all detail into the L channel, doesn't have this problem. We simply select the affected areas and apply curves to the A and B, possibly using the L for added depth, as I did in the lips in Figure 7.8.

If you have experience in this type of face work, you are probably sneering to yourself at this point at the choice of correcting eyes and lips, when in an image of this nature, it is far more likely that the client will call for something to be done to the hair.

> **L**AB is the best choice for big color moves. That means it is also where we want to be when the job involves any major move away from reality.

If you have no such experience, let me explain that the others are sneering because they think I took the easy way out. The eyes and lips are excruciatingly easy to select. Something soft-edged and irregular, like the woman's hair, is not, especially when it, as here, butts a background of a similar color. Otherwise sane individuals have been known to spend hours creating an accurate hair mask.

If the background had only been more neutral, or, better yet, if it were green rather than reddish! There might then have been ways of improvising a mask from one of the RGB channels, but in this case, the colors of the hair and background are just too close—unless we are in LAB!

The smallest of differences can be exploited, if we can only learn to think in the weird, color-antagonist LAB mindset. The issue is not whether the hair is more red than anything else, but whether it is more, er, red vs. green than anything else. It is not, which rules out use of the A.

As against that, while the hair is not much more yellow than the background, it is, by a wide margin, more, er, yellow vs. blue. Its B value is typically around 30, which is 10 points more positive (that is, more yellow vs. blue) than anything else in the

Figure 7.10. *When an original features closely similar colors throughout (left), curve maneuvers in the A and B channels can add life. Here, steepening the red-green A curve brings out color contrast in the forest, right.*

image. Discovering this, making a copy of the image and applying a super-steep curve to the B results in incredible edge definition of the hair. The sneerers need no help from Figure 7.9, for they know thousands of ways to make the mask from this point.

For the rest of the world, one easy method to complete the mask is to discard the new L and A, saving the B as a grayscale image. Then adjust its contrast to make the background black and the brightest areas of the hair white, and invert the channel so that the hair becomes black and the background white. This yields a lovely soft-edged mask in a fraction of the time of any other method I am aware of.

This sort of issue pops up more than you might think. Going back to Figure 7.2, there was a gray and white cat against a light background that could best be described as dirty blue. If we had wanted to select the irregular outline of the cat's fur, doing so in CMYK or RGB would have been a royal pain. The white fur would be lighter than the background and the gray darker, regardless of what channel we were looking at. The fact that the background had an even slight blue cast, though, means that it could have been isolated in the B channel, which does not care how dark the cat is, but only that it is neutral.

Simultaneous Contrast via LAB

The AB curves are so ill-tempered that, in general, one should confine their use to images with grave color difficulties, such as the redhead of Figure 7.6. There is, however, a major exception, typified by the rainforest image of Figure 7.10.

A well-known anomaly of the human visual system is that, when confronted with similar colors in close physical proximity, we perceive more difference between them than is actually there. This phenomenon, which color scientists call *simultaneous contrast,* means that when shown, as here, lots of greens, our brains exaggerate what variations we find, so that we seem to see more flavors of green, some lighter, some darker.

> **O**rdinarily, steepening a curve emphasizes detail, giving more apparent contrast. But in the A and B, a steeper curve creates color variation.

Since cameras and scanners employ no such mental process, their product can seem rather tepid. This rainforest picture is dominated by shades of green. How do we get the greater variation in them that our subconscious wants us to see?

Surely not by moves in CMYK or RGB, and not by saturation adjustments either. No, this is a job for LAB, and a comparatively simple one at that.

Ordinarily, steepening a curve emphasizes variation in detail, giving more apparent contrast. But since the A and B do not carry detail, a steeper curve there emphasizes *color* variation.

Here, as with the redhead image, we can simply pivot the A curve counterclockwise around its midpoint. That adds color contrast throughout the red-green continuum, breaking the greens apart.

This image demonstrates another helpful use of LAB: the ability to control neutrality. The redhead image had nothing that we wanted to portray as white or gray, but here the top of the waterfall plainly should be neutral.

It is easier to represent a neutral color in LAB than in either RGB or CMYK, since we only have to deal with two channels. As long as both the A and B are at or near zero, an object will be neutral regardless of what is happening in the L.

In this case, before applying the steepening curves to the A channel, we measure the white area at the top of the waterfall. If it is more than a couple of points away from zero, it is simple to move the curve to the left or right to compensate.

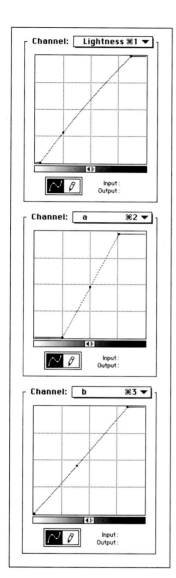

Figure 7.11. *Brightening up the colors in a gray original is another area in which LAB excels. In addition to the steepening of the A and B channels to give more color variation, note how the stong yellowish cast is eliminated by moving the B away from yellow and toward blue.*

The L channel can also help bring out more depth in the greens. Measuring the L in several regions of the forest yields values of from 55 to 25. This information suggests construction of an S-shaped curve. We find the lightest part of the waterfall, and set the L value to 95, and the darkest shadow to 10. Then, we place two more points on the curve at the values measured for the greenery, lowering the 55 and raising the 25. This gives steepness between the two points, increasing contrast in an appealing manner.

> For psychedelic special effects, LAB can get you weirder faster than anything else.

Steepening the A and/or B is also a key maneuver in images that lack color punch, as opposed to simply being too flat. Three quick examples come to mind:

- You are preparing a series of pictures for a real estate brochure. Obviously, you want bright, happy colors throughout: blue skies, green lawns, etc., whether or not these are the colors of the original art.
- Your file is in CMYK, but you have to convert it to RGB because, say, you are putting it on the Web. The brightest RGB colors are out of the CMYK gamut and hence will not be found in your original. Steepening the A and B is a pain-free way of bringing them back.
- You have an image like the Quebec snowscape of Figure 7.11, where lighting was bad and all colors are clustered closely together.

This one seems like a good one to end a series on LAB with, since it caters to several of the themes we have covered. When originals have a color cast, as here, setting the range is best done in the L channel, rather than in CMYK or RGB. Proper control of unsharp masking will be critical here, so once again the L is the best choice.

Since the colors in the original are so muted, steepening the A and B seems the way to go, and at the same time we can correct the color cast, by keying into those parts of the snow that we are sure should be white, and setting them to values of zero in both channels. How far to go in boosting the colors is of course up to you; you may not agree with how far I've gone here, but it is unlikely that you would want to leave the colors the way they were, either.

Just the Beginning

If you are one of those who has been frightened away by the snarls and threatening gestures of this obviously powerful creature, you are certainly not alone. The idea of taming LAB is very recent, so there are not too many experienced people to ask for advice on how to do it. Most of the techniques illustrated here are my own, and presumably can be improved.

But even knowing as little as we do about it, certain conclusions are clear:

- The L channel is the best sharpening space.
- The L is also the easiest way for a non-expert to set proper highlight and shadow range.
- When the move desired is a big one—either because the original is grossly defective or because we want to make some major move away from the art—LAB is much better than RGB or CMYK.
- For noisy, grainy, or prescreened originals, or when merging one image into another, blurring the B and/or A is the most effective, cost-free option.
- When trying to pep up the colors of an image, or when trying to get closely similar colors to show more variation, consider steepening the A and/or B curve.
- If you are having trouble making selections of irregular, soft-edged objects, often the best way to isolate them is found in the A or B.
- For cloning small areas of an image, or extending a background, LAB is the colorspace of choice, because the three channels can be cloned independently of one another in many cases.

It should also be obvious that for psychedelic special effects, LAB can get you weirder faster than anything else. Try sharpening the A and B heavily, or applying an unusual curve to them, and see for yourself.

LAB does not solve all problems. It must be used in conjunction with either CMYK or RGB, as it is too musclebound to deal well with finesse situations such as balancing a highlight. And, of course, if it is not treated with the respect that such a powerful entity deserves, why, you probably know what happened to the young lady from Niger, who smiled as she rode on a tiger.

The virtues of working in a way that separates color from contrast, however, are a compelling argument for everyone to learn to use LAB as a *second* colorspace. I've shown a few of the hoops that it can be enticed into jumping through, and wish you success in finding further ways to domesticate it. ●

Afterword

The two original columns that are combined into one here appeared in mid-1996, so the reaction from readers is not yet in. LAB correction is getting a lot of word-of-mouth attention these days from people who know or suspect that it is a very big deal, but nothing this complete has ever appeared about it in print.

These 20-plus pages, along with the other three columns that make up this section, will, I trust, put to rest certain myths about my alleged CMYK chauvinism. From time to time I get called dinosaur or worse; those who haven't plumbed all the capabilities of CMYK tend to believe that its advocates just believe in it because they are used to it.

While I am certainly a CMYK aficionado, it's not because of any lack of experience in working in RGB, I assure you; quite the contrary. When I wrote *Professional Photoshop*, which is aimed at print production, I used CMYK as the base, because everyone who works in print has to get there sooner or later, and because anyone who has mastered CMYK will have no trouble with the less complicated RGB, while the converse is not true.

So, for the record, here are the workflows I recommend:

1. If your original files are CMYK and your destination is CMYK as well, don't convert to LAB without a good reason, but don't be afraid to do it if you have one. If you have certain channels that lack detail, you may wish to consider use of other colorspaces, by converting copies of the original to LAB and/or RGB and making use of the channels there for blending. If you are good enough to take advantage of what LAB has to offer you should be plenty good enough to reverse the small quality loss in the CMYK-LAB-CMYK conversion. Refer back to Figure 6.1 if you aren't convinced of how small that loss is.

2. If your originals are RGB and your destination is RGB also, feel free to do work in LAB; there is zero quality loss. But if your final destination is a high-resolution film recorder, be aware that unsharp masking in LAB or otherwise is normally undesirable. Cases where it is best to take RGB work into CMYK for some specialized correction exist but they are rare.

3. With CMYK originals that need to go to RGB, convert to LAB first. Highlight and shadow should ordinarily have a greater range in RGB, and this can be arranged by adjustment of the L. Also, CMYK colors will seem somewhat desaturated when converted to RGB, so steepen the A and B in the way shown in Figure 7.11.

4. With RGB originals going to CMYK, if it's not a quick-and-dirty kind of job where you really don't want to spend much time, convert to LAB. Before doing so, inspect any brightly colored areas in RGB. If any of these areas are completely lacking in detail, often this is the fault of a single RGB channel, which can now be corrected by blending, before the problem migrates to several

other channels. Once in LAB, set range and sharpen, then convert to CMYK for final adjustment of highlight, shadow, neutrals, and fleshtones.

In this particular RGB-LAB-CMYK scenario, I see little merit in correcting in RGB. If you are going to be working the curves in LAB the inherent inaccuracy of that space will force you to do some final touchup in CMYK. However, if you are more comfortable adjusting color in RGB, it won't cost you anything except a little extra time.

If in any of these cases you desire to do color correction or retouching, do so in whatever colorspace you like. The greater your skill the more you will be able to exploit the advantages of CMYK as opposed to RGB. But the greater the problem that you face with the image, the more LAB has to offer. It's an offer I don't think you can afford to refuse. ●

Jargon Watch

channels The subdivisions of a digital image file. CMYK documents have four channels, one for each ink, while RGB and LAB files have three. Additional channels are sometimes added by the operator for use as masks or templates.

cloning In image retouching, the duplication of parts of an image into other regions. Often used to repair damaged areas or to bring additional detail.

color balance To what extent an image appears to have neutral ambient lighting; the presence or absence of a color cast.

dodging and burning In conventional photography, the lightening or darkening of small areas of the image, carried out in the darkroom during the developing or printing process. Adopting the terminology, Photoshop incorporates a tool that does the same thing. It can be applied overall or to any channel.

gamut The range of colors that can be accommodated by a given process. CMYK cannot produce certain vivid colors, particularly blues, so it is said to have a smaller gamut than RGB, which in turn has a smaller gamut than LAB.

highlight Used generally to indicate the lightest areas of an image; sometimes used (*the* highlight) to refer to the area the scanner operator or image technician uses as a base point for setting range and color balance. Under this second definition, the highlight must be the lightest area of the image other than those intended to depict flashes of light; but it also must be an area that the oper-

ator is prepared to represent as *white*. If both prongs of the definition are not met (which happens in about 25 percent of all photography), then the image has no highlight.

moiré An undesirable interference pattern, generally caused when one pattern is superimposed on another. For example, if the subject of the image has a strong gridlike pattern (such as the texture of a nylon stocking), either the scan itself or the process of halftone screening may cause a moiré. The case mentioned in the column involved preprinted images. Since a printed image has been screened, and reprinting imposes a second screen on top of it, weird-looking moirés can develop.

neutral Whites, grays, and blacks; any area of an image that has no prevailing color.

noise In digital image files, the presence of seemingly random pixels that have nothing to do with either detail or color. Noisy originals look grainy at best and silly at worst, so noise is usually thought undesirable. There are some special cases, however, so most image processing applications have some means of *adding* noise to an image if desired.

quartertone A somewhat nebulous term intended to encompass ranges that are roughly a quarter as dark as the shadow regions. A quartertone is darker than a highlight and lighter than a midtone, but there is no fixed number where one begins and the other ends.

selection In image processing, the isolation of an area prior to altering it. When portions of the image are selected, other areas are locked and cannot be changed.

shadow The darkest neutral areas of an image. Sometimes also used to refer specifically to *the* darkest such area, the point that a scanner operator or image technician uses to set range and color balance.

sharpening See *unsharp masking.*

smudge A primitive Photoshop retouching tool, intended to give the effect of dragging one's finger through paint. It is rarely used in professional work. The suggestion of using it in restoring a background was an in-your-face kind of thing.

unsharp masking An artificial method of making an image appear to be more in focus. Can be accomplished manually on a stripping table, optically on a drum scanner, or by algorithm in an image-processing application such as Photoshop. In any case the method is to exaggerate transition areas so that they will appear more pronounced. The edges of dark areas are darkened and the edges of light areas are lightened. When done subtly, it is unnoticeable; when carried to extremes, halos begin to appear. The halos can become ugly rapidly when USM is applied to more than one color channel. In the picture of the woman in the red uniform in Figure 7.3, the green background is a dark area in the cyan channel but a light one in the magenta. USM, as described above, darkens the edge of the cyan but lightens the edge of the magenta at the point where the background touches the red uniform. The combination of extra cyan and decreased magenta causes an offensive green halo.

Dialog Box

I have a CMYK printer's file (Scitex CT format) that now needs to be retouched and then output to 4×5 transparencies. I can do the retouching in CMYK but need to convert to RGB for output to film recorder. Any suggestions as to setups to make this conversion as accurate as possible?

Depending on the characteristics of the image a number of approaches may be right. However, as a rule, the following will work well. The basic problems with just doing a CMYK>RGB conversion are a) a film recorder supports a heavier shadow than a press does, so the darkest parts of the image are presumably too light at the moment for your intended use; b) colors will not seem saturated enough. Therefore,

Reverse logic: how to prepare a CMYK file for output on an RGB recorder

1. Once you are happy with your retouch and overall color in CMYK, convert the image to LAB.

2. Find and measure the darkest point in the image, reading the L value in the Info palette. For a normal CMYK scan that value is probably 6 to 12 (lower equals darker). For RGB work it should be about 2 or 3.

3. Open the Curves dialog box, and in the L channel, take the top right point and move it horizontally to the left until the darkest point in the image reads 2 or 3. (In these instructions, I am assuming you have set up the curve so that the dark side is to the right of the dialog box.)

4. Switch to the A channel curve and change it from a 45-degree straight line to a steeper, say 50-degree line, by moving the lower left and upper right points in equal amounts horizontally toward the center, making sure that the center of the line still crosses the center point of your curve grid.

5. Ditto the B channel.

6. Convert to RGB. ●

PART III

What Goes Around, Comes Around

*the ground rumbles beneath the
feet of the professional photographer*

8

How Much Image For a Dime?

The business of stock photography reels, as digital entrepreneurs introduce royalty-free CD-ROMs of quality images at prices that seem too good to be true.

Just about ten years ago, I had occasion to purchase the entire Mergenthaler typeface library in digital format. A marvelous collection it was, some 1,200 faces, representing some of the best work of the best designers of the last five centuries. The package was offered at what was, by the standards of the time, a huge bargain, but to get the bargain I had to commit to buy every additional face that Mergenthaler, now Linotype-Hell, released in the next five years, at a usurious fee.

I do not have the stomach to recollect the exact figure I paid, but in today's money, it would come to something just over $100,000.

That is not quite a hundred times what one would pay for an equivalent package today from leading vendors, such as Adobe, Agfa, or Monotype. Furthermore, the overall quality of the letters and the font metrics is today a lot better than it was when I dropped my hundred grand.

Several smaller firms, however, have discounted much more deeply. Packages priced at a dime per typeface are readily available, although quality and, sometimes, ethics, can be variable.

Figure 8.1. *The knock against royalty-free stock photography used to be that the selection wasn't specific enough. No more. These photos come from 100-image CDs entitled (you'll have to guess which is which): Decorated Pumpkins; English Pub Signs; Cactus Flowers; and Doors of San Francisco. The images are pennies apiece in quantity, from low-price leader Corel.*

The collapse of type prices is old news. Something very similar, however, is happening in stock photography, and we'll now take a look at some images that have broken through the dime-per-image floor.

The Old Order Changeth

If, for advertising purposes, we decide that we need to use an image of, say, the Statue of Liberty, the way this has historically been done is for us to approach a stock photo agency. The agency typically has several hundred thousand images available against the time that we will come calling, and of these, a dozen or more will be apt to be of the Statue of Liberty.

> **Previously, nobody bought a stock photo without definite plans to use it. Now, one buys a hundred or more, on pure speculation that one may one day come in handy.**

Once we examine their catalog and make a selection, negotiation about price commences. We are cross-examined about what we intend to do with the image, which will determine how much we pay. If the image is going on the cover of *Newsweek*, we will be charged much more than if it is going on the cover of *Computer Artist*. If instead it is being used in advertising, a third set of prices will apply. In each case, we will be asked to agree not to use the image for any other purpose. The fee for one use of the same image can vary from very low to tens of thousands of dollars.

Acquiring rights to a stock photo in this fashion takes time and is moderately inconvenient. This, coupled with the difficulty of predicting what the price is going to be, has limited stock photo usage.

The digital age has given the agencies an opportunity to remedy this. What everyone wants to do (and several fledgling services already more or less succeed) is to allow us to dial into a large database, specify that we want an image of a blond man standing in front of a green Oldsmobile, and have the system spit back at us low-resolution versions of the fifteen images in the world that fit that description.

This is a definite improvement, but the disagreeable negotiated price remains. Some entrepreneurial types felt that a radical departure was in order. The advent of CD-ROM drives on the desktops of most computer artists gave them the opportunity to prove it.

This concept, which as far as I know dates back only to 1991, was to sell a whole variety of images on CD, with more or less unrestricted reproduction rights.

What a revolutionary idea! Previously, nobody ever bought a stock photo without having firm plans to use it. Now, one buys a hundred or more, ordinarily on pure speculation that one may some day come in handy.

It took a while to catch on, but in 1994 sales exploded, and a host of new vendors have entered the market. Selection has drastically increased, to the point that one can easily acquire for home use royalty-free libraries comparable (in size, at least) to that of small stock houses. Now, there is no shortage of digital Statues of Liberty, as Figure 8.2 demonstrates.

What usually happens in such cases is now at work. Instead of advertising to an audience unfamiliar with the basic concept of royalty-free stock photos, the vendors are stressing their own strengths and knocking down the competition.

Quality has become a competitive issue. Those vendors whose photos are already in CMYK trumpet the greater convenience; those using drum scanning are attacking those using Kodak Photo CD; those whose resolutions support printing at full-page sizes make much of other vendors' inability to match.

The licensing agreement has become a competitive issue. Most firms' licenses call for unlimited, credit-free usage as long as the photos are not redistributed in digital form. Occasionally there are prohibitions against usage in pornography, in advertising products that compete with the vendor's own, or in products where the image itself is the primary value. A couple of the leading names in the field have licenses that are less broad, such as restricting use in products that are offered for sale. This has had the predictable result that ads for their competitors generally have the words "completely royalty-free" and "unrestricted use" in large, boldface upper case letters, with at least three underscores.

The caliber of the photographer has become a competitive issue. Many vendors now have deals with some very fine photographers, whereby a single disk, or a set, is devoted to the work of one named individual.

And, perhaps above all, price has become a competitive issue. Has it ever. The first royalty-free CDs retailed for around $300, and some vendors are holding the line there. But, as more

The scanner issue on royalty-free stock pretty much resolved itself in 1995 as virtually all players went to drum scanning. Some of the work produced on the lesser scanners was really quite good (and better in many cases than some of the drum scans being peddled by competitors). But the advertising alluded to here did its job, and market forces triumphed, as they usually do. Kodak's decision to open up the Photo CD standard (see Column 4) allowed Photo CD users Corel and Digital Stock to retain their format, but switch to higher-quality scanners.

labels have entered the market, some prices have come down. At first we saw $200, then $99, then $50. How low can the price go for, say, a 100-image CD of reasonable quality?

Well, would you believe $9.95 a disk? Would you believe $4.00 in quantity?

Believe it.

Enter, Stage North, a 600-Pound Gorilla

Figure 8.2. Royalty-free collections have strong selections of familiar objects. On these two pages: variations on a theme by, from left to right, Aztech, Corel, Digital Stock, PhotoDisc, and Hammerhead.

The course of this competition between small entrepreneurs has been seriously disrupted by a presence that, like a 600-pound gorilla, no one dare ignore. Corel Corp., the mightiest name in PC-based graphics, entered the fray in late 1993. Things have not been the same since.

In this market, the average vendor struggles to put out 20 titles. Corel releases 20 *per month* in its Professional Photos series, and had 350 available at the end of 1994. In this market, the average vendor struggles to find enough money for a quarter-page ad in *Computer Artist* or some other trade publication. Corel advertises its CDs with full-page ads on the back of the sports section of *USA Today*, along with extravagant use of the trade press. Although no reliable numbers exist, I would guess that Corel's advertising budget for this product is greater than the *gross sales* of any of its competitors, possibly than of all put together.

One of the big selling points of the stock-photo houses against the interlopers has been that the CD selections are not specific enough. Corel has cast serious doubt on this. Among its titles—100 images per disk—are *Waves, Bonsai and Penjing, English Country Gardens,*

Kitchens and Bathrooms, and *Ice and Icebergs,* in addition to the titles cited in Figure 8.1.

Corel's financial power was also one of the main factors in persuading professional photographers to allow their work to appear in this form. Since many feared little or no royalty from this unknown medium, Corel offered its photographers the option of a flat cash payment instead. For a full 100-image package, Corel offered $CDN10,000 (roughly $US7,000 now, but more back then). In late 1993 and early 1994, the market for professional photography, particularly in Ontario, was not such that people were inclined to turn down sums this large. Especially not for shots already taken, however high their quality, that otherwise might never be used.

How Low Can It Go?

But most striking of all has been Corel's relentless price-cutting. When the product was first introduced, the list price was $49.95 per CD, which already was just about the lowest in the industry. Today, the same disks are available at street prices of three for $40, a little over a dime per PCD image.

In 1994, Corel introduced sets of 25 preselected CDs, at highly attractive prices, but those who, like me, tried to order them, encountered long waits: Corel was not able to manufacture enough to meet the demand.

Corel reacted to this good news in typical fashion. It sent the rest of the market a message by slashing the price even more (at this writing, street price is $149 for the 25-disk sets) and introducing an even bigger bargain: a set of 200 CDs, 20,000 royalty-free images, for $800 street—four cents an image.

The growth in sales of the Corel product continued strongly in 1995, and its low prices held. It even introduced a new variant: 10 pre-selected CDs, 1,000 images, at a street price of $39. You can read more about Corel's progress in Column 9.

These tactics paid dividends. In a market where most vendors are happy to sell a couple of thousand of any title, Corel has moved 1.2 million CD-ROMs. Of these sales, according to figures released in January 1995, more than half—650,000 units—came in the last quarter of 1994 alone.

Companies this aggressive make enemies. Among stock photo houses, Corel is about as popular as the 1994 hockey lockout was in its home town of Ottawa.

The other CD-ROM vendors, oddly enough, are by and large delighted by Corel's presence. They may wish that Corel did not cut its prices quite so low, but they recognize that its advertising benefits everyone in the industry, and they are happy to ride along on Corel's coattails.

The Aztech product is now marketed under the name Photofile World Image Collection.

Not that Corel was the first to offer large sets at a very low price. That honor, as far as I know, goes to another Ontario company, Aztech New Media, which publishes a 25-disk, 3,000-image collection, World Bank. The set features scenic and cultural shots from many different countries, but as you might expect, with this many images, there is plenty of miscellany. At $200 (street) the set, it isn't quite as cheap as Corel's, but at seven cents an image, it is still well below the rest of the industry.

Hammerhead released less than half the number of disks it predicted in 1995. In February 1996, it was purchased by CAM, Inc. The line of CDs continues, but at $19.95 apiece.

Meanwhile, Hammerhead Interactive has announced plans to eat some of Corel's lunch. Its first Photo CDs shipped in January 1995. It hopes to release 100 titles in its first year. And, unable to match Corel's advertising muscle, Hammerhead has decided to undercut its price: the CDs are $9.95 apiece!

In the next year, we'll find out whether Hammerhead is jumping onto a passing train that other vendors are standing in the path of. Corel and Hammerhead, though they value the graphic arts community's business, do not see it as their primary market. That is why Corel advertises in *USA Today*. If enough people will buy these disks as screen savers or whatever, these very low prices will hold.

Figure 8.3. *The Canada goose, a major pest in many areas, is also a considerable nuisance to color-correct when the original scan is as poor as the Corel one above. Getting a respectable printed version out of it is possible (below), but is not for the inexperienced.*

Figure 8.4. *Right, the image is seductive, but so is the price: $9.95 for 100 such swimsuit shots, from Hammerhead Interactive's first CD release. Left: subsequent Hammerhead disks retain the low price, but explore topics more suitable for general advertising.*

Selection and Quality

This is, of course, great news for graphic artists—provided that the quality is there. It isn't always.

There are three major criteria to consider: 1) how well executed are the original photographs; 2) how many of the photos on the CD are actually useful; 3) how good is the digital rendition of the photograph (cleanliness, depth of detail, and color fidelity).

As to photography, things are getting better in all CDs, but it is still not what you would get from a conventional house. This is because, naturally, such agencies deal only with experienced professionals. One of the great things about the new products is that they are a wonderful opportunity for gifted amateur photographers (if you have 100 high-quality images on an interesting theme that you'd be willing to take $10,000 for, give Corel a call—they won't ask for your union card).

> **These CDs, according to an opponent, "have generated more antagonism between photographers, art directors, stock agencies, CD publishers and clients than any other practice in recent history."**

Some of this work is indeed quite good, but it is not as consistent as that shot by professionals. As stated before, however, more and more of these photographers are seeing the writing on the wall and signing on with the digital stock companies.

As to selection, there seems to me to be a clear advantage in the more expensive CDs. In the $200-$300 range, industry leaders PhotoDisc Inc. and Digital Stock Corp. and texture specialists ArtBeats and Vivid Details show great familiarity with what the advertising artist is looking for. Their disks are full of useful, interesting images. Many of the cheaper vendors, it is painfully clear, have fallen victim to the fifty-decent-images-and-fifty-to-fill-up-the-disk syndrome, and we wind up paying for images we will obviously never use.

Since this column appeared, PhotoDisc has switched to exclusive use of drum scanning and has re-released its earlier disks with new, higher resolution scans of the same images. Many of these can in fact be used at or close to full-page size. Aztech size is unchanged.

Before selecting a CD, you need to know how big you intend to print the images. If full page or larger, that would exclude PhotoDisc and Aztech products, neither of which have enough resolution for such purposes.

More to the point, though, you had better ask yourself how good you are at color correction, especially if you plan to use Corel CDs, which are exceedingly inconsistent. Early on, Corel decided to use the Kodak Photo CD format, which made sense.

However, it also allowed its photographers to furnish PCDs from their local supplier, rather than original chromes. This was a big mistake.

When PCD first came out, Kodak told the world that all scanning variables had been so compensated for and automated that the machinery could be operated by baboons. Quality, therefore, would be very consistent, if not indistinguishable, from one supplier to the next.

Experience has shown this claim to be entirely wrong. The Kodak scanner may leave the operator less room for error, but when an error is made, it is a beaut. As a result, there are entirely too many images with appalling color casts, such as the yellow one in Figure 8.3, or where significant detail is missing and unretrievable without major effort.

To be sure, the majority of Corel images are not this bad, and those that are can be resurrected—if you know what you're doing. I gave this one out as an exercise in a color correction class, and, as you can see, one student blew right by it without ever making a local selection. He did, however, make corrections in three different colorspaces. Such techniques are not for the timid. Most of the professional retouchers in the class could not make an acceptable image out of this goose.

Corel is responding to the quality problem, taking more control of the scanning process, including doing some drum scanning and color correction before writing to the PCD format, as opposed to giving us a raw PCD scan. This is showing up in significantly better recent releases, but the packages now being sold aren't much affected.

Of the three ultra-cheap vendors, Hammerhead's first disk, a collection of swimsuit poses typified by Figure 8.4, is perfectly workable for quality, but how this will be maintained under their ambitious production schedule remains to be seen. Aztech, which provides CMYK TIFFs, has generally good scanning, but if you intend to use the images in print advertising, beware: many don't comply with SWOP standards for maximum ink density, and publications may bounce them.

Don't suppose that Corel has a monopoly on inconsistency. Speaking as someone who scans a lot of stuff from conventional stock houses, sometimes one receives first-class original transparencies and at other times a dupe of a dupe of a dupe, and the scanner operator gets blamed for the printed result looking sick.

The Ordeal of Change

The stock photo industry is indeed changing in much the same way that the typesetting industry did. Stock houses are severely threatened by the new technology, as are many photographers.

In the old days, if somebody liked the picture of the woman in Figure 8.4 enough to plan a national ad campaign around it, the photographer would have hit a jackpot. Today, the advertiser can go to Hammerhead, and the photographer's royalty will be half a cent or so. Assertions that the puniness will be made up for by the hugely increased volume of stock photo purchasing may seem small consolation to this photographer.

The head of a major committee of the American Society of Media Photographers, a strong opponent of unlimited-use CDs, summed it up: "These disks have generated more antagonism between photographers, art directors, stock agencies, CD publishers and clients than any other practice in recent history. They are subjects that none of us can ignore because they are turning the business of photography upside down."

At least two lawsuits are pending between stock houses and CD vendors. A Chicago-based stock house is suing Corel over the appearance in a Corel-sponsored contest of a line graphic that was plainly derived from a copyrighted photograph. Suits and countersuits are flying between Digital Stock, its ad agency, and a stock house over an ad that compared a Digital Stock photo favorably to one belonging to the conventional supplier.

The Digital Stock case, which involved allegations that magazines were being pressured not to run their ads, has since been settled. The more interesting Corel case drags on, as both U.S. and Canadian courts wrestle with the question of to what extent artists are entitled to appropriate snippets of work copyrighted by others. That law is not yet settled, largely because the whole legal question is so new, having been brought about by the advent of desktop publishing programs that allowed the practice.

Because of these and a host of other recent cases charging unauthorized use, there may be an argument against creating advertising using images from the smaller firms, if the images have an identifiable person in them, which most of them don't. Under existing law, which is rather unsettled, if we use such a picture in advertising, there is the awful possibility that a model who never signed a release may emerge from out of the blue to sue everyone involved. The fact that we did not believe we were doing anything wrong will not excuse us from being held as liable as the photographer and the vendor.

If the deep-pocketed Corel is our co-defendant, we will be nearly as happy about it as the plaintiff's lawyer. I have great confidence that all of Corel's models sign unconditional releases in front of batteries of priests and notaries public. When dealing with a small CD vendor whose pockets may not be as deep even as ours, however, caution may be in order.

Although an article like this is protected regardless, when I decided to use the image of the woman in Figure 8.4, I asked Hammerhead to prove they were legally entitled to license it. Within half an hour they faxed me what appeared to be proper, comprehensive releases from both model and photographer.

The Lessons of History

If the business of stock photography continues to emulate the path of the business of typefaces—and I think the chances are it will—one may expect the following.

- A proliferation of independent vendors, as barriers to entry fall. If you have an attic full of interesting pictures, very little stops you from going into the royalty-free CD business for yourself.

- A move by conventional houses toward alternate electronic methods of purchase, such as unlockable CDs and archives that are searchable through on-line services. To the extent, however, that they are less convenient to the user than royalty-free CD-ROM, these alternatives will fail.

- Despite the current rancor between conventional and digital stock companies, there will be many mergers and strategic alliances.

- Steadily plummeting, then eventually stable pricing. Large differences between the prices vendors charge may still be possible, if the higher-priced ones can convince buyers they have better quality and selection. (This analogy may break down: in typography, nobody dominated the market the way Corel does; and the larger firms were also the higher-priced ones, whereas Corel leads the price cutters).

- Conventional houses will hang on for some time, but when the end comes, it will be sudden.

- Think of this: an advertising agency that purchases lots of stock photography can today, for about $10,000, purchase substantially every royalty-free CD on the market. This would yield a library of 70,000 images or so, of which many are not too usable. The number is impressive, but it is not what a good stock photo house can offer. Yet.

- There will be no place for the medium-sized stock houses in the new order. Of the larger ones, those who ignore the lessons of history will, of course, be condemned to repeat them, but the savvier ones will survive.

- In the long history of type, there has never been a time even remotely comparable to today in terms of the number of meritorious faces being released, including revivals of worthy faces that have not been seen for many years. The end-user of type is far better off than under the old system. The same thing, I think, will happen to stock photography. ●

Afterword

The relentless momentum toward more use of color graphics everywhere created the royalty-free CD industry, and there's no sign that the growth will stop soon.

The predictions in the last few paragraphs, which were written in late 1994, have held up well, at least through mid-1996, the time of the present writing. Some of the 1995 developments in the industry are covered in the next column in this book, but to hit the high points:

In spite of the furious growth rate in 1994, 1995 grew faster. Tens of new vendors entered the competition, mostly at prices somewhere between the very low ones and those at the top of the market.

Prices were stable for the most part. Corel street prices have drifted down slightly, and the company has released two more 200-CD sets, meaning that for less than $2,500, we can buy 600 CDs, 60,000 royalty-free images.

Scan quality improved almost everywhere, particularly in Corel's case. Bad images such as in Figure 8.3 are now rare.

Professional photographers have faced up to reality and have become much more willing to deal with the digital stock companies, so the caliber of what's available on CDs has gotten much better.

Meanwhile, it is a huge blessing for us. So often, we need not just a specific image but a specific item. In *Professional Photoshop* I showed an outdoor scene where the layout required more sky than the photographer shot, and the sky had to be attractively blue, but cloudy. In another case, the problem was to eliminate the glasses a woman was wearing, which unfortunately left her without any eyebrows. In both cases, I commented that it was certainly lucky that, thanks to the large volume of images I process, I had both an appropriately sized spare cloudy sky and set of eyebrows.

Thanks to the royalty-free explosion, this is no longer so impressive. Today I have more spare digital cloudy skies and sets of eyebrows on my bookcase than a service bureau has excuses for late deliveries.

Want another example? It was not the original plan for this book to include all the correspondence from readers that are found in the Dialog Box sections at the end of most columns. By the time the publisher and I realized that it made sense to do it, we were getting close to deadline.

I wanted to illustrate some of them, but when people fax or e-mail me questions about images, the image in question doesn't customarily come along for the ride. Even if it did, my legal right to print it here would be dubious.

So, while the images in the columns proper had long since been taken care of, I found myself suddenly in need of (for these are the images the readers specified):

- A new car, bright red, with relatively quick transitions to dark shadow areas in its trim;
- A pizza that could be silhouetted;
- The business side of a deck of cards, showing plenty of black pips;
- A slew of faces of persons of disparate ethnic origins.

I put it to you that, if this had come up *even at the time the foregoing column was written,* it would have been a problem without a solution. In mid-1996, however, it is, if not a piece of cake, at least not a dose of castor oil.

The remaining difficulty, now that we are swamped with royalty-free images, is how to find them. That is one area where the old-line stock houses had a huge advantage. Their high prices justified expensive catalogs and salespeople with enough familiarity with the library to offer clients helpful suggestions. The problem often is that we are not sure exactly what we want; we are after a feeling, not a specific image.

The royalty-free vendors, by and large, give us thumbnail prints of their images, too difficult to judge quality by. And in any event, the selection has gotten so great that we really need some better method of narrowing down the possibilities.

Computerized search engines are only as good as the keywords the designers program into them. Recently, a client asked me to come up with an image of a spider web, you may guess for what purpose, so that they could purchase the disk. Using Corel's computer index, I searched for *spider, web,* and *insect,* finding two dubious candidates.

Silly me! The keyword I was looking for was *arthropod.* Corel has a whole disk by that title, and the spiders aren't cross-referenced as spiders. Too late—I had found something better using PhotoDisc's much more comprehensive routine, costing my client $250 to license the image rather than $15 from Corel.

By traditional standards, either price is low. The time of someone searching for exactly the right image, often under very tight deadlines, is another story. ●

Dialog Box

In *"How Much Image for a Dime,"* you noted that one of your students used three different colour spaces for colour correction. I am wondering if you would tell me (since I live in New Zealand and cannot attend your course) what the benefits of this are, and in which order you would charge through if you started with LAB. I haven't done much colour correction, as I usually do my scanning myself or at least over-see it, but I bought this Photo CD which is kinda bad.

Now, tell me the story about the goose and the three colorspaces...

The image of the goose in Figure 8.3 is not typical at all because of the monstrous color cast. I ordinarily advocate working in CMYK. However, in a case this extreme, a preliminary color-correction may be done in LAB, which is a considerably more volatile space. Curve-based corrections in LAB are not for the faint of heart, but they can overcome enormous color casts, such as the one in this image.

Because LAB is so powerful, it is imprecise. A subsequent CMYK correction is necessary to finalize highlight and shadow values. Also, in this case, the LAB correction to eliminate the yellow cast was so inaccurate that it caused the grass in the background to assume a blue color. As this was the only instance of such a color in the image, the indicated procedure was to correct it using Photoshop's Adjust Hue/Saturation command, which in effect works in the HSB colorspace.●

For further coverage of color correction techniques using LAB, see Column 7.

Bring a CD image into a service bureau, and you don't get no respect

I am a commercial photographer who works with many different vendors, printers and service bureaus alike. I don't get much respect when I show up with CD images, regardless of the quantity or quality of the work. I get the message of *"leave it to the pros (read, 'us')."*

Do you find this particularly surprising? You're taking their work away from them, not telling them they won the lottery.

The problem is usually with color, not dot gain or overall density. Output devices that are accurate are way out of my budget so I am looking for a reasonably inexpensive, fairly credible way to check the numbers off my densitometer. I thought that if I could purchase a Pantone book that would show the CMYK breakdowns of printed inks, that would put me in the ballpark. Is using Pantone inks as a recognizable standard a way for me to confirm the numbers I see on the screen?

Nice idea, but not practical because of Pantone's color definition convention. They use maximum amounts of black for everything whereas it is standard practice in color photos to use minimum amounts of black. Therefore, in a fleshtone, for example, Pantone would give lots of black and no cyan at all, while a normal fleshtone has significant cyan and practically no black.

There is a kludgy workaround for this. Set Separation setup to Light GCR, define the background color as the CMYK Pantone values, then open an RGB file and fill it with the background. Now, open up the Info palette and ask it to display CMYK values. It will show you how the Pantone values would reseparate at a more normal black setting.

I see myself using this to check out my neutrals and fleshtones.

That's exactly where you *shouldn't* need it. The appropriate numerical values for neutrals and fleshtones are well known and you need no Pantone swatches to achieve them.

If you give yourself a good highlight and shadow, and meet the requirements for neutrals and fleshtones, chances are you should have very good color everywhere. Sure, sometime you may say afterwards, the numbers are all OK but the grass still is too yellow or something, and in that case you do some additional work on it. But as a rule, good numbers equal a good image.●

Using CD images without a license, and the chances of being caught

I work for a computer company. I recently purchased a machine for my home. As a favor for a friend, I did artwork for a music CD which she is self-producing. I'm not a professional graphics artist nor is my friend a professional musician. There will be 1,000 CDs published.

Her intent is to use these CDs as "self-promotion" of her talents as a songstress. The CD will not be sold through commercial channels.

My original artwork was digitally photocomposited with a stock photograph which came on one of the dozen or so CDs which I got with my PC and various software I purchased. My original intent in using the stock photos was to present ideas.

In any case, the actual CD cover has been printed from my electronic files. I have no explicit photo release. The blanket release states that I have unlimited personal use of the picture (I can use it in reports at work for example) or up to 10,000 copies can be distributed in software that I might produce. It also states I can use it for promotional purposes. It seems like they just want me to not "sell" the image.

Do you happen to know who the CD vendor was? For most, but not all of these vendors, the license agreement would permit you to do what you are doing. Some of them, however, say you can't use the image on anything that you take money for, and others say you can't use it except on a list of specifically permitted things (and it sounds like you might be running afoul of that here.)

Do I have a legal problem given the quantity and intended use of this image?

If, for the sake of argument, you are in violation of the license, neither I nor any lawyer can give you a straight answer as to how you might do in court. The Copyright Act of 1976, which governs this, establishes a whole gang of exceptions, buts, ifs, and whereases to the copyright holder's general protection. The question of to what extent one can use copyrighted art as a small part of a larger unrelated project is still very much up in the air. Now that technology has made such "borrowing" of snippets possible, there have been a few court cases, including the one alluded to in this column where the winner of a Corel-sponsored contest did essentially just what you are doing. However, the law has not really taken shape. It will probably take a Supreme Court case before it does.

Let's put it this way. You have a legal problem if somebody sues you—a big, big problem.

Does it make a difference that I made no income from the job and the fact that the artist will (probably) generate no income from sales of the music? Sorry to bother you, but I enjoy your various columns and thought you might help me decide what to do. I don't want to open a legal can of worms if I don't have to and the artist is completely unaware of the issue.

Legally this helps you a little. Practically speaking, nobody is going to sue you, unless 1) they find out and either 2) you happen to be wealthy enough to make it worthwhile or 3) they really want to send you or somebody else a message.

Most of these CD companies are pretty small operations themselves; the chances of them hearing about what you did are next to nil, and if they do find out they are unlikely to want to be bothered dealing with you.

You never know, though. Maybe some morning the president of the CD company will wake up and stub his toe or have an argument with his wife and because he is in a foul mood he will call up his lawyer and tell him that unauthorized usage is getting out of hand and it's high time an example was made of someone, by God.

And maybe the first name that the lawyer comes up with will be yours, and you will be in for tens of thousands of dollars worth of hassle.

If this extremely remote possibility is enough to keep you awake even a few extra seconds some nights you might ask yourself whether it would not have been worth it to buy a cheap CD from Corel or Hammerhead, because both of these companies have license agreements that would definitely permit you to use their images in the manner you did.●

9

What Goes Around, Comes Around

The desktop publishing revolution has in many ways been merciless, wiping out entire classes of jobs. Guess what group looks like the next victim?

ogi Berra, Aristotle, and other famous philosophers have long been fond of pointing out that history repeats itself. Here in the tenth year of the desktop revolution, several developments remind us that, indeed, what goes around comes around.

Some of these throwbacks are good things. Among them, I would count the reemergence of the graphic arts specialist, the one who is an expert illustrator, or retoucher, or layout artist, rather than being a jack of all three and master of none.

Despite its wonders and achievements, though, our revolution has been merciless. It has wiped out whole classes of highly skilled people, making them irrelevant, forcing them out of an industry that no longer had work for them (but which was the only industry they knew) at great suffering to themselves and their families.

That many committed professional suicide by refusing to acknowledge the rumblings of the nascent volcano beneath their feet

Figure 9.1. *As royalty-free libraries of prescanned stock images continue growing explosively, certain categories are becoming saturated. Thousands of background and texture images are now available, at very reasonable prices. Most, like the seven shown here, are detailed enough for at least full-page magazine size, some even larger. This is great news for the digital artist, but not so good for the professional photographer: with this broad of an inventory available, who in their right mind will ever hire a photographer again to shoot a background?*

does not diminish the sadness of the event. Typesetters, dot etchers, strippers, board-bound art directors: they are all gone now. The more successful they were, the more they assumed that they were somehow exempted from what was happening. Worse, no group seemed to learn from the fate of the others.

Those who cannot remember the past, wrote Santayana, are condemned to repeat it. That epigram is appropriate for the dilemma being faced by the next group of potential victims of the revolution, professional photographers.

More on that later. Let me first explain how this column came to be more philosophical than my usual nuts and bolts.

The Specialist Returns

A little over a year ago, I decided to write a column on a modest trend: the professional-level Photoshop plug-in. Plug-ins, as you doubtless know, are image-processing filters that are usually written by third parties. Typically, they are once-in-a-lifetime special effects, such as the Adobe's own Twirl or Pointillize filters.

At least, that's what they used to be. Now, many aim squarely at the specialist. Some, like A Lowly Apprentice's PlateMaker or Visu Technologies' Co-Co, allow a printable fifth plate in a CMYK document, the lack of which feature is a major Photoshop failing. Others have advanced color-correction capabilities, special attributes for handling Photo CD images, or can generate masks purportedly more accurate than Photoshop's. Or, for $6,600, you can acquire Visu's complete separation engine, ICISS (Figure 9.2)

Photoshop, FreeHand, and Illustrator are now so deep that it has become impossible for a person to be completely expert at any one, let alone all of them.

The thing that soured me on this column plan was the emergence of complex hybrid plug-ins, aimed simultaneously at the creative type and the image-processing drone. Chief among these was KPT Convolver, from MetaTools, nee HSC Software.

KPT stands, of course, for Kai's Power Tools, one of the earliest and most successful of the third-party plug-in packages, a potent way of generating textures, mostly fractals. KPT Convolver, while it can certainly be used for such weird stuff, also has a robust set of color adjustment and sharpening tools.

It is not, however, one of these doodads that you just install and sail into production with. It is complex, and, once I foresaw

Figure 9.2. *The return of the specialist is confirmed by new plug-ins and standalone applications that make no pretense at all of being for the home user, particularly in terms of price. For a mere $6,600, Visu Technologies' ICISS augments Photoshop's abilities with, above, creation of additional printable channels for hi-fi color and other purposes; below, scripting; and bottom right, remapping of hues prior to separation.*

a learning curve in the tens of hours, it was transferred to the mountain of software that I intend to investigate in depth—at a future time.

Said list is by no means limited to Photoshop, since third-party additions have been the great software growth area of the past couple of years. It started with the Quark XTensions program, which has generated hundreds of products, some of great sophistication. It also forced Quark's competitor, PageMaker, to open up its own program to similar outside manipulation.

Meanwhile, Photoshop-compatible plug-ins have become usable not just in other photo-manipulation programs, but in Illustrator and FreeHand. In 1995, the first plug-ins specifically designed for these two emerged, with MetaTools leading the way. Its product, KPT Vector Effects, has plenty of special-effects filters, but also some highly intelligent capabilities not to be found in the base programs. Figure 9.3 demonstrates one of its riffs on a simple base shape. And, sigh, to make full use of its powers requires yet another extensive investment of time.

The base programs are now sometimes scarcely recognizable. Some sites are so XTension-happy that a Quark expert from off the street would need considerable reeducation to fit in.

But this is not really the main reason for the return of the specialist. The main reason could have been deduced from history, which tells us that data and applications expand to fill whatever amount of disk space and RAM is available.

Once upon a time, believe it or not, installing a DTP application, even one of the majors, consisted of inserting a floppy into one's Mac and drag-copying its contents to the hard drive. As the programs got more sophisticated, compression and/or multiple floppies became the rule, but the growth has continued

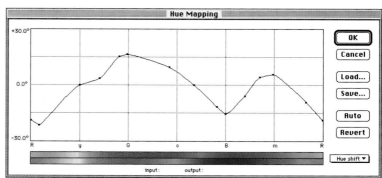

exponentially and unstoppably. PageMaker 5 weighed in in 1993 at 7.4 megabytes installed; 1995's PageMaker 6 porked out to 31.7 mb. Not only that, PageMaker 6 can't even be run on a standard Mac with 8 mb system RAM, as it requires that much for the application itself. In this, it follows the lead of Photoshop 3, and even Microsoft Excel.

The purpose of this flab is not just to compel us to buy bigger and better computers and peripherals. Each rev of software must match whatever features competitors have recently introduced, plus raise the stakes considerably, if users are to be expected to pay for the upgrade.

Over the years, the applications have thus become confoundingly difficult. The illustration programs now can do serious typography and page makeup. Led by the just-released Illustrator 6, they are starting to get strong in bitmap imaging as well. The line between word-processing and page makeup applications is similarly blurry, and the greater power of the majors has wiped out many niche applications.

Photoshop 3's hunger for computer power left a market void. The older, less demanding version, Photoshop 2.5, is no longer sold. In mid-1996, Adobe introduced a new product, PhotoDeluxe, as sort of a Photoshop Lite, to cater to the non-professional user.

This trend has discouraged use of the main programs by dilettantes. Microsoft Word 6 is powerful, but an inconceivable dog on older Macintoshes, so Word 5.1 hangs on. Photoshop 3 is slow, if it runs at all, on older machines, so Photoshop 2.5 lives and thrives.

Photoshop, FreeHand, and Illustrator now are so deep that it is next to impossible for any individual to be completely expert at any one, let alone all. Contrast this to five years ago, when one could assume that a professional could exploit the full range of capabilities of Quark, Photoshop, Illustrator and Free-Hand, plus be at least familiar with two or three other apps.

We have therefore become a crew of specialists running programs written for professionals, just as was the case before DTP. We have in fact improved on that model. Yesterday's dot etchers and strippers had no more idea of how to scan chromes or set type than of how to install a set of SIMMs. But today, even the most hard-core Photoshopper can place images in a page, or make simple shapes in an illustration program.

We have also become a crew of survivors. Our future survival obviously depends on using our energies effectively. With so many hucksters assuring us that their product is the next killer app, when do we make the investment in new learning? When do we know that a change is inevitable, and that we must buy in?

Those of us who did survive are the fittest, naturally, and generally the youngest as well. So young, in fact, that many of us are unfamiliar with some of history's teachings. I will devote the rest of my space here to discussing some of these, including the answer to the above question, before returning as promised to the current plight of photographers.

A Conservative Revolution

Conventional wisdom in DTP is not revolutionary, but conservative. The major programs have become virtual monopolies. Confounding expectations, this has become worse recently.

In software, the most glaring example is in page makeup programs. PageMaker has always led in overall market share, thanks largely to Quark's catastrophic early decision to copy-protect its software. Once this was removed, however, QXP rocketed into a dominant position among professionals, due to better precision, speed, and support of color.

Adobe, and earlier Aldus, reacted to this bad news in exactly the right way. They matched Quark's features, gave us the Additions technology, upgraded twice, and provided a consistent interface with other Adobe products.

In this effort, they could scarcely have asked for more cooperation from Quark, which has not released a major upgrade in five years, whose announcement in 1995 of an imminent competitor to Photoshop

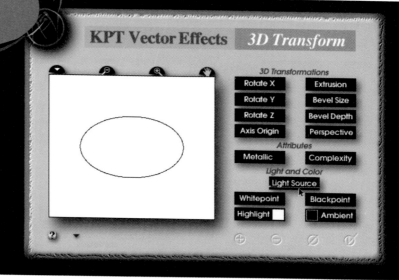

Figure 9.3. *Plug-ins for illustration programs, such as KPT Vector Effects, have become massively powerful. Three tweaks of various filters, without a single command from the application proper, transform the simple blue oval at top above into the complexity below it.*

has proven to be vaporware, and which has notoriously poor relations with its customers.

In short, everything in recent history has gone right for Page-Maker—except for the bottom line. As nearly as I can tell, QXP is *more* entrenched in the professional market than it was before PageMaker eliminated the performance gap.

In hardware, an even more striking illustration exists in the Mac itself. The Power Mac is powerful indeed, and priced competitively. But during the two years before it was introduced, and during its shakeout period, one could clearly have gotten more computing bang for the buck (not to mention cheaper peripherals) elsewhere. A substantial group of prognosticators therefore predicted the imminent demise of the Mac, given how important computing performance is in graphic arts applications.

Precisely the opposite occurred. The Mac today dominates graphic arts more than it did when these historical illiterates gave it two years to live.

When a DTP product achieves a dominant position, it can normally only be dislodged by its own blunders, not by improvements from its competitors. A poor upgrade (such as Word 6.0 or FreeHand 4.0) can cost market share. But a Photoshop, which has near-total dominance in image processing, will keep it, unless it self-destructs. This is why there is so much emphasis on plug-ins, and why Fractal Design's Painter and Macromedia's Xres, which could be made into reasonable *competitors* to Photoshop, instead position themselves as adjuncts, offering features (in one case the strong painting tools alluded to in Figure 9.4, in the other great speed) that complement rather than compete with the giant.

Shortly after this column appeared in April 1996, Macromedia launched an ad campaign touting Xres as "The Photoshop Companion." If ever there was a concession to the conservatism of the marketplace, this is it, since Xres has almost all of Photoshop's capabilities. It would have been reasonable, if suicidal, for Macromedia to have titled its ads "The Photoshop Replacement."

Solutions in Search of a Problem

For the same reasons, one has to be wary of products that seek to dislodge the current way of doing things. For example, trade publications have spent much of the last few years tediously trumpeting the forthcoming triumph of stochastic screening.

Read anything about it *recently*?

You must remember stochastic screening: the high-tech method of generating extremely small, randomly placed spots of ink rather than the comparatively large, uniformly placed dots of conventional printing. It was supposed to yield images that looked continuous-tone, like a photograph. It did—but nobody could get the color to look right.

Stochastic is not dead in the water, but it is barely alive, in spite of all the erstwhile frenzy. It still attracts experimentation. But the trade press has rightly written its one-time darling off, thus justifying the views of those columnists who declined to waste their space on it when it first came out, citing a lesson of history, namely: beware of solutions looking for a problem.

Conventional screening is a time-tested technology that is simply not all that horrible. Stochastic has advantages, but not enough to compensate for what it brings along as baggage, at least in the commercial market; the only place it has caught on at all is in newspapers, which *do* have color quality problems.

Grandiose color management systems, which the marketplace has been rejecting for more than ten years now, continue to emerge now and then with grandiose claims of the impending transformation of the industry. They preach repeatability in scanning, and worship a nebulous deity known as "device-independent color." Some of the solutions are technically quite interesting, and if only there were a serious problem to begin with, might well justify the considerable time and expense of adopting them. The fate of Cachet, and the propensity of knowledgeable QXP users to avoid headaches by simply deleting the EfiColor XTension from their systems, is something to keep in mind before getting terribly excited about Apple's ColorSync.

Even when a new solution is incontestably better than the old way (and the above ones are not), it won't take off if it causes the user undue difficulties. For years now we have all been

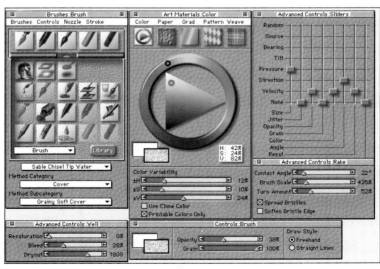

Figure 9.4. *With Photoshop having a hammerlock on the image-manipulation market, its natural competitors have to position themselves as adjuncts, rather than rivals. At right, Fractal Design's Painter 4 offers a staggering variety of brush effects as part of its strategy to differentiate it from the leader.*

PHOTOGRAPHERS' DILEMMA, END USERS' JOY: THE ROYALTY-FREE EXPLOSION CONTINUES

One year ago, this column (see Column 8) profiled the business of digital stock photography, which was rapidly changing the old-line stock houses as well as the lives of photographers. 1995 was a year of even more explosive growth, so it's time for another look.

Nothing is now simpler or cheaper than for a frustrated photographer to put some shots together for royalty-free use and to start advertising a CD of "professional" advertising shots for $100 or whatever. The market has become deluged with new entrants, some of whom offer excellent quality and others garbage. By my estimates the number of royalty-free digital images now on the market is well into the six figures, and, if you are a big user of stock photography, it is not beyond reason for you to buy them all. What exactly you will do with them is, regrettably, another story.

At the low-priced end of the market, Corel Corp. continues to pour forth 20 new disks per month in its Professional Photos series. By now they have more than 600 CDs, each with 100 images on a given theme, each image with enough resolution for a full magazine page. As we go to press, Corel has just released its third library series, consisting of 200 disks, 20,000 royalty-free photographs, at the flabbergasting street price of $700. This hyperaggressive pricing, supported by massive advertising, yields volume: Corel reported sales of its royalty-free line to be around $12 million in 1995, double 1994's rate. That represents six percent of Corel's gross corporate revenue, and a whole lot of stock photography by anybody's definition.

Unlike Corel, most other vendors are not public companies and so don't have to release sales figures, but it appears that 1995 was a banner year almost everywhere. Many, such as Digital Stock Corp. and Vivid Details, both of whose disks retail for over $200, intend to release enough titles in 1996 to more than double what they have available now. Industry leader PhotoDisc, which also sells in that price range, has moved into electronic distribution as well as CDs, through a Web page it claims to be highly successful.

That Web page is characteristic of a maturing industry, one that is looking for new ways to increase customer satisfaction. Corel, PhotoDisc, and Digital Stock have all, for example, moved away from past practice and toward using drum scanners in creating their product. Many vendors have also invested in better catalogs or computerized searching to allow their customers to more quickly find images that meet a specific need. Several now also include Photoshop clipping paths in appropriate images, a useful feature.

Photographers are now more inclined to accept the legitimacy of this new market. All of the above-named vendors report that they are becoming more and more selective as they are being presented with more and more images to choose from. There is also a lot of competition from talented amateurs. Corel, for example, pays its photographers a flat fee of around $7,500 for the 100 images included in a disk. Some professionals turn up their noses at $75 an image. It's big bucks to others.

As the price of color printing continues its freefall, demand for stock photography naturally has gone up. That may compensate the stock houses for the business lost to the digital upstarts—but one wonders how long it will last. Many are floundering about trying to get some kind of digital capability, through unlockable CDs, on-line search engines, alliances with the royalty-free houses, and the like.

Conventional stock houses still have advantages. The computerized search capabilities the digital vendors are using are very nice, but they are not a substitute for talking to someone who is familiar with a number of images and can offer helpful suggestions. Most digital libraries are also weak in images involving people, since it is still tough to get models to agree to the unconditional releases needed.

On the other hand, certain categories are now so full that conventional competition stands no chance. Under the general heading of backgrounds and textures, Corel alone has nearly 5,000 images, and every vendor competes; some of the variety is shown in Figure 9.1. Furthermore, several software packages offer attractive, realistic, and infinitely variable computer-generated backgrounds (see Figure 9.5).

In the face of this, who needs to pay the price of conventional stock for backgrounds? And who needs to pay a photographer to go out and shoot a background on special assignment? If you can't find what you are looking for in the massive selection currently available on CD, let alone the avalanche that will be released in the next year, you have got some kind of serious problem.

Cheap, plentiful, high-quality stock photography on a wide variety of subjects: what's not to like? This is, indeed, a better way—from the end user's point of view. Obviously, it also has been profitable for the digital entrepreneurs. For the professional photographer, things have not been so rosy. With so many more competitors and uncertainty about what the future will bring, stock houses both conventional and digital are driving harder bargains, especially concerning unlimited rights.

Meanwhile, as royalty-free inventory swells, opportunities for custom shoots go down. Shooting for background was never the mainstay for most professional photographers, but by the same token it was also a significant revenue source for some. The photographers I know say that it is gone.

In recent months, the ancient SyQuest technology has finally started to look vulnerable. Fast, convenient drives from Iomega are taking hold in a way that mini-opticals never did, and have a good shot at becoming the new standard.

complaining about the speed, reliability, and inconvenience of SyQuest-compatible removable disks, which are nevertheless our standard. Remember when it was announced that mini-optical disks would run them out of town? Didn't work that way.

Where a problem actually exists, new ideas, even stochastic screening, *can* latch on. Consider the case of five overprinting colors, the same issue addressed by the plug-ins previously mentioned. On press, we face a difficult choice of what screen angle to use for the fifth plate. The wrong decision will either sap the strength of one plate or cause a moiré. With conventional screening on the first four plates and stochastic on the fifth, however, the problem vanishes. Moreover, the disadvantages of stochastic screening (excessive dot gain and difficulty in managing the process) are minimized, since fifth colors invariably add color depth, not detail.

Figure 9.5. *As if photographers didn't have enough competition, a new generation of fractal-based texture generators can create surprisingly detailed backgrounds out of nothing but zeroes and ones. This one was generated with MetaTools's KPT Bryce package.*

The Locomotive Looms

When a compatible and user-friendly better way emerges, though, those in the way of the locomotive had best watch out. That is the position of photographers today. They stand on the tracks, and the train of the digital revolution is headed right at them. Two of their choices are quite unpalatable. They can

remain where they are and find out who will survive the inevitable collision. They can also cede their territory and their business, by stepping aside.

There exists, however, a third alternative: getting a running start, so that when the train roars by they can jump on board.

There are those who pooh-pooh this, just as the type houses did a few years back, pointing out the many areas in which conventional photography is, at least for the moment, undeniably superior. Regrettably, this is irrelevant: digital photography only has to be superior in *some* ways. And it already is.

The lesson of the implosion of typesetting is this: pull a few bricks from the foundation, and the structure collapses.

I will admit to thinking at one time that the collapse of the type shops would be followed by the demise of the color separators. That hasn't happened, although there has been a considerable shakeout, and the industry has restructured.

Color avoided type's fate for several reasons. Although middle-sized separators are in the process of being squeezed out, there are plenty of color jobs big enough and/or with tight enough deadlines that only a separator with a big staff can handle them. The large shops have therefore survived. No such need existed in typography, and the big, proud houses died.

At the time the revolution began, the type industry was already in trouble; many shops were losing money and lacked the resources to invest in new technology. The color industry, by contrast, was strong and profitable, and accustomed to spending lavishly on equipment.

Scitex, the Israeli company that dominated the electronic color separation market in the 80s and early 90s, reported its first major loss in 1995. It has refocused, concentrating on imagesetters and workflow solutions, rather than its historical strength, dedicated color workstations.

There was no dominant front-end system vendor in typography, certainly not in the sense that Scitex has dominated that part of prepress. Vendors who are on death's door themselves are in no position to give much help to other patients. Scitex had the wherewithal to flow with the tide and adjust its own manufacturing and marketing.

Although much color work has gone to freelancers or coalitions thereof, not every Tom, Dick, and Harry can compete, the way they did with the type houses. Serious expenditures of time and money are required before one can enter the color market.

Also, clients really do care how their color looks, far more than worried about the kerning of their type. Quality is and will therefore continue to be a major issue.

Most of these mitigating factors do not apply to the

professional photography industry. Anyone with any kind of camera can compete, or try to. There are no huge conglomerates of photographers with the advantage of sheer size. The industry is not used to spending big bucks on equipment, particularly equipment that does not last for a long time, yet the pressure to buy now is almost irresistible.

The digital process does not have to be superior to film, any more than DTP had to be better than old-fashioned typography. The mere fact of significant market erosion was—is—enough.

> *Suppose only 20 percent of film-based photography is lost to the digital interloper, suppose only 10? What do you think will happen when the same number of suppliers chase after only 90 percent of the business?*

Already, digital photography has taken over most catalog shooting. The advantages are just too stark: no film expense, immediate results, no later scanning, much shorter approval cycles. And, for those relying on the old saw that digital will never equal film's quality, at March 1996's Seybold conference, the following history-making claim was made. Dicomed, maker of what most consider the preeminent high-end digital camera back, said in a release that its product yields "excellent image quality *that is superior to film*" (emphasis added). One normally discounts such braggadocio from vendors, but I don't work for Dicomed, and I think they are right.

With the industry reeling from several lean years, all we need now is a little more competition. Buying into Dicomed's technology will set one back more than $30,000, out of range for many photographers but low enough to attract printers and service bureaus who see a way to pick up business at the photographer's expense. Meanwhile, the explosion of digital stock libraries (see page 214) has wiped out most stock shooting assignments.

It gets worse. Most high-end digital cameras, including Dicomed's, expose so slowly that they are as a practical matter limited to still-life studio work. But, confounding expectations, Dicomed announced in March 1996 that it will—in 1996—introduce a camera with no such limitation.

Suppose for a moment that this new product doesn't work, and that effective digital field work remains pie in the sky. So what? There is still plenty of damage, even if digital stays confined to the studio.

Suppose that only 20 percent of film-based professional

photography is lost to the digital interloper; suppose only ten? What do you think will happen when the same number of suppliers, if not more, chase after 90 percent of the former business?

The same thing that happened to type houses, that's what. Cutthroat tactics; suicidal price cuts; irrational distrust of vendors and new technologies; the best people looking for ways out; rapid failure for those failing to adjust.

It's happening already. When the top film vendors introduced the APS system, which allows digital data as well as a photograph to be recorded on film (but requires a new model of camera), a horde of photographers charged conspiracy. And many of those photographers who have accepted reality and sold their work to the royalty-free stock vendors are being castigated as traitors, prostitutes or worse by their colleagues.

Incorrigible conservatives will undoubtedly go down without ever even knowing their enemy. The great majority, however, now face the crucial decision. If they can bring themselves to reflect upon what has happened to others, and why, they will survive. If not, we will all see a demonstration of a notorious corollary to Santayana's wisdom: that when history repeats itself, it does so first as tragedy, then as farce. ●

Afterword

As technology advances, there is always the question of when to jump into it. Exceptions to the normal rules of the marketplace are not suspended for new products just because they happen to be digital. Usually there are pros and cons.

Digital photography, in certain applications at least, is not like that. If you produce catalogs in which the products illustrated do not move and can be shot in the studio, you have to be *crazy* not to do this digitally. Film photography has nothing to be said for it; no advantages at all. Digital catalog production is much cheaper, much faster, and higher quality to boot if handled correctly.

Similarly, for texture and background shots, one would have to be nuts to do things the old-fashioned way. We have a better selection now, ten times as convenient and a fraction of the price.

This happened very quickly, as quickly as the slide rule was obsoleted by the electronic calculator. Naturally, there is great turmoil now. Some, giddy with the success of the new technology, predict that film will be dead by the turn of the century. Those whom psychiatrists might characterize as being in denial claim such enormous superiority for film that they say it will *never* go away.

Not being a photographer myself, I

can refrain from both wild-eyed enthusiasm and burying my head in the sand. However, this throws me into a no-man's-land into which snipers fire from all sides.

When people's livelihoods are threatened, rationality is often a victim as well. You may recall how a correspondent in an earlier column had convinced himself that color separators were conspiring to sabotage his files. With photographers, it's worse. Those who don't accept the reality of change are capable of great vindictiveness, not just toward suppliers like Kodak and Fuji, but toward columnists who attempt to talk about historical lessons. Believe me.

For the perceptive photographer not all is gloom and doom. The very trends that are obsoleting them give them new chances. Even forgetting the opportunities in the Internet and multimedia, the cost of producing color documents in print has fallen through the floor, with predictable results: vastly more color printing is being done. Especially, more color printing of small quantities is being done. It's not that the cost of printing itself has gone down, quite the opposite. But for short runs, prepress costs, which *have* plummeted, can be a big percentage of the total job cost. Whereas, in runs of 200,000 or so, the prepress cost is negligible. Reinforcing this trend, databases mean companies know more and more about their clients and can tailor their advertising more precisely. In the old days, printing a hundred different versions of something in quantities of a thousand each, as opposed to 100,000 copies of a one-size-fits-all document, would have been unthinkable. Now, it's fairly common.

The printers who saw this coming and invested accordingly are for the moment highly profitable. Printing presses come in all configurations, and all specialize in certain size and run lengths. Printers who sunk money into the biggest and fastest web presses find that these expensive behemoths are sucking in wind rather than paper; now that they realize they should have bought sheet-fed presses or half-webs, it is too late. A press is made to order. You can't just go out to the press store and buy one; you are dependent on the manufacturer to get you one as fast as possible. And with everybody wanting to buy one, for the smaller presses the wait can be a couple of years, by which time who knows what the economy will be like?

A photographer who ignores the digital revolution may be able to buy equipment quickly, but the requisite knowledge is another story. Those who do obtain the knowledge, though, and realize that they are in the communications, not the photography, business now, will prosper. Everybody can produce color now, but not everybody can take good original photographs, any more than everyone can design a Web page. Being able to offer such services is a decided plus.

As you must know by now, this is not my typical kind of column. I wrote it in the hope of shocking certain people into realizing that their best hope is not in ignoring or attacking instructional writings on prepress, but in *reading* them. Mine, or anybody else's. ●

Jargon Watch

APS Advanced Photography System, a film-based technology that allows capture of digital data along with an analog image.

bitmap imaging The support for photographic or other resolution-dependent graphics inside a vector program such as Illustrator or FreeHand, whose artwork has previously *not* depended on resolution.

Cachet A software package that promised an intuitive method of color-correction, this is another in the seemingly bottomless pile of artificial color intelligence and color management systems that have failed. From the same company as EfiColor.

chrome High-quality positive color film, ordinarily shot by professionals.

ColorSync Apple's system-level color management system, which theoretically will allow us to "profile" all the color devices we use, thus allowing closer matches in color between them.

EfiColor An ill-fated color management system chiefly known for being included as a default in QuarkXPress 3. Most users delete it as being unnecessary and in many cases damaging.

filters Routines within imaging applications that alter originals according to some formula. Filters range from the most fanciful special effects to prosaic items like unsharp masking.

fractal A computer-constructed image based on the concept of a single pattern that evolves through slight variations in size and shape. It doesn't sound plausible, but this is also the way nature seems to construct objects in many cases. As a result, fractal images, though obviously computer-generated, can have an incredibly realistic feel.

mini-optical A magneto-optical drive using a 3.5-inch disk as opposed to the larger ones used by conventional optical drives. Mini-opticals normally have a capacity of 256 megabytes as of this writing. At one time the conventional wisdom said they would displace SyQuest drives, but the conventional wisdom was wrong.

plug-ins Mini-programs that drop into and add capabilities to major graphics applications.

Power Mac The generation of Macintoshes based on PowerPC processors, introduced in 1994.

scripting Writing a routine that will automatically perform several commands or steps, rather than having to manually call for each one.

SIMMs Single in-line memory modules, the way that one adds RAM to certain models of Macintosh.

stochastic A halftone screening method that uses extremely small, seemingly randomly placed dots, as opposed to the conventional method of a fixed number of dots per inch.

SyQuest Historically, the leading manufacturer of removable disk drives, a fixture on the desks of professional graphic artists. Now threatened by a variety of technologies, but not dethroned yet.

Dialog Box

I have a question that I'm sure you've been asked 7,000 times—but never by me.

Your column touched on the Mac/PC conflict and since I am at that moment of moving from traditional graphics presentations to a major buy to get rolling I have to admit it's a mindboggler.

I have had some crash training with a larger photo lab/computer graphics supplier, and they are VERY committed to Mac. In addition to preparing things like brochures, point of purchase displays and

Should one buy Macintosh or Wintel for graphic arts work, Rev. #7,001

magazine advertising, I also freelance automotive photo/feature stories, and notice that most of them seem hooked to Macintosh as well. Okay, so it would appear that that's the way to go.

But my local computer mad scientist, a guy who basically puts together custom systems that do great things for low prices, sees PCs as the FUTURE. He talks about hardware, exploding software deals, and an all around friendlier market.

The question then is, is Macintosh for professionals and PCs for amateurs, or are PCs going to blow right past Macintosh?

I have to factor in the financial situation of Apple, their apparent cavalier attitude, and the way the market seems to be shifting. Correct or not, I see the Macintosh/PC situation somewhat like Beta vs. VHS, where one was superior, but the other won out through hard work, low price, and customer preference.

So, there it is. I will be using the computer gear to earn a living, not play games, but I admit to liking the all-conquering attitude of PC marketers.

Okay. Which direction would you go if you were in my position, Beta or VHS?

If you are getting into professional graphics you should buy a Mac. You are getting seduced by qualitative comparisons. I don't question that you can get the same computing bang for the buck, if not more, with a Wintel unit. The software available is almost as good. With Macs dominating the field the way they do, certain things are not yet available on PC. Examples: there is no adequate color-management system on PC, no support for Multiple Master fonts, many of the better scanning programs run only on Mac, as do some high-level applications such as Live Picture. But, to be sure, the main programs, QXP, PageMaker, FreeHand, Photoshop, Illustrator, will run on either platform.

The problem for the would-be PC user is that the rest of the world is on Macs. Your local supplier is absolutely typical. If you try to do high-end stuff on a PC people will laugh at you, justifiably or not. Several of the companies I have worked for would as a matter of policy not take your business. Why? Since professionals work on Macs almost exclusively, the very fact that you are not doing this suggests you are inexperienced and therefore a problem customer. Not to mention, if they do take your work, and some problem develops, they will not be nearly as familiar with the proper solution. Unfair, yes, but life is that way at times.

Your local mad scientist may be quite correct. Everyone, myself included, is worried about Apple's future. But is this any worse than two or three years ago, when Macintoshes were both more expensive and performed worse than PCs? As I mentioned in the column, lots of mad scientists said then that the Mac was finished. Instead, it became even more entrenched. Not just in prepress, but in video, multimedia, sound, and management of digital photography. Two years ago, I'd guess that 95 percent of high-end work was done on the Mac; now it's closer to 99 percent. Although Apple's current financial position is most worrisome, there is no evidence (yet) that the Mac is even beginning to lose its graphics dominance.

The question is, can a possible decline in the Mac's popularity (or Apple's going out of business) affect you over the useful life of your computer? You say you are going to become a serious computer artist. If so, the bad news is that whatever you buy will become so totally obsolete in the next two to three years that you will have to replace it. In that way, computers are not like cameras. The good news is that many of the things you buy today—the monitor, the disk drives, conceivably the RAM, will still be useful in 1998 regardless of what computer you buy then. There is nothing at all to prevent you from buying a PC in 1998 if it looks like that is the way to go at that time, and you most certainly are going to have to buy *something*.

You need to be more short-term in your analysis. Is it possible that the PC will take over? Certainly. Is it possible that this will happen by 1998? No. Is it possible that you will regret a Mac purchase by 1998? No. Is it possible you will regret a PC purchase by 1998? Yes, it is an absolute certainty; you will be swimming against the tide for most if not all of that time. By the time (if it comes) that PCs dethrone Macs, the PC you buy today will be nearly worthless anyway.

The Beta/VHS analogy is not quite accurate. I would think a better one might be VHS/8mm. When 8mm was introduced as an alternative, a lot of people believed it would eventually take over. They might have been right. But a sane buyer would have said, even if they are right, we are in a VHS world right now; I will really be isolating myself from the huge majority of users if I buy now. If things change in the future I can always get into 8mm at that time. Meanwhile, I'll get full use out of my VHS.

Therefore, I would consider your present decision to be a no-brainer—in May, 1996. June may be another story. ●

PART IV

Typographic Fashion For Our Time

*after 500 years, the architecture
adapts to the age of color publishing*

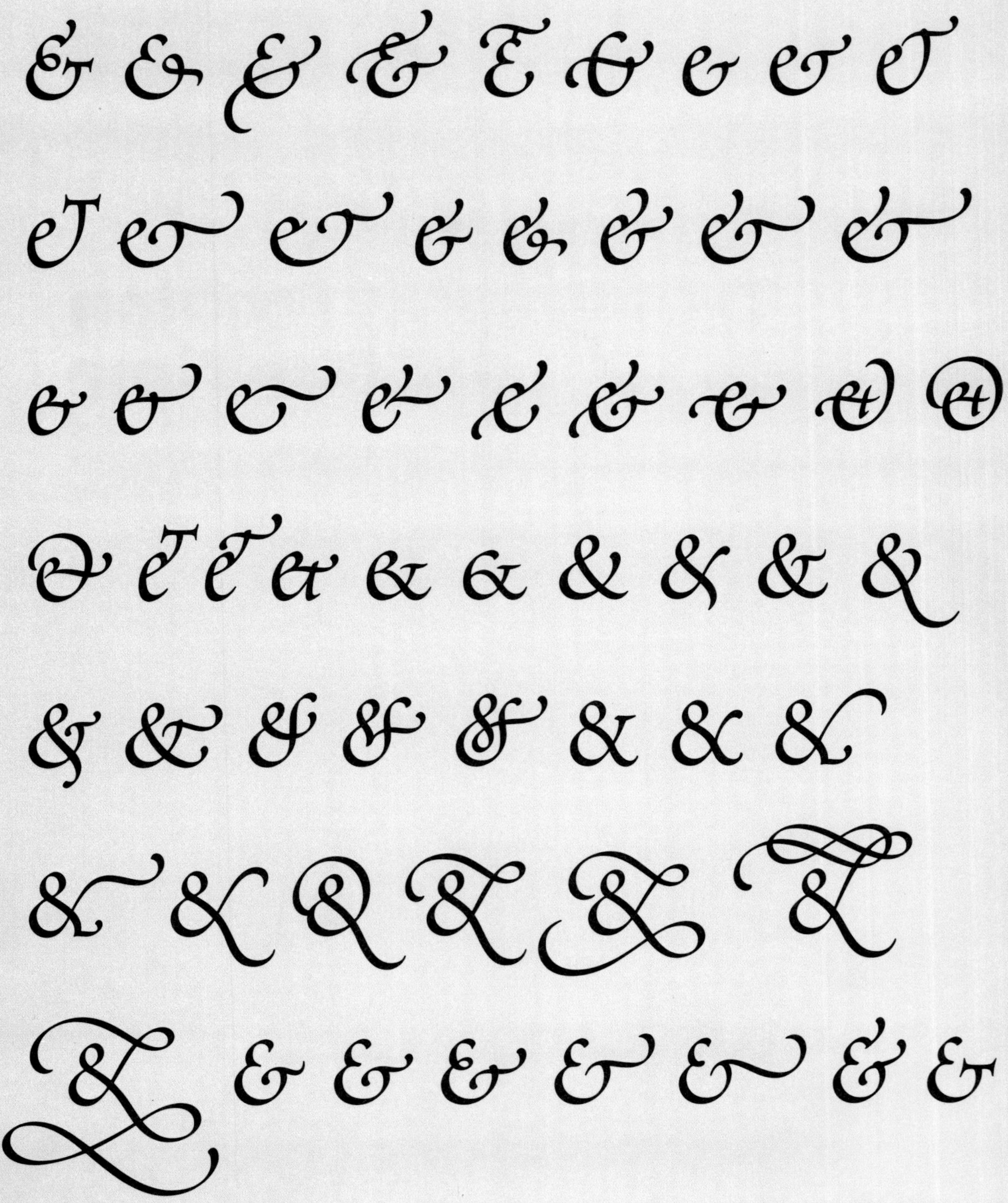

10 Typographic Fashion For Our Time

With thousands upon thousands of new typefaces being released, there's something for everyone. Yet, even in remakes of the classic designs, there is a distinctive nineties style.

W hen I first had to think about acquiring a business wardrobe, back in the seventies, I rejected, thankfully, an option known as a "leisure suit." For those who do not remember, leisure suits were almost a parody of traditional men's attire. Proudly polyester, they had a jacket and trousers, but everything that defined previous fashion was hideously distorted. Lapels were made wide enough to trip over. Instead of the usual grays, browns, and blacks, leisure suits customarily came in such shades as hunter green and bright orange.

If you are a fan of the history of typography, you are probably aware that typographic designs of a given time tend to mirror the tastes of most other art forms, such as music, architecture, or men's fashion. It is therefore not much of a stretch to call the seventies the age of leisure-suit typography.

The most memorable faces of that forgettable era were designed along leisure-suit lines. Traditional faces were "updated" by exaggerating everything that gave them individuality, and forcing them into a larger x-height and a ridiculously tight letterfit.

Figure 10.1. *Today's tools let typeface designers indulge their whims. The secondary headline above is set in Poetica, a 1993 revival of a Renaissance bookhand. With traditional design methods, such scripts were extremely difficult. Freed by the desktop revolution, though, the designer, Robert Slimbach, created not just one Poetica font, but 21. Including, believe it or not, the 58 alternate ampersands shown here.*

227

Nowadays, our tastes are considerably more subdued. Men and women alike prefer natural fibers; earthtones are our favorite colors, and even our rock music is quieter and more subtle. Is it any wonder that type has, for the most part, followed suit?

An Embarrassment of Riches

Before launching into what defines the style of the new typefaces of the nineties, a few words need to be spoken in praise of the incredible choices we now have, in comparison to preceding generations.

The growth in the number of typefaces available is just staggering, and most of it has happened very, very recently.

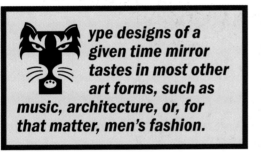

ype designs of a given time mirror tastes in most other art forms, such as music, architecture, or, for that matter, men's fashion.

Between mid-1994 and mid-1995, Agfa, the second-largest typeface supplier after Adobe, added 500 faces to its library, almost a 50 percent increase in one year. During the same period, Monotype Typography, number three, added nearly a thousand faces. In a move as aggressive as this unprecedented growth, Monotype in November 1995 also acquired FontHaus, one of the largest resellers of type worldwide, and with it the right to sell thousands more fonts.

The reason for this embarrassment of riches is the same one we are so familiar with in other areas of the graphic arts. What used to require months of work with impossibly expensive equipment now can be done on the desktop, so hordes of fledgling type designers are now finally able to spread their wings. Their tool of choice is Macromedia's Fontographer, which now has a near monopoly among serious type designers, having left a couple of opponents for dead along the way.

In principle, the characters of Fontographer typefaces are drawn with the mouse, using Bézier curves in exactly the same manner one would in Illustrator, FreeHand or Photoshop. Individual letterforms can freely be imported from such programs. But Fontographer also supports drawing using a pressure-sensitive tablet.

The tablet's capabilities have a lot to do with the sudden glut of two kinds of faces that were previously almost unknown. The more obvious, because it is so flamboyant, is the class of face of this column's headline, Agfa's Escalido Gothico.

Various names have been proposed for such type. I favor "distressed," but "grunge," "garage," or "deconstructive" typography are equally reasonable. The idea is that the designer has willfully and with malice aforethought sabotaged a face by mangling its edges, throwing in garbage, misangling or misaligning the letters, or any combination thereof.

In spite of the horror that such practices inspire in typographic purists, there are legitimate reasons for these to be faces of our time, which we will get to later.

A Labor of Love

The second great advantage of working with a tablet is that Fontographer interprets a variation in pressure as a request for change in stroke weight.

The English translation of this is that it is now vastly easier to design something calligraphic, such as a script or a medieval bookhand. Such faces have traditionally been excruciatingly difficult to execute. They are no walk in the park even now, but enough tablet-proficient designers are being tempted that we are now deluged with new scripts as well as relatively accurate renditions of various European hands of several hundred years ago.

The secondary headline on the opening page of this column is in one such, a chancery hand, technically speaking. The face is Poetica, designed by Robert Slimbach of the Adobe Originals design group, about which we will hear more later.

International Typeface Corporation (ITC) was the leading source of new type designs throughout most of the seventies and eighties. Its releases were licensed, with a hefty royalty, to most type manufacturers. Nowadays, with type being priced as a commodity, ITC sells its faces direct, but most of them are also available through the major typeface vendors.

Script work exerts a peculiar spell on the type designer. One puts in far more time than can possibly be justified by economic considerations. This differentiates it from, say, distressed faces, which can be tossed off rapidly. If we make a mistake in designing a distressed face, it looks like we did it on purpose.

But scripts take a long time, and when you consider their relative inapplicability to real-world jobs, you have to wonder what it is that motivated the designers and foundries that supply Agfa to have produced no less than 15 new historical-model scripts in 1995. If you wish to try your hand at such a face, it would be unlikely that anyone other than Adobe or International Typeface Corporation would be able to sell more than a few hundred copies of it. Both are very selective. Absent the involvement of one of these two giants, there is no way, at $50 or less retail, you can come close to making a profit once all the middlemen take theirs.

If today's type prices seem low, just wait until tomorrow. The price of the $49 script special mentioned favorably here dropped to $39 in early 1996.

The reason the scripts keep coming nevertheless, of course, is that they are a labor of love. This is why Slimbach, far from contenting himself with a single cut of Poetica, designed the 58 different *ampersands* shown in Figure 10.1, in the course of producing a monumental 21 variant fonts off the basic design. You can buy the lot in two packages from Adobe for $140 total. Or, Adobe will sell you four Poetica variants, along with six other unrelated scripts, for $49. That's $49 for *all ten*, not for each one.

The Postwar Experience

Given that independent designers are not in it for the money, it is not surprising to find a number of ridiculous novelty faces, some of which, according to the vendors, sell as few as ten copies apiece.

Agfa, for example, markets a new face called Alligators. Every letter consists of one or more gators. For ailurophiles, Monotype has one named Catastrophe, featuring guess what in every letter. Adobe competes with one called Critter, which has a different animal for each letter. If you look very carefully, you may be able to find an example of each in this column—but enough weird stuff. Let's turn our attention to some bread-and-butter kinds of typefaces, to see whether historical generalizations about what sorts of faces are developed in what periods really hold true in the nineties.

The best test of an era's typography is neither its scripts nor its display faces, but rather what might be called classical book faces: workhorse, conservative serifed cuts suitable for most text applications.

The huge volume of spirited new text typefaces in the nineties is all the more remarkable in that it comes on the heels of a long drought. To illustrate this, consider, decade by decade, what has happened in type design since the end of World War II.

1946–1955 featured the brilliant debut of Hermann Zapf, who produced Aldus, Melior, Optima, and what I and many others would consider the finest face of the century, Palatino. These faces alone would make the decade a distinguished one, but there was in fact considerably more.

Good as it was, however, on the whole it did not match the next decade. Between 1956 and 1965 there were two outright masterpieces, both based on Garamond designs: Jan Tschischold's Sabon and Francesco Simoncini's Simoncini Garamond.

Both of these faces will be around as along as humans set type. Three other faces, if not quite up to this high standard, were surely of the first magnitude. I refer to Aster, Berling, and the forerunner of the leisure-suit typography of the seventies, Méridien. And behind these came a dozen or so text faces worthy of inclusion in serious libraries.

1966–1975 fell well short of this level, and, with the leisure-suit phenomenon in full swing, 1976–1985 was worse still. Not a single face was designed during that decade that could be put in the same league as any of the ones mentioned above. What we now call ITC New Baskerville was released and displaced many previous cuts of Baskerville, but the popularity of the new face was more because it offered additional weights than that it had any intrinsic superiority in design.

The best original faces of this sorry period were Basilia, Berkeley Old Style, Linotype Walbaum, and Galliard, which, although not really meant to be a book face, has frequently been used as such. All of these are nice and deserve a look now and then, but they are unlikely to last, in my view.

The Decade of the Century

Those of us who were praying for a little rain to end this creative dry period were rewarded instead with a typhoon.

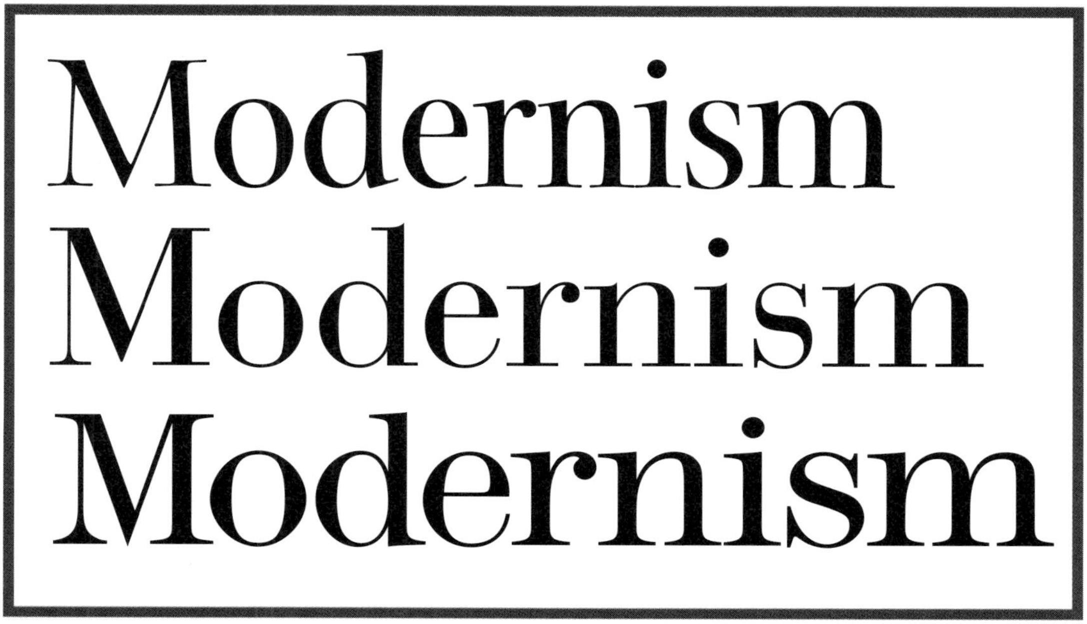

Figure 10.2. *Three variations on an old typographic theme: these faces all feature a vertical stress and extreme contrast in stroke weight, characteristics of the early nineteenth-century designs of Giambatista Bodoni. One of these is in fact a Bodoni cut; one dates from 1982; and one was released in 1995. Can you guess which is which?*

Modernism
Modernism
Modernism

The best-known book faces introduced in these extravagant ten years are undoubtedly those of Slimbach and his Adobe Originals group, who don't even use Fontographer. The popularity is deserved. Their initial two text offerings, Adobe Garamond and Utopia, manage the difficult feat of balancing elegant design with legibility. These faces are right up there with anything designed this century.

Adobe Caslon and Minion followed shortly thereafter, and, in early 1996, Adobe Jenson, based on fifteenth-century principles but with a distinctly contemporary feel, was released to somewhat mixed reviews.

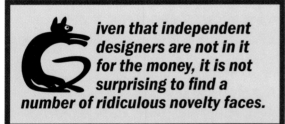

iven that independent designers are not in it for the money, it is not surprising to find a number of ridiculous novelty faces.

Meanwhile, at least 20 other meritorious text families (let alone all the not-so-hot ones) have recently come to market from a variety of other sources.

In-house designers at Monotype, which traditionally has had the strongest text face library but has suffered from lack of exposure in the United States, have given us new text families such as Columbus and Amasis, as well as the best revival of a historical form in recent years, Monotype Bulmer. All of these, like the Adobe faces mentioned above, have at least three different weights.

Most encouraging of all is the slew of new text faces from independent foundries such as Font Bureau and Elsner & Flake, and from solo designers. Agfa, with its Creative Alliance program, and Monotype, with its similar Typeface Designers of the World, are licensing these new faces at a rapid pace. They are also available through independent type resellers.

The technical glitches that plagued early releases of PostScript type have long since gone. If today's offerings are inadequate, and some of them certainly are, it's the fault of the designer, not the process.

The lack of poorly thought-out faces from leading designers, however, is one of the most striking features of our desktop age, and reinforces my view that in terms of type design, we are living in the best decade of the century. It is entirely too easy for purists to pine for the days of Benton, Goudy, Dwiggins, and Zapf. No question, these men have left a brilliant legacy. Each of them also left a fair number of worthless, howling dogs.

Technology may partially explain this: it is easier now for a designer to spot problems and start over than it was in the days of metal matrices. But whatever the reason, the Adobe Originals group has been more consistent than any of the legendary figures listed above. More years of work of this quality are needed before one can really say they have surpassed that lofty competition. But at the moment, in my opinion, that is exactly what they are on target to do.

Weight-Watching in Type

The design signature of the nineties may not be as blatant as in the leisure-suit era, but it is certainly there if we look for it. Some of the characteristics are dictated by the new uses to which type is being put nowadays, but some are simply an expression of the taste of the times.

Figure 10.3. *Three examples of type design of today, contrasted with two time-honored warhorses. The contemporary faces are narrower, have larger x-heights, and are tuned for adverse printing conditions.*

Hamburgefont
Apolline (Agfa, 1995)

Hamburgefont
Baskerville (c. 1780)

Hamburgefont
Caslon No. 540 (c. 1735)

Hamburgefont
Columbus (Monotype, 1992)

Hamburgefont
Utopia (Adobe, 1989)

As a weight-conscious society, it is perhaps unsurprising that we are now favoring skinnier typefaces. This is especially true in headlines, where bold, very condensed sans-serif faces are the current rage. Many of the trendiest and sauciest of these come from Emigre Graphics, one of the most successful of the new small design houses.

Text faces are conservative by definition, but one can still see the trend. The best faces being designed today may not be much narrower than their classic predecessors, but the change is there nevertheless. Book faces got slightly more condensed in the nineteenth century, but they bulked up in the early 1900s, and haven't shed the extra poundage until now.

Not only are today's faces skinnier, they are taller. The x-height (the relative height of the lower case letters vs. the caps) has come down from the absurdities of the seventies and eighties, but it is still significantly higher than classic practice. This yields easier legibility in smaller sizes, a more important factor today than it was when the major use for typography was in books.

In Figure 10.2, we have variations on a theme by three of the most distinguished designers of their respective eras—which are readily identifiable.

Figure 10.4. Today's text faces are not only attractive and readable, they often come in more than two weights. This is a big help when the type has to work in conjunction with color elements. Both Apolline and Columbus (top samples) have a semibold; Utopia (bottom sample) adds a black weight as well. In all three, note how as weight increases, more of the stroke contrast that was absent in the light version reappears.

abcde   abcde

Apolline (left) is the text face for this book. This paragraph, and the sample at right, are set in Monotype's Columbus. These similar faces are technically Venetian Old Styles, the oldest variety of text face. But there is a twentieth-century difference—the thinnest part of the stroke is much heavier than it used to be, as you can see from the vowels in Figure 10.3. That means that the newer faces will hold up better than their ancestors would if printed over a color, as here. **And if printing conditions are less favorable yet, a semibold cut (this sentence) can solve the legibility problem without losing the flavor of the face.**

abcdefghi   abcdefghi
abcdefghi   **abcdefghi**

Figure 10.5. *Knocking the upper-case Q out of a four-color tint is asking for trouble with classic faces like Baskerville and Caslon (second and third from left): the thin stem may well wash away. Designers of the three contemporary faces (Apolline, Columbus, and Utopia) took this modern design practice into account—and still managed to retain the individuality of the character.*

The middle version is in effect the work of Bodoni himself, and typifies his style: great simplicity, a strict vertical emphasis, and, especially, a radical contrast between the thickest and thinnest strokes.

At bottom is a design of the leisure-suit school, as executed in 1982 by one of its foremost exponents, Ed Benguiat. The defining characteristic of this style is an overwhelming x-height, easily visible here. Secondarily, all detailing is exaggerated. Bodoni's faces aren't noted for detail, but you can see how Benguiat has emphasized the flourish at the end of the *r*.

Sometimes this approach works nicely. Avant Garde, for example, is a leisure-suit version of Futura, and yet is useful and distinctive. But the face shown here, ITC Modern No. 216, is already all but forgotten.

The top line of Figure 10.2 won't meet with the same fate, in my opinion. Arepo is a 1995 release from Sumner Stone, who founded the Adobe Originals program and designed several of its earliest faces. Stone is now independent and has given marketing rights to Arepo to Agfa.

This is typography for our time. The face is narrow. The x-height is large but not overpowering. The detailing is mannered, not assertive: here the *r* is the least prominent of our three examples, but subtle diagonal emphasis is added. Bodoni's face is clearly the starting point for both twentieth-century versions, but Benguiat's version is a parody while Stone's rendition has much originality.

Faces done in this style are notoriously difficult to print, because of the characteristic thinness of their strokes. Arepo is no exception. Yet in the base of the *d*, where the angle of the serif is opened, making a printing snafu less likely, we see another hallmark of contemporary style: a concession to the fact that we live in an age of nasty printing conditions.

Form Follows Function

Caslon, Baskerville, and Bodoni never had to cope with a laser printer. If they had, they would have designed differently.

In Figure 10.3, contrast two classic faces, Caslon No. 540 and Baskerville, with three from our time: Apolline, a 1995 design by Jean-François Porchez made available by Agfa (and the text face I have chosen for this book); Columbus, a 1992 release by Monotype's Patricia Saunders; and Slimbach's 1989 Adobe Original, Utopia.

> *he type of the nineties reflects the reality that it is more likely than ever to be used in, over or next to color—possibly even knocked out of a color photograph.*

Laser printers have a tough time with the thin lines shown in the Bodoniesque faces of Figure 10.2. When designing in Bodoni's style, thin lines are unavoidable, but see to what extent our present-day designers have avoided thin lines in the other examples. Apolline, Columbus, and Utopia should by rights have more stroke contrast in their base weights, but the designers downplayed it, as seen in Figure 10.4. The contrast is visible in the bolder weights, but not in the base Roman.

Type of the nineties also reflects the reality that it is now more likely than ever to be used in or over color—possibly even knocked out of a color photograph. It's asking a lot of any typeface to retain legibility under such circumstances.

Q, a letter that invites whimsy in form, is quite beautiful in both Caslon and Baskerville—in black and white. Knocking it out of a four-color tint, as in Figure 10.5, is a terrible design practice, especially in small type sizes. There is too big of a likelihood that the thin stem will wash away. In the three contemporary faces, what washes away is the printing problem. And yet the individuality of the Q is retained in all three.

The problems of color printing also argue for more weight flexibility than the traditional light and bold of book composition. If a headline is fighting for attention on a color page, a standard boldface may simply not be loud enough. This is an argument in favor of a distressed or similarly flamboyant face, but sometimes that just won't work.

Similarly, even the sturdier lightfaces of today may not hold up at small sizes when color is involved. Printing in bold may solve this particular problem but it will hardly be tasteful.

The situation cries out for the use of a semibold weight. And, more often than not, today's type designers are giving us one. All three of our featured contemporary faces have a semibold version, as shown in Figure 10.4.

In the types of our time, design thus follows technology. The result is a whole class of faces that are both distinctive and responsive to our needs. They are stylish, yet conservative, just like our taste in fashion. To bring a contemporary flavor to any design, they should be part of any art director's repertoire.

With the huge volume of faces now being released, there is of course something for almost everyone. If the leisure-suit school appeals to you, Treacyfaces, an independent foundry, specializes in this style, but does it rather more convincingly than it was done in the seventies.

And the good faces just keep on coming, faster and cheaper. All three major vendors have just released new unlockable CDs, often accompanied by general price reductions and/or special deals. Whether the typographic fashion of our time is a sound one is debatable. That, typographically speaking, we live in the best of times, is not. ●

Afterword

In spite of the explosion of available faces, about which I have more to say in the next column, the market's appetite for new designs appears unabated. My own experience with my book *Professional Photoshop* is a good illustration.

Bembo, the earliest face that is still in common use, dates from around 1492, and it is as fresh today as it was then. I own several versions, and would have been proud to have used any of them. As you have just read, there is also no shortage of admirable faces designed in *this* century, let alone the other classics of the first 400 years of professional type design.

As a commentator on the contemporary type scene, it would hardly have been politically correct for me to have chosen something from pre-DTP days. Accordingly, in late 1993, after consideration of several other worthy recent faces, I decided on Utopia, one of the faces featured in this column.

With so many hundreds of other conceivable choices, I was convinced that *Professional Photoshop* would have a somewhat unique look.

It does, but not because of the typeface. Shockingly, no less than three other Photoshop books have since appeared using Utopia as their text face, to say nothing of all the Photoshop books I have no desire to read that use it as well for all I know.

What accounts for this coincidence? That both Photoshop and Utopia are Adobe products did not influence my decision, nor presumably anyone else's. Utopia isn't included for free in most systems, the way Palatino and Helvetica are, so it can't be that either. None of the other authors write about type, to my knowledge, so they were under no constraints to choose a recent face.

I conclude the obvious, that whoever designed the other titles felt the same way I did, that Utopia is an outstandingly elegant and legible face. Plus, given Utopia's large x-height, it is a good choice when the publisher is screaming to keep page count down, since such faces can retain legibility at relatively small sizes.

For the current title, I am using Apolline, and not just because it was released recently enough to deter other Photoshop authors. It has many of the same advantages for printing on coated paper, discussed in Figure 10.4, that Utopia has. Furthermore, it is a sturdy-looking face, just what is wanted in a book full of color photos. As pointed out in Column 3, the choice of a light typeface often prompts the pressman to increase the flow of black ink. Such a press move often results in the artists who prepared the digital files cursing out Photoshop for giving "muddy seps," especially if they didn't change the Separation setup defaults.

If you stick with the intelligently designed faces for our time, the question of whether the muddy-looking sep is your fault or the pressman's may well never come up. ●

Jargon Watch

Benguiat, Ed (1927—) American type and logo designer and hand letterer. Among his 500 or so faces are Barcelona, Korinna, Souvenir, Tiffany, Benguiat, and the Bookman that is a base font on today's computers.

Benton, Morris Fuller (1872–1948) Prolific American type designer, long-time head of production at American Typefounders; credited with the concept of assembling types into extended families. Among his works are Century Schoolbook, Franklin Gothic, Alternate Gothic, and Cloister Old Style.

bookhand Any of the several mannered, ornate styles — scripts, uncials, blackletters — used in books prior to the invention of printing.

calligraphic Having the characteristics of mannered handwriting, particularly a variation in the thickness of the stroke, emulating what happens when a pen is applied to paper with different pressures.

distressed 1990s typeface phenomenon, a class of typefaces that is intentionally roughed up to look punkier, the headline on Page 227 being an example.

Dwiggins, William A. (1880–1956) American calligrapher, illustrator, and type designer, best known for his Caledonia (1938). Electra and Metro are also Dwiggins faces.

foundries Companies specializing in the production of typefaces, often with their own staff of designers.

Goudy, Frederic W. (1865–1947) Designer of well over 100 faces, one of the pivotal figures in American and world type history. His specialty in text faces was a sculpted, angled look. Among his best-known designs in this genre are Goudy Old Style, Kennerley Old Style, Deepdene, and University of California Old Style, which in a revised version (ITC Berkeley Old Style) is enjoying renewed popularity.

sans-serif Serifs are the horizontal bars at the bottom of most letters in the majority of typefaces, including the one you are reading now. Sans-serif typefaces, such as Helvetica, or the face used for captions in this book, do not have these serifs.

tablet Pressure-sensitive computer input device used to supplement or as an alternate to the traditional mouse. An electronic pen is used to establish position; some programs, such as Fontographer, can also react to variations in pressure on the pen.

x-height The height of lower-case characters in comparison to that of capital letters.

Zapf, Hermann (1918—) German designer and authority on type. Working for the Stempel type foundry in the 1950s, he cemented his place among the greatest designers of all time with, in rapid succession, Palatino, Melior, Aldus, and Optima. His subsequent faces have not been at that exalted level, but his work lives on: three Zapf faces (Palatino, Zapf Chancery, and Zapf Dingbats) are included as base fonts on virtually every computer.

Infinity
Infinity
Infinity
Infinity
Infinity
Infinity
Infinity
Infinity
Infinity
Infinity
Infinity
Infinity
Infinity
Infinity
Infinity
Infinity
Infinity
Infinity
Infinity

Copious
Abundant
Bountiful
Unrestrained
Overload
Scads
Bounteousness
A Whole Lot
Unconstrained
Plenteous
Endless
Abundant
Bountiful
Oodles
Plenitude
Limitless
Profusion
Overload
A Whole Lot
Endless
Unbounded
Plenitude
Plenteous
Scads
Unbounded
Profusion
Oodles
Bounteousness

Ample Ample Ample
Ample Ample Ample
Ample Ample Ample
Ample Ample Ample
Ample Ample Ample
Ample Ample Ample
Ample Ample Ample

Limitless
Copious

11

The Case for Cross-Breeding Fonts

With tens of thousands of typefaces on the market, why in the world would one want to morph existing ones? The creative designer may find some reasons.

 aniel Berkeley Updike, the foremost type historian of this or any other century, would be appalled at the thought of the proliferation of fonts we have available today. Nearly 100,000 faces are now being marketed, and even though many are the same fonts issued under different names by different vendors, the number of discrete families of type must be close to five figures.

Updike, writing in 1922, took the view that *seven* families of type (and he named them) were all a composing room needed. He was full of scorn for anyone thinking that more are necessary.

"We are told that if we know the truth, it will make us free; and *it will*," he seethed. "If we know the truth typographically we shall be freed from using the many poor types that are offered us. There are hundreds of pages in founders' specimen-books; and yet examples of almost every type that the world ought ever to have seen could be shown in a thin pamphlet."

Figure 11.1. *Multiple Master fonts allow virtually unlimited, first-generation variants of a single design. Everything on the opposite page derives from four Adobe originals. At left, Ex Ponto, a script, varies as to boldness only. Bottom right, 1996's Adobe Jenson adds an optical-sizing axis: as the sample moves left to right, the type becomes thinner and more elegant, more suitable for larger-size printing; as the sample moves down, the type gets bolder. Scattered throughout the page in blue is Jimbo, and in red is Nueva. Both of these vary not only in weight but in width.*

It is with no small amount of trepidation that I risk rousing Updike's ghost by discussing an even more incendiary means of feeding the typeface explosion.

In the same way that our friends in the motion picture industry can "morph" images—that is, create intermediate versions of two endpoints—technology now allows us to create hybrid typefaces that bear some of the characteristics of two different parents. Consequently, it is now possible, with some difficulty, to generate a nearly infinite number of typefaces, of which 99 percent are entirely useless.

This column is about the other one percent.

In the approximately two years since this column was written, the situation has not changed. There are still only two non-Adobe Multiple Master faces available as far as I know, and non-Mac users are out of luck.

Those wishing to embark on this dubious adventure have three different tools at hand. Of these, the purest and cleanest is to use a Multiple Master font, if you can find one. Unfortunately, less than a dozen exist now, they only work on the Macintosh, and only two, to my knowledge, are available from any source other than Adobe.

Masochistic readers may try their luck with a dedicated font editor such as Macromedia's Fontographer. This program allows us to mix any two typefaces in any format in any percentage. The technical results are, to put it as charitably as possible, highly variable, and a good knowledge of the editing features of the program is necessary to clean up the inevitable bad or missing characters in the hybrid face.

FontChameleon was discontinued in June, 1996, when Adobe purchased Ares. See the Afterword to this Column.

A third alternative is about to be released by Ares Software. Its FontChameleon program (available for either Mac or Windows at about $200 street price) carries descriptors of 200 standard fonts in a proprietary format, set up to match their Adobe equivalents for spacing. The actual fonts can be generated as is, or obliqued, and/or condensed or expanded, and/or with a larger x-height, or as morphs with other Chameleon faces. Non-Ares faces don't work, and at present there are no italic faces or scripts.

When Chameleon first was announced, breathless press releases trumpeted the fact that we now could make a typeface that was a cross between Avant Garde and ITC Bookman. When I read this, I thought of the old drinking song, mourning the loss of a comrade who was

> *Regrettably, no longer here:*
> *He tried to mix Cointreau and beer.*

WHAT IF THE HEADLINE DOESN'T FI

The Squeeze is On

Many has been the time, over these past years of writing, that I have visualized with some pleasure my hands around the neck of the individual who decided that the headline of my *Computer Artist* column would consist of one line of 30 point Futura Bold Condensed caps, set to a maximum width of 33 picas. That miserable excuse for a design allows me around five words for a title. Writing something to fit the space of Figure 11.2 is child's play by comparison.

This is a more realistic example of where one might want a hybrid face. Since the style of this headline is supposed to match others in the magazine, we can't change its specs very much. Nobody will notice if the point size is reduced by one, and we can tighten letterspacing a little, but we can only get so far with these measures.

We can gain quite a bit more by condensing the shapes of the letters themselves. Just about every desktop application permits changing width without affecting height.

Doing that without torpedoing quality is not so simple. Futura Bold Condensed is what typographers call a "grotesque" sans-serif. There is nothing derogatory about this term; most popular sans-serif faces, such as Helvetica, Franklin Gothic, and Univers, are grotesques too. The defining characteristic of these faces is that the weight of the stroke is the same everywhere.

It follows that if we change width without changing the height, the whole identity of the face goes down the tubes.

Consider "Helvetica Narrow," a standard "font" on almost every printer. The reason for the quotation marks is, Helvetica Narrow is not a true face at all; it is just Helvetica, with width reduced to 82% of normal.

In Figure 11.3, observe how the tops and bottoms of the rounded letters on the third line are thicker than the sides. Forget about it! A real typographer cannot use an atrocity like this.

As the second line of that sample shows, a condensed version of Helvetica exists that is faithful to the original. That isn't big news, but what *is* big news is that we can now create any number of intermediate semi-condensed faces that split the difference, and there should be little or no deterioration in quality. This approach could also be used to create a face darker than Helvetica, yet lighter than Helvetica Medium.

If the font we want to use is one of the few available in Multiple Master format, that is the best option. All of the sans-serifs currently on the market are two-axis fonts, meaning that one can produce correctly proportioned faces that differ not only in width but weight. This yields a frightening variety of fonts: Adobe's Myriad face lives up to its name by offering 247,016 possible variations. More frightening still is the inability to name the results sensibly. If we generate a font that is roughly Myriad Semibold Semicondensed, its name is going to be something like MyriaMM_504 wt 420 wd, so if we use more than one of these hybrids, telling them apart will not be easy.

Crossbreeding a typeface with a different member of its own family, as Futura with Futura Condensed, frequently works without a hitch in Fontographer. Things get tougher if the two parent fonts are not related. Even slight variations in the way characters are drawn cause undesirable artifacts, as in Figure 11.4. If the shapes of the letters are completely different—which often happens with *a, g, W,* and others—the program gives up.

FontChameleon niftily finesses this problem, allowing the user to specify which of the two parent fonts will take precedence if there are characters that are completely incompatible. This allows us to undertake the dangerous but occasionally rewarding task of making a true hybrid out of two unlike faces.

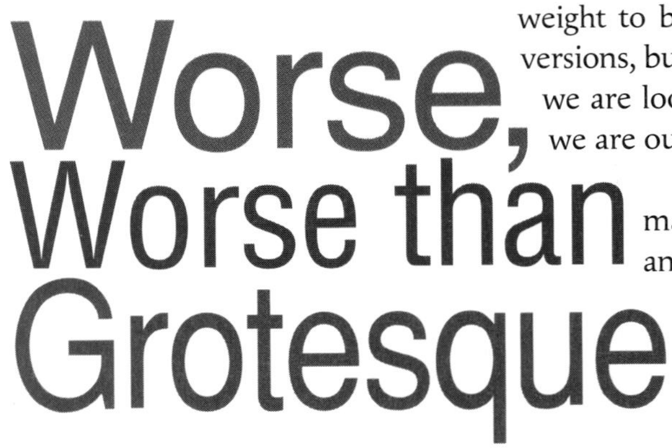

Figure 11.3. Artificially condensed faces, such as Helvetica Narrow (third line) can be detected by an unnatural narrowness at the sides. Contrast the shape of the o with that of the true Helvetica Condensed (second line) and the base face (first line).

Moderation and Mugwumps

The most obvious reason for morphing faces from two different families is when there is no choice. If a face ranges from book weight to bold we can create many different versions, but only at points between the two. If we are looking for a light or an ultra weight we are out of luck.

Going back to Figure 11.2: we may need to condense the face to fit an occasional extra letter, but there is no member of the Futura family narrower than the one we are currently using. Therefore, nothing to cross-breed with—except a

Worse, Worse than Grotesque

member of another type family. Univers, which *does* have an ultra-condensed cut, is a clear choice. Cheating by mixing 85 percent Futura Condensed and 15 percent Univers Ultra-Condensed should not be detectable.

Fifteen percent is a good maximum to keep in mind for blends. The dangers of going higher are clearly seen in Figure 11.5 in the four letters set in a face I call Mugwump Roman, a 50–50 FontChameleon split between Times Roman and Bodoni.

Even forgetting the problem at the base of the *b*, this typeface is worthless. It can be printed, it can even be technically classified as a transitional face, in the same group as Baskerville and Fournier. But overall it merits the name I have given it. It straddles the fence between two contradictory positions, with its mug on one side and its wump on the other, looking forlornly in every direction at once, without a future because it has no past, an ugly child tormented by competing, incompatible memories of its elegant, eminent parents.

And yet, blending in moderation can be a positive thing. The face we now call Caslon No. 540, one of the Updike Seven, shares a drawback with most of its eighteenth-century brethren. They were designed for exactly what the main use for them then was: printing in books. Naturally, since coated paper did not exist at the time, Caslon judged how good his design was by how good it looked when printed on uncoated paper.

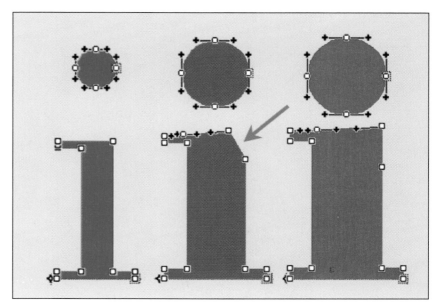

Figure 11.4. *A slight variation in letterform can be enough to throw off a program's morphing capability. Faces in the same family should work well, but here Fontographer's attempt to generate an intermediate weight (center) of Bodoni Antiqua is derailed by the slightly different shapes of the top of the letter in the two parents on either side of it.*

Those working with halftones know that dot gain is much less on coated than uncoated paper. Nobody who knows what they're doing would dream of printing the same color picture on both sheets without compensation. The same principle holds in type. When Caslon No. 540 prints on an uncoated sheet, it spreads. But on a coated stock, such as in a magazine, it looks peculiarly insubstantial.

If we compensate for this by generating a new font that is 95 percent Caslon No. 540 and five percent some bolder face, not only will we have a better type for a magazine, but we will actually be indulging in one of typography's best traditions, the modification of form to take account of adverse conditions.

Using 9-point or smaller type is an adverse condition. Having newsprint as the paper is an adverse condition. Being forced to use a laser printer rather than a high-resolution imagesetter is an adverse condition. And, with the wide variety of color and graphic effects we now can achieve, there is every opportunity for designers to engineer in further adverse conditions, such as printing across images, or in light colors, or over a similar color,

Figure 11.5. *Blending typefaces runs into problems where the two parents have different characteristics. Here, FontChameleon attempts to combine Bodoni, which has a spur at the base of the lower case b, with Times, which doesn't. The combined letter is therefore not a success.*

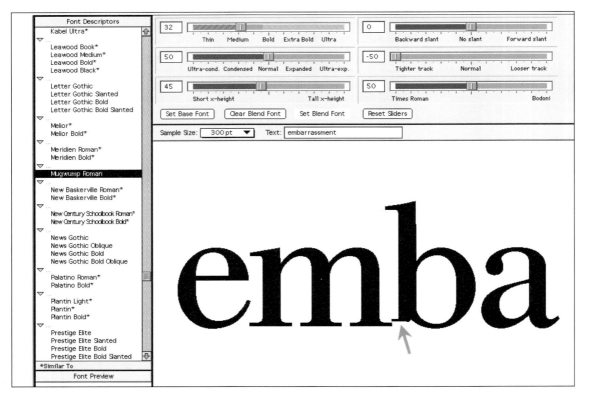

in addition to the old reliables, knocking out of a dark background or setting in all capital letters.

The sensitive typographer responds to adverse conditions by emphasizing legibility. That usually means some sacrifice of elegance and style.

C.H. Griffith's 1931 face Excelsior, shown in Figure 11.6, typifies a group of faces—Corona, Gazette, Imperial, Ionic, Textype—that were designed for the most horrible of all printing conditions, namely, a newspaper. Standard book faces were not legible enough for the demands of newspaper publishers. This class of faces therefore avoids subtle detailing. There are no fine lines that might fail to print. X-heights are large, enhancing readability at small sizes. Acutely angled stroke intersections, where ink could build up into a blotch, are ruthlessly excised.

Excelsior and its prewar kin succeed in doing what they were designed for. They are, however, so lacking in style and grace that it is extremely unusual for anyone to want to use them for any other purpose than newspaper text. Up until now, that is. If we'd like to make a face more legible, what could be better than blending in five percent Excelsior, the champion of clarity?

The Size-Dependent Design

This brings us to the lost art of optical scaling. When type was set in metal, a "font" meant one size of a given typeface. Each size had to be mastered individually, instead of generating every size from the same design, as we do today. There was thus no technical reason for 6-point Times Roman to be the same typeface as 12-point Times Roman—and a persuasive artistic reason, the difficulty of printing at small sizes, for it *not* to be.

Consequently, the designers of metal faces used the dinosaur equivalent of blending with Excelsior. That is, they made the x-height larger as size decreased; they cut down on contrast between thick and thin strokes; they lessened inktraps; and they put more space between letters.

In the desktop world, these nuances were nonexistent until the release of Adobe's Minion Multiple Master face. This font adds a third axis, optical scaling, to width and weight. Figure 11.6 displays three of the 2,792,292 possible Minion variants that this Multiple Master can spit out.

Note how the "72 point" sample at bottom, like the Galliard below it, has a stylized, sculpted look. Very elegant—as long

Technology changes terminology. In the metal days, "font" meant a single size of a single face. Although one still sees that definition from time to time, it is obsolete: now, "font" is synonymous with "typeface." Prior to Multiple Master, one could redefine "font" as meaning the minimum package that one could purchase from a type vendor. That inclusive definition would have covered the metal days, when one had to buy different sizes separately. Adobe prefers to use the term "instance" for an individual face that has been generated by a Multiple Master, but a lot of people call it a "font" anyway.

as the type is large enough for us to appreciate it. At smaller sizes, the sculpting detracts from legibility. Neither face is effective at 10 point or smaller, in my opinion.

In the early nineteenth century, typographic fashion called for simple, classic letters with no diagonal stress, and for extreme, not to say ridiculous, contrast between the lightest and thickest parts of the stroke. The principal practitioners of this "modern" style, Italy's Giambatista Bodoni and France's Firmin Didot, took advantage of advances in metal-cutting technology to create such thin lines in their designs that printers have been cursing their names ever since.

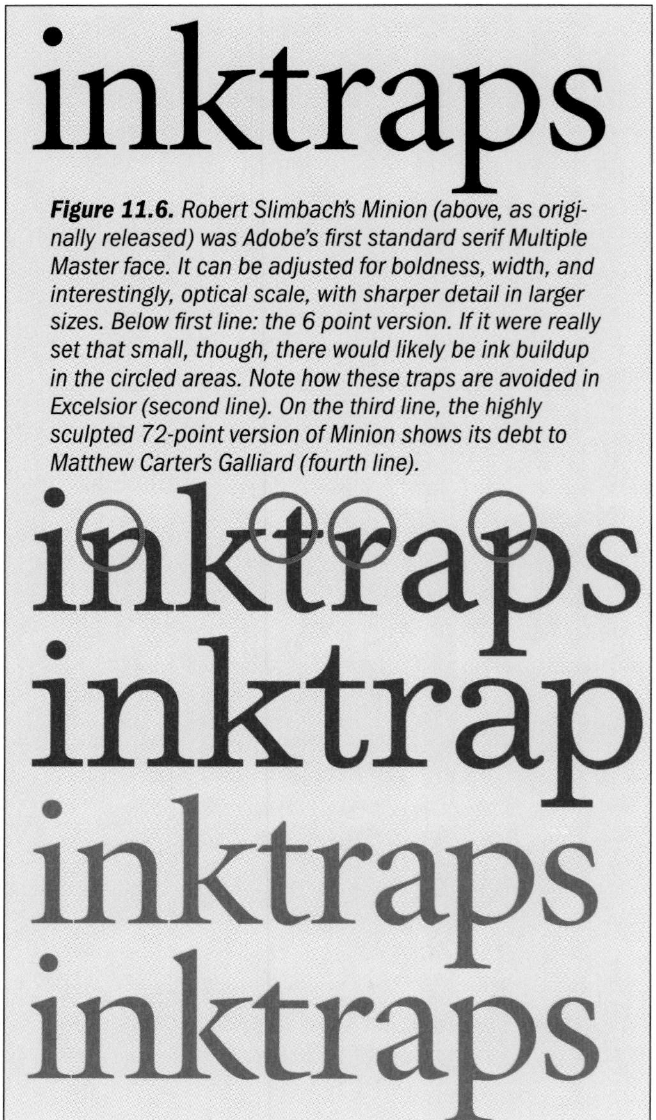

After being dormant for most of the century, there has been a recent revival of interest in these faces for advertising use. IBM, Delta Airlines, and Hilton Hotels, among others, use "modern" faces as their corporate identity fonts.

Modern faces are the obvious argument in favor of optical scaling. Having only one base drawing will either get lines that are too thin to print in text sizes, or that are too thick in large sizes (let alone a letter as large as that of Figure 11.8), or, more commonly, both problems at once.

Holding the fine lines of modern faces is trying enough when dealing with black type on a white background. Under any other circumstances acceptably

Figure 11.6. *Robert Slimbach's Minion (above, as originally released) was Adobe's first standard serif Multiple Master face. It can be adjusted for boldness, width, and interestingly, optical scale, with sharper detail in larger sizes. Below first line: the 6 point version. If it were really set that small, though, there would likely be ink buildup in the circled areas. Note how these traps are avoided in Excelsior (second line). On the third line, the highly sculpted 72-point version of Minion shows its debt to Matthew Carter's Galliard (fourth line).*

legible printing becomes impossible, as Figure 11.9 indicates.

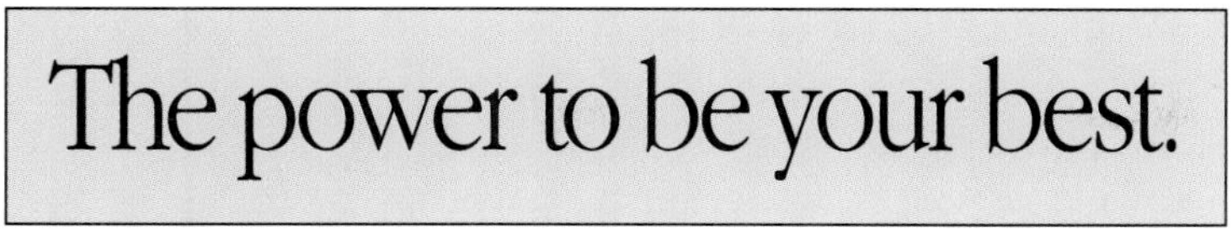
The power to be your best.

***Figure 11.7.** Art directors for Apple Computer conceived of cross-breeding ITC Garamond and ITC Garamond Condensed, and wound up with one of the world's best known advertising looks. The morphed face, originally called Apple Garamond, was some years later released under the name ITC Garamond Narrow.*

It is tempting to attack this problem by cross-breeding Bauer Bodoni and Bauer Bodoni Bold. That might work if the entire typeface were too light, but not here. Bauer Bodoni Bold has the same thin areas as the text weight. Blending with it will leave us as badly off as before.

What we really need for this is a typeface with no thin strokes. There is exactly such a class of typefaces, the Egyptians or slab serifs. Like the grotesques, these faces have no variation at all in stroke weight. The only difference is that they have serifs. Examples of this kind of face are Memphis, Rockwell, and Stymie. For the comparison in Figure 11.9, I used a more recent face, Glypha, which also has the plus of a large x-height. I hoped to retain the overall feel of Bodoni while beefing up the lighter areas.

Knowledge and Taste

Further growth of these technologies will depend on how important a force they become in the design community. There have been few Multiple Master font releases, presumably because they are hideously difficult for the designer to create.

Fontographer and its competitors will likely get more intelligent in their abilities to morph unlike faces; for the time being, considerable typographic expertise, not to mention intestinal fortitude, is required to even think about using this method.

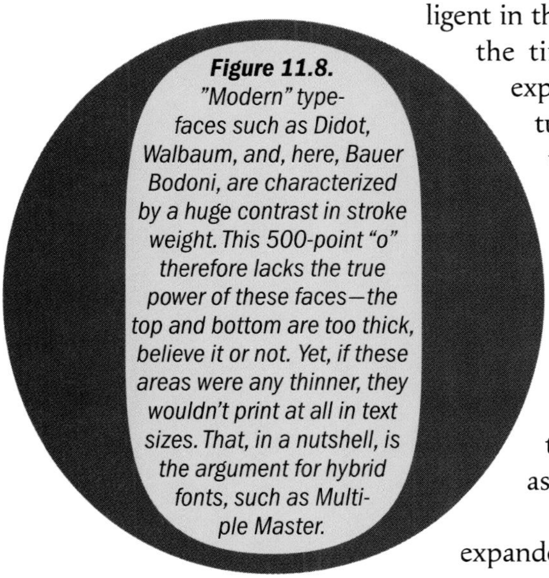

***Figure 11.8.** "Modern" typefaces such as Didot, Walbaum, and, here, Bauer Bodoni, are characterized by a huge contrast in stroke weight. This 500-point "o" therefore lacks the true power of these faces—the top and bottom are too thick, believe it or not. Yet, if these areas were any thinner, they wouldn't print at all in text sizes. That, in a nutshell, is the argument for hybrid fonts, such as Multiple Master.*

FontChameleon, the simplest tool to use by far, produces fonts of reasonable but variable quality from its proprietary outlines. In its first release, its lack of any italic faces prevents its use as a low-cost method of acquiring a type library. (Ares states that italics and scripts will be released as an upgrade later this year.)

It would be much more useful if it expanded the range of available morphs by exaggerating the cuts of some of its types. Instead of bundling a face with its standard condensed and bold partners, Ares would be better advised to release it with a super-condensed and an ultrabold. A Bodoni-like face with thin areas optimized for 100-point and up would also be helpful in generating new fonts for use at large size.

Millions upon millions of new typefaces. When will we ever have enough?

The slogan in Figure 11.7, as familiar to graphic artists as the half-breed typeface that states it, suggests an answer.

Or, to look at it another way, one of Updike's seven base fonts was a Scotch-style roman called Oxford, dating from 1798. He used it for the text of his seminal book *Printing Types,* explaining "It seems to me a type of real distinction." In 1946, Griffith

ab **Figure 11.9.** *The thin lines of Bauer Bodoni (left; and top sample below) invite disaster if knocked out of a colored or black background, such as the one below. A font cross-bred with something more legible (right; and bottom sample below) preserves the flavor, not the problem. The quotations are from Daniel Berkeley Updike.*

There is, therefore, little excuse for thinking that conditions of labour to-day are very different from those that long preceded them; and it is important to realize that these conditions were all along factors, as they are now, in the problem of turning out good printing. Types and books reflect the state of the arts around them, because on one side typography is an art; but they are influenced by trade conditions, because it is also a trade. Not to face these two facts, or to neglect either one or the other, is merely to fool one's self!

The outlook for typography is as good as ever it was—and much the same. Its future depends largely on the knowledge and taste of educated men. For a printer there are two camps, and only two, to be in: one, the camp of things as they are; the other that of things as they should be. The first camp is on a level and extensive plain, and many eminently respectable persons lead lives of comfort therein; the sport is, however, inferior! The other camp is more interesting. Though on an inconvenient hill, it commands a wide view of typography, and in it are the class that help on sound taste in printing, because they are willing to make sacrifices for it.

reworked Oxford for use in a biography of Thomas Jefferson. He called the revised face Monticello, and it was a remarkably fine effort, later marketed by Mergenthaler.

You guessed it. For all the superabundance of faces on the market today, you can't find either Oxford or Monticello.

No matter how many new faces may be released, no matter how many hybrids we create, the best artists will always be plagued by the nagging suspicion that, maybe, just maybe, somewhere in history — or somewhere in the future — there is a type that is the one and only right one for the next job. ●

Afterword

The secret of FontChameleon's great flexibility was an extremely compact and efficient way of storing font descriptions electronically. Typically, a Chameleon base font description was less than a tenth the size of an equivalent PostScript Type 1 printer font.

This fact was not lost on industry leader Adobe, which in June 1996 bought FontChameleon's parent, Ares, largely for its font compression technology — and promptly scuttled Chameleon.

Though Chameleon may be dead, its influence will therefore presumably live on in future generations of laser printers. It never made much of a dent in the market in its nearly three years of existence, a testimonial to the difficulty of the cross-breeding field.

Multiple Masters, despite enthusiastic support from Adobe, have not caught on either. It is correct that many of Adobe's best-selling font packages are Multiple Masters. On the other hand, nobody else is manufacturing them, although anyone who uses Fontographer, which supports the creation of Multiple Master faces, could conceivably do so. And shockingly, Multiple Master fonts still work on Macintosh only.

Font blending, however, remains a hot topic for the serious typographer. In his 1995 book on type design, *Fontographer,* Stephen Moye includes not just a section on how to do it in Fontographer but also one on Chameleon. He concludes that regardless of how one starts, final touchup in Fontographer is almost inevitable. If so (and I agree that it is) that is a pretty severe limitation for those who aren't type specialists.

Moye has little use for the intricacies of Multiple Master. His only practical suggestion for the format was to use it to impose heavier kerning and tighter letterspacing as the font increases in size — without risking the consequences of altering the shape of the characters.

The two most ambitious and widely publicized type design projects of our decade each, in its own way, demonstrated the frustrations and dangers that go hand in hand with the undoubted virtues of Multiple Master.

The two projects resembled one another, in that the foremost American typographers of our time headed teams trying to produce updated versions of the works of classic Italian designers; that extended trips to Europe were taken to investigate the typographical detritus left by the Italians; that the projects were hyped as being the last word in historically informed type design, combining the brilliance of the old masters with the advantages of the Bézier curve; and that those who were waiting for results from all this research were in danger of dying of old age before finding any.

For the reasons stated in Figure 11.8, Bodoni faces seem like the most tempting possible target for Multiple Master treatment. So, when International Typeface Corp. commissioned a team led by Sumner Stone for a remake, to be called ITC Bodoni, it announced that the final product would be a Multiple Master.

Several years and lots of dollars later, a pretty decent series of faces emerged, but *not* as Multiple Masters. There were in fact multiple versions of each face, each with its thinnest areas optimized for a certain range of sizes, but the execution of the Multiple Master was evidently too difficult even for so august a group.

Column 12 will give you an idea of how much I admire the designs of Adobe's Robert Slimbach. Nevertheless, had I written Column 2 ("The Curse of Trying Too Hard") after the 1996 release of Slimbach's Adobe Jenson, I'd have used Adobe Jenson as an example of where too much sophistication hurts.

Nicolas Jenson (1420–1480), a Frenchman known mostly for his work in Venice, was the first to make successful use of what we now call Roman type. His designs were the clear forerunners of the faces now classified as Venetian Old Style. Francesco Griffo's 1492 Jenson remake, now known as Bembo, is the oldest face still in common use.

Jenson paid the price for being first; his types were pleasing but inconsistent and difficult to read. That's virtually the opposite of Slimbach, whose style is one one of smooth precision. In trying to reconcile the two, Slimbach was seduced by the Multiple Master format into leaving in too many of the eccentricities of Jenson's experiment. For example, in the bottom half of Figure 11.1, you can see in the Adobe Jenson *e* a useless spur on the outside of the cross-stroke. Elegant in very large sizes, perhaps, but counterproductive in the overwhelming majority of uses. The overall design was nice, but Slimbach would have been better off releasing two separate cuts than a single Multiple Master.

Bleeding-edge font morphing may not be for everyone. The idea of modifying existing fonts, though, is decidedly mainstream. Nowadays, it is commonplace for designers to use an illustration program to convert the shapes of existing types into editable outlines, so as to alter them for use, say, in a corporate logo. And diehard type aficionados who design full alphabets in Fontographer often begin by opening and using a complete existing font as a base, which is then modified extensively.

Updike and Jenson must be turning over in their graves. ●

Jargon Watch

axis In the Multiple Master lexicon, one of the variables, such as width, boldness, presence or absence of a serif, etc. Most releases have two axes, generally weight and width, although several have only one. Minion, which also has an "optical scaling," axis, is the only current example of a three-axis Multiple Master.

condensed Said of a typeface with relatively narrow letters. There is no clear definition of what constitutes a condensed face, but those faces generally considered condensed are at least 15 percent narrower than their standard counterparts.

grotesque A sans-serif typeface where all parts of the stroke forming the letter are of nearly equal width. Helvetica and Univers are examples of grotesque faces; Optima is a sans-serif face that would not be classified as grotesque.

halftone The imposition of a screen during the printing of photographic images on film or paper; hence, any printed photograph.

instance In a Multiple Master font, a particular one of the many possible variant faces that can be generated.

modern Technical term describing a typeface with the general design characteristics of those of the early nineteenth century, as opposed to the *old style* and *transitional* faces of earlier centuries. Modern faces, such as those of Giambatista Bodoni, have a strong vertical emphasis and great contrast between thinnest and thickest areas.

morph To create intermediate versions of artwork, having some of the characteristics of two unrelated parents. Also used to describe the video technique of showing a series of such morphs in rapid-fire succession, leading to the illusion that one parent is changing seamlessly into the other. It has been so frequently used in negative political advertising recently that it has become a cliche: clips that show a local Congressional candidate morphing into Newt Gingrich, and so on.

Multiple Master A PostScript type technology, introduced by Adobe, that allows intermediate faces to be generated between two extremes, in fonts that have Multiple Master capability.

Scotch-style A variety of typefaces that has sharply fallen from favor over the years. Scotch-style faces have a vertical emphasis, considerable contrast between thick and thin, and have capital letters that appear bolder than the lower case. Caledonia is based on Scotch-style forms but has been heavily modified. The headlines on the front page of *The Wall Street Journal* are in a Scotch-style face; other examples are rare today.

serif The short, horizontal base on which many letters appear to rest. Some typefaces, such as Helvetica, remove serifs as a design element; these faces are termed *sans-serifs*.

x-height The height of the lowercase letters in relation to the upper case. A large x-height is not very elegant, but it makes the type more legible.

Makeready"*kn0*kt0*ra0*rb0*d0*p(0,21,0,14.45,0,0,G,"U.S. English")*t(0,0,"2 "):
Ps100t0h100z11.5k0b0c"Black"f"Apolline-Regular">
@Subhead=[S"","Subhead"]<*L*h"Dan's Ragged"
*kn1*kt0*ra0*rb0*d0*p(0,0,0,14.45,13,0,G,"U.S. English")*t(0,0,"2 "):
PBs100t-2h100z14k0b1.9999c"Black"f"MEllington">
@Makeready Text 1st Graf=[S"Makeready Text"," Makeready Text"]<*J*h"Dan's Makeready"
*kn0*kt0*ra0*rb0*d0*p(0,0,0,14.45,0,0,G,"U.S. English")*t(0,0,"2 "):
Ps100t0h100z11.5k0b0c"Black"f"Apolline-Regular">
@Makeready Text:The success of the Internet has brought code-driven typesetting back into the forefront. If you want to make yourself a web page, you will have to become familiar with a structure known as <H>html<k20>—<Hk0>hypertext markup language. It is duck soup for anybody who has ever used a code-driven type system, or who is familiar with XPress Tags. Other mortals have been known to tear their hair out over its complexities.
@Subhead:Kerning and Letterspacing
@Makeready Text 1st Graf:The modern programs benefit from the superior capabilities of PostScript type, which can be adjusted very finely.
@Makeready Text:<Hh105.0003>89p<Hh100> was limited by its output devices, which generally could space only in the relatively coarse increments of <h10 313z8k-30b4.1999>1<h100z11.5k-20b0>/<h108.3313z8k0b0.6999>54   > <h100z11.5>of an em. Type sizes were in half-point increments, and l   ts.
<H>pm<H> improves considerably on this, and   >pm<H>
accesses both type and leading in incre   >in
thousandths of a point. <H>qxp   ing are
in<H> <Hh108.3313z8k-2
20b0>/<h108.331   <H> is only
half this se

<H
20b
<H>p
comes   typeface
size ind   size: as
12.2 ma   gure
<H>qxp   us
letterspac
lines that a   e,
but changing
If we can onl
<Hh105.0003
In 1989, comm
<Hh105.0003>8
plenty for most p
Nowadays, fonts a
letters in the middl
This means that if w
pairs rW, rB, and eM
Aldus<H>'<H>s respo   >pm.
<H>This generates a b   programs.
<H>qxp<H> can use su   er and dirtier fix with
an easily editable kern ta
On the other hand, if we s   then say, rats, we should have done it

12 Desktop Publishing vs. "Professional" Typography

How do today's page layout programs stack up next to their very expensive predecessors? In a Quark-PageMaker shootout, a ringer steps in to find out.

ive years ago, the professional graphic arts community generally believed that desktop publishing would never attract the serious user. The hardware was inadequate, the software idiotic, and there was no base of people who knew how to use either.

Now that the dinosaurs who held this view are extinct, it makes sense to ask ourselves, could they have been right? Do today's desktop programs really offer the functionality that dedicated "professional" systems took for granted in 1989?

The answer depends on the field. In illustration programs, desktop wins by default: tools as sophisticated as we have now simply did not exist in 1989.

For handling color photographs, some pretty fair systems were available in 1989, for a million dollars or so. 1994 readers of *Computer Artist* can easily afford desktop systems that blow their doors off in both performance and capabilities.

Figure 12.1. *Code-driven typesetting systems have many advantages, to go along with their long learning curve. QuarkXPress's editable XPress Tags format (sample at background left, using text that appears on Page 260), is one way of getting away from the limitations of WYSIWYG. The 1989 edition of the software of Penta Systems, featured in this column, had many coding possibilities that are sorely missed in today's programs. Inset at left, its useful White Space Fill command, as described in its operator's manual. No cognate method of white space insertion exists in either QXP or PageMaker.*

255

But typography, which started the whole desktop revolution, is a bit dicier. Unlike color imaging, type is not very compute-intensive, so increases in power are not so important. Furthermore, since type was computerized long before pictures were, in 1989 professional type systems were relatively more mature than their graphic counterparts.

Both of the leading desktop page design programs have recently released upgrades, so it is a good time for a little head-to-head comparison. To spice up the competition, however, I am adding a third contestant, a ringer: a professional-level typesetting system, vintage 1989.

> **U**nlike color imaging, typesetting is not compute-intensive, and in 1989 it was far more mature than its graphic counterparts. A professional system from 1989 will be a worthy opponent for today's desktop champs.

Computer Artist's readers have no use for the kind of review that emphasizes useless bells and whistles and how neat and how keen the various menus are. Instead, we will approach these products as tough-minded typographers, ignoring minor differences in ease of use. Being typographers, we will also place our heads firmly in the sand and ignore all graphic capabilities.

WYSIWYG and WYSIMOLWYG

The contestants, alphabetically:

At the time this column appeared in early 1994, Aldus was an independent company. It was acquired by Adobe Systems that August, and Adobe has continued and upgraded the PageMaker line.

Aldus PageMaker 5.0 (PM), which has the largest market share of any page-layout program, but has historically lagged behind in some high-end features, particularly support for color separation. Version 5.0 is an ambitious upgrade to previous editions. The street price for this program is around $600.

From 1989: a PentaPro front-end typography system (89P), one of the leading and highest-quality systems employed by type houses, noted for the caliber of its book pagination routines and its typographic power. Four-user configurations, running on Data General minicomputers with slave terminals, ran about $100,000. Fast Unix-based descendants of this system, but with a modern graphical user interface, are still available.

QuarkXPress 3.2 (QXP), the preeminent desktop program for professional publishers, known for great precision, speed, and ease of handling graphics. An open architecture enables development of third-party "XTensions" that add functions, but XTensions will not be permitted in this contest. Pricing is comparable

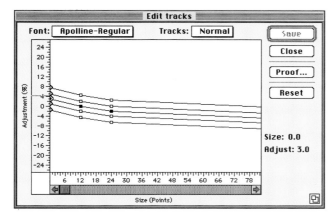

Figure 12.2. *Page-Maker comes with typographic tracking by default, but unless the user edits the values (bottom dialog box), some faces will look rather abnormal (top line) when the "normal" value is selected. There is no tracking in the second line.*

to PM. In fairness to 89P, one must point out that these prices do not include a computer.

Today's programs have won the toss and elected to start with today's strengths: cheap computing power, and accurate monitors.

In terms of processing speed, it is no surprise to learn that 89P eats the dust of both PM and QXP. While I can't get my hands on a 1989 system to run time trials, my impression is that QXP performs H&J—hyphenation and justification—at least ten times as fast as 89P. The speed of PM is slightly less impressive. More annoying, PM's printing is slower, generally about half again as time-consuming as QXP's. It also takes much longer to open files.

89P terminals show stick figures with or without serifs to represent fonts; they were dismissed by some with the pejorative WYSIMOLWYG: What You See Is More Or Less What You Get.

In the age of Adobe Type Manager, that technology does not impress. When adjusting letterfit, creating a tight contour around a graphic, or trying to lose or gain a line of copy by creative typography, PM and QXP are much superior. With 89P, these circumstances required repeated trips to the laser printer.

[j1]The Case for Coding[cm

Point-and-click is not always the best approach. 89P is code-driven, and its suite of commands is astonishingly powerful. They can be combined into repeatable formats, and applied much more precisely than in either PM or QXP.

The two desktop leaders use the same analog to 89P's formatting: user-definable "styles." Each can be applied only to complete paragraphs, a huge shortcoming. When changing from one style to another, further problems develop. Both will over-ride the previous style, preserving italicization. If, however, the text contains elements where the size or face has been changed manually, as inexperienced operators are wont to do, PM over-rides these specifications also. Although this is probably the correct thing to do most of the time, it is awfully tough on those of us who use pi fonts such as Zapf Dingbats in text.

QXP leaves these alone when changing directly from Style 1 to Style 2, but going from Style 1 to No Style to Style 2 will wipe out everything. Including, sad to say, all italicizations, fractions, small caps and superior and inferior characters.

THE XTENSION ADVANTAGE

QuarkXPress's greatest strength may well be that its structure enables third parties to create "XTensions" that interact closely with it to give it new capabilities. Quark vigor-ously supports the developers of such XTensions. Hundreds now exist, ranging from the ridiculous to the incredibly powerful. Most are available for Macintosh only.

Pricing ranges from free, for several XTensions written by Quark itself, to $6,000 for AdManager, which can take advertising size information and dummy up an entire publication, placing all ads in appropriate locations. Conveniently, most XTensions, including all those mentioned here, are available from a single clearinghouse called XChange, although there are several good shareware XTensions as well. Even Penta markets an XTension that allows files prepared on its current systems to be imported directly into QXP, preserving Penta formatting. Some other favorites, each of which exceeds in power some of the comparable aspects of 89P.

Dashes ($200) gives QXP a much better hyphenation engine. Shortline Eliminator ($99), a widow-killer, tries several new ways to H&J paragraphs whose last line would otherwise be too short. Several XTensions offer enhanced tabular capabilities, including horizontal and vertical straddling. Xtags ($299) enhances the already powerful XPress Tags command language and offers greater control of imported text.

Em Software's Xdata ($299), a must for serious database publishers, takes fielded information from databases, including pictures, rearranges it if necessary, and imports it, properly formatted for style, size, and layout, into a QXP document. Many conditional statements are supported; the user manual is 200 pages long and by no means exhausts all the XTension's possibilities.

Although XTensions can add great functionality to the program, they can easily triple its price. Some of them are also memory hogs, or conflict with one another to cause system crashes or other undesirable events. Experienced users, therefore, load only the XTensions that they will actually need in the current session.

PageMaker 6, released in late 1995, addressed the ligature problem with an addon that puts in ligature combinations—no matter what. This is not as good as QXP's implementation, which, intelligently, disallows ligatures in letterspaced copy.

QXP and PM can only apply leading to a full paragraph. QXP can only turn automatic kerning or automatic ligatures on and off in the *entire document,* whereas PM can access kerning by paragraph, and, in a serious omission, ligatures not at all. None of these issues trouble 89P, which can turn any feature on and off at any time, and can override any style on any line.

Very simple tasks can become onerous without these capabilities. Five years ago, most publications' typographic style was to set their picture captions justified, with the last line centered. In a system like 89P, all that was needed to achieve this was a quad-center code at the end of the final line. In either PM or QXP setting this kind of caption is absurdly difficult, which is why, in my estimation, most publications now set captions flush left.

This column's treatment of subheads illustrates the power of code. In QXP and PM, I must use three separate styles: one for the bold subhead with extra space before, one for the first paragraph after it, which has no indent, and one for subsequent text, which does. I must click and point to each one each time. Should my editor be so foolish as to rearrange the order of my text, he will probably have to click and point all over again, because styles travel with the text they affect.

89P has a vastly better way. With the one-time code [dj1][ol22][oio][sp[cf3,9][cm[ep[rp[oio][ef I do all this at once, and am immune to my editor's depredations.

This coding information uses the values in the magazine. A format for the subhead structure of this book would look exactly the same but sizing and leading would be slightly different.

The above mnemonic code translates as follows: define job format #1; override the current leading and substitute 22 points for this line only; override the current indent and substitute no indent; save all typesetting parameters in memory; change face to 3 (bold) and size to 9; copy will merge here; end of paragraph; restore the previous parameters; one more line of zero indent; end format definition.

When each subhead occurs, I merely code it as in the subhead on page 257, and everything clicks neatly into place. The format definition can, at my choice, apply to this file only; to all my *Computer Artist* files; or to all files, period.

Note the "hole" in this format that waits for the subhead to be entered before resuming the routine. There is no limit on the number of such holes, so as repetitive steps become more complex a single format will still work.

The advantages of coding are so apparent that QXP offers it as an alternative. Its XPress Tags commands can be generated by direct export from a Quark document. An XPress Tags text file, such as the one shown in Figure 12.1, is editable, and when the text is imported into QXP, the commands will be honored. In a complex job, it pays to use these tags, and they also afford a useful method of making alterations via search and replace. PM has no such feature.

The success of the Internet has brought code-driven typesetting back into the forefront. If you want to make yourself a Web page, you will have to become familiar with a command structure known as HTML—hypertext markup language. It is duck soup for anybody who has ever used a code-driven type system, or even XPress Tags. Other mortals have been known to tear their hair out over its complexities.

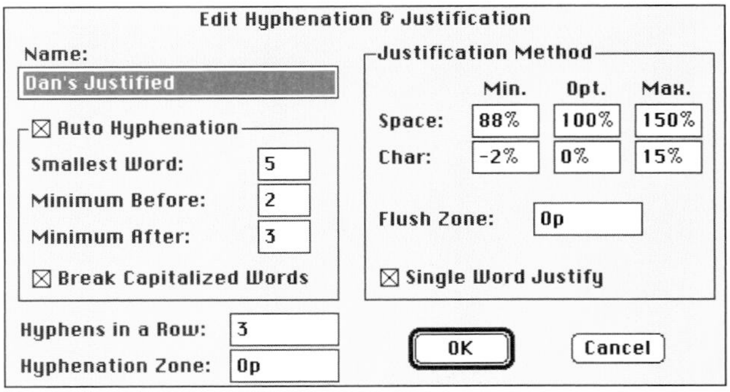

Figure 12.3. *All three programs allow the user to specify not just minimum and maximum values for a spaceband, but also an optimal value, not to mention the amount of letterspacing that will be acceptable. PM, below, leaves out an important option by not allowing the user to specify the minimum number of letters before or after a hyphenation. As against that, QXP, above, overhyphenates spectacularly.*

Kerning and Letterspacing

The modern programs benefit from the superior capabilities of PostScript type, which can be adjusted very finely.

89P was limited by its output devices, which generally could space only in the relatively coarse increments of $\frac{1}{54}$ of an em. Type sizes were in half-point increments, and leading in quarter-points.

PM improves considerably on this, and QXP is best of all. PM accesses both type and leading in increments of tenths of a point, QXP in thousandths of a point. QXP's automatic letterspacing and manual kerning are in $\frac{1}{200}$ em increments; PM is only half this sensitive in manual kerning, although in its H&J it beats QXP by using $\frac{1}{400}$ em increments.

PM joins 89P in offering traditional "tracking." Each typeface comes with five alterable "tracks," from very loose to very tight. Tracks vary with type size: as size increases, letterspacing is reduced, which is usually what we want. It is not, as Figure 12.2 makes clear, *always* what we want.

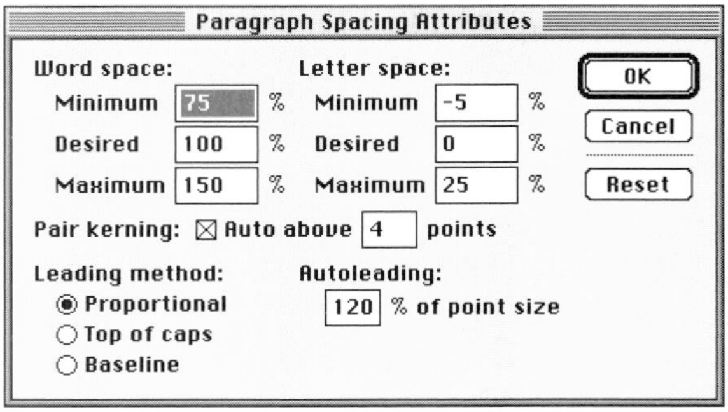

QXP defines tracking differently, as the ability to impose very precise plus or minus letterspacing on a block of copy. This capability is needed, among other things, to make lines that are slightly too long fit. A QXP tracking of minus one is scarcely noticeable, but changing PM tracking from "normal" to "tight" is quite apparent.

If we can only have one of these "tracking" methods, QXP's is better, but 89P has both.

In 1989, commercial fonts did not carry their own kern tables, so users of 89P had to write their own. These were limited to 500 pairs, which is plenty for most purposes, but not exactly extravagant.

Nowadays, fonts are kerned, but as against that manufacturers are prone to put capital letters in the middle of product names, as in LaserWriter, PowerBook, and, yes, PageMaker. This means that if we are engaged in advertising the products we will have need of the kern pairs rW, rB, and eM, which it is unlikely the font designer thought necessary to include.

Aldus's response is to include Agfa's KernEdit program with each copy of PM. This generates a brand-new font metrics file that can also be used in other programs. QXP can use such an altered font, but it also provides a quicker and dirtier fix with an easily editable kern table that works in QXP only.

On the other hand, if we start to fix kerns by hand and then say, rats, we should have done it with a new font or a kern table, QXP is the only program of the three that doesn't give us an easy way to kill all manual kerns. If there are a lot of them, the best alternative is to export the entire mess using XPress Tags, open the XPress Tags file in a word processing program, search for and destroy the kerning codes, and reimport the file into QXP.

Justification of the Righteous

All three programs approach justified copy in the manner shown in Figure 12.3, with user-definable minimum and maximum wordspace and letterspace values. Each uses an editable dictionary to store hyphenation information but is capable of taking guesses at unknown words. Each allows us to specify the number of consecutive lines that can end in a hyphen. Only PM does not let us choose a minimum number of letters before and after a hyphen: it permits two before and two after. Most typographers would disagree.

With these similarities, one would think that justified output of the same text would be approximately of the same quality on all three systems. It's not.

PM, alone among the three, uses a preferential hyphenation scheme. I use the word *Photoshop* a lot in my writing, and all three programs recognize that the word can break after either *o*. Obviously, though, the second *o* is better. Using 89P or QXP, my best choice is to change the dictionary to permit that one alone, condemning myself to a loose line when only the first one fits. PM lets me have my cake and eat it too, by saying that both are legal, but the second is to be used if possible.

E nglish being an illogical language, when computers try to guess where a word should be hyphenated, watch out.

Yet PM's dictionary almost completely ignores this powerful tool. *International* and *polyethylene,* for example, are treated as though all hyphenation points are equal.

To test H&J capabilities, I ran the first 20,000 words of *Moby Dick,* justified to three different column widths using identical H&J parameters in PM and QXP. Penta kindly agreed to run the same test with one of its 1994 systems. *Moby Dick* is suitable for this because of its many archaic and long words.

The test was in 10-point Times Roman at widths of 13, 21.5, and 35 picas. Since H&J is mostly the massage of wordspaces, the more spaces to juggle in a line, the simpler. The 13-pica version is considerably more difficult than one normally finds in book work, and the 35-pica version much easier.

PM and the "professional" system were close: the Penta algorithm has a couple of useful bells and whistles that made for a slightly better product, especially at the narrow measure, where it had an overall smoother appearance, and 20 percent fewer hyphens than either opponent. PM suffered unduly at narrow measure because of a bug: em dashes, a favorite Melville device, are legal as points to end a line, but it is also kosher, if less desirable, to *start* a line with a dash. PM wouldn't do this, and paid for it with some dreadful lines.

QXP trailed badly in the wider measure copy. Inexplicably, it always tries to hyphenate the last word of a line before seeing whether wordspacing can be adjusted enough to avoid the hyphen. The result is a wildly excessive pattern of hyphens. In the narrow measure test, QXP had only a few more hyphens than its opponents, but in the medium measure it had half again as

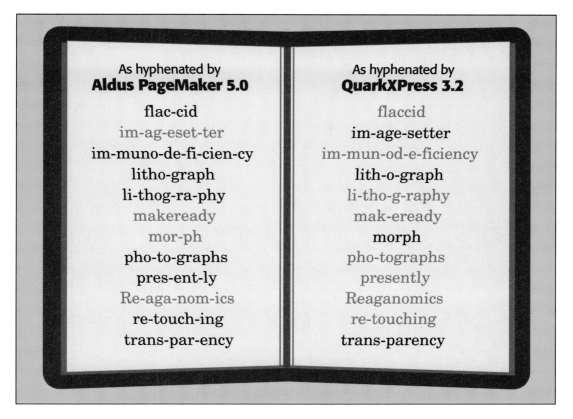

As hyphenated by **Aldus PageMaker 5.0**	As hyphenated by **QuarkXPress 3.2**
flac-cid	flaccid
im-ag-eset-ter	im-age-setter
im-muno-de-fi-cien-cy	im-mun-od-e-ficiency
litho-graph	lith-o-graph
li-thog-ra-phy	li-tho-g-raphy
makeready	mak-eready
mor-ph	morph
pho-to-graphs	pho-tographs
pres-ent-ly	presently
Re-aga-nom-ics	Reaganomics
re-touch-ing	re-touching
trans-par-ency	trans-parency

Figure 12.4. *Typography programs have built-in dictionaries, supplemented by computer logic, that decide where a given word may be hyphenated. The results are not always accurate. Words in red above show either a failure to find an obvious hyphenation point or, worse, finding an illegal one.*

many as either, and in the wide measure, where hyphens should be rare, it had seven times as many.

English being an illogical language, when computers try to guess where a word should be hyphenated, watch out. PM and QXP, as Figure 12.4 suggests, get quite different results. The PM algorithm is aggressive, often overly so, whereas QXP's often throws up its hands and refuses to hyphenate at all. Either approach has its pitfalls.

In the narrow-measure test, PM made two outright errors. QXP had none, but two lines were unacceptably loose because the program failed to find an obvious hyphenation. Surprisingly, 1994 Penta had four outright hyphenation mistakes and one avoidable badly loose line. (In the two wider measure tests, there were no errors in any of the three programs.)

Although their 1994 sample was best overall, in 1989 Penta was much more prone to bum hyphenations. Therefore, the winner by a eyedash of the justification contest, in a huge upset, is PageMaker.

THE TALE OF THE TYPE

STABILITY: freedom from major bugs, scarcity of crashes, historical reliability, compatibility of updates with previous versions and with other applications
QXP Very Good   PM Good   89P Fair

JUSTIFIED COPY: producing justified copy with few loose or short lines, rivers, or incorrect hyphenations
PM Good   89P Good   QXP Poor

PERFORMANCE: speed of opening files, H&J, operation, and printing, demand on system resources
QXP Very Good   PM Good   89P Poor

RAGGED COPY: ability to create an aesthetically pleasing rag with limited numbers of hyphens
89P Excellent   QXP Fair*   PM Poor

KERNING AND LETTERSPACING: being able to address intercharacter space easily and accurately
QXP Very Good   PM Good   89P Fair

SEARCH AND REPLACE: ability to search for common errors, and to correct foreign text
89P Awesome   PM Fair   QXP Poor*

TYPOGRAPHIC REFINEMENTS: inclusion of extra features commonly requested by skilled typographers
89P Good   PM Fair   QXP Fair*

TABULAR & DATABASE: ability to import copy and format difficult tables
89P Very Good   PM Poor   QXP Poor*

*XTensions are available that would improve this rating.

When we move from justified to ragged right composition, the rankings change drastically. 89P offers scintillating quality by restricting both by how much and how little any line can vary in length from the ones above and below it. If a line would ordinarily fall outside of these user-definable limits, one can write a style sheet that sets forth, in order, the steps 89P should take to try to solve the problem (including, as a final alternative, giving up).

The style sheet can specify up to 15 tries, and 99 style sheets can be kept in the system.

QXP cannot achieve a shadow of this quality: its best method is to limit hyphenation by means of high minimums, like four letters both before and after any hyphen. PM lacks even this and is consequently the worst of the three. It does offer a definable zone in which hyphenation will not occur. This will still result in some two-letter hyphenations, which is unacceptable in ragged copy, period.

The Power Tools

The formatting features of 89P give it an overwhelming advantage in jobs with repetitive styles, particularly if complex. In tabular work, for example, one can easily switch the order of two columns of numbers, or make one column bold, even after the table has been completely set.

89P's tabular capabilities crush its opponents under a variety of straddling commands, vertical and horizontal rules, and interlinking text routines. An even more striking inequality is in handling import and export of foreign files such as databases, for 89P has a feature virtually unknown on the desktop: a *conditional* search and replace.

Any of these three programs can search for text and replace it with something else wherever it appears. Only 89P can replace it unless (say) it is simultaneously in bold, in a headline or on the first page of an even-numbered chapter that happens to start on a right-hand page.

The real power comes when reflowing a foreign document into 89P's command language. If there is any pattern at all in the imported file, it can be sniffed out and coded in one pass. That XPress Tags did not exist in 1989 would not stop 89P from reading (and, if necessary, exporting) an XPress Tags file today.

By contrast, PM has but rudimentary search-and-replace capabilities, and QXP is worse yet. For example, all these programs have a command that forces a line break that is not considered the end of a paragraph. That command is especially needed in a program like QXP, which doesn't H&J particularly well on its own.

In justified composition, one frequently forces a line break in lesser-of-evil circumstances. If we have a very loose line, for example, but the line above it ends with a *to* or a *the* or some other short word, we can force that line to end earlier, giving us two acceptable lines. 89P's H&J routine looks for such two-line opportunities automatically, but the desktop programs do not, so our text winds up having a number of forced breaks if we care at all about quality.

Naturally, if we change the column width later—for example, say, if we had a column written for the specs of a magazine and then wanted the text to flow into a book format—the presence of these hard line endings will be a considerable nuisance, and they will have to be deleted. That is a problem in QXP, since its search-and-replace routine can't find this command, among many others. The best way to handle this is by code: export the text in XPress Tags format, search for the hard line endings there and eliminate them, then re-import the XPress Tags text.

The desktop programs lack many of the sophisticated nuances found in 89P and its ilk. Top on the list is the ability to

The very useful auto-
mated paragraph-
numbering capability
was added to PM in
late 1995, with the
release of version 6.
QXP still does not
have it.

set punctuation "hung" into the margins: 89P lets us specify what punctuation and what margins we are talking about and a percentage of hang.

89P and other such systems have a code indicating, set a number here. This means we can have numbered items that will change dynamically if we make additions or deletions. In QXP and PM if one numbered paragraph in a group of a hundred changes, we are going to key a hundred new numbers.

In typography, two consecutive spacebands is a no-no. Since it is quite easy to key them by accident, it will be necessary for me, when I am finished typing this column, to perform a search-and-replace for any stray double spaces. Intelligently, 89P saves this step by ignoring double space-bands, and also single spaces at the start of a line.

Those who use double space-bands for alignment purposes should, of course, use the fixed spaces, the em, en, and thin. We call them "fixed" because if any tracking or spacing is applied to parts of the line, the spaces will hold their width—that is, unless we are using QXP, which gets this wrong.

Picking a winner between 89P and the two modern programs is not necessary, since the market has already done so. A wistful look at its strengths, however, points out how far we still must go.

A typographic problem unique to PM is in the handling of SMALL CAPS and superior/inferior figures. If you don't have a font with true cut small caps and have to generate your own, just setting capital letters in a smaller size than text will look too skimpy, as in the example three lines above. Therefore, one expands the horizontal scale to compensate. Such expansion (SMALL CAPS— looks better, right?) is a default in 89P and all similar systems, and is an option in QXP. But PM left this capability out.

And the Winner Is...

Over the years PM and QXP have adopted so many of each other's features that, in my estimation, there is little to choose between them. PM wins for book work because of better H&J as well as indexing capabilities. QXP is better for advertising because of its precision.

If forced to choose only one, I would go with QXP, but mostly because of the availability of specialized XTensions, not for any real superiority in typography.

Picking a winner between these two and 89P is not necessary, since the market has already done so. A wistful look at 89P, though, points out the improvements possible in future upgrades to PM and QXP.

Our programs do have strong points. 89P's advantages show up as documents get longer and more complex. For single-page advertisements, equally skilled operators will produce higher quality work in either QXP or PM than in a "professional" system, and will also do it quicker.

The fact is that which system produces the best type will normally be determined by which system is being run by the best typographer. If PM and QXP have not achieved full parity with traditional systems, they are at least close, and gaining. They have democratized the process, and typography as a field is better for their presence. In their continuing contest, the real winner is *us*. ●

Afterword

Product reviews date themselves rapidly, which is why I try to avoid them. The major improvements in PageMaker 5 were enough, however, to make an exception to this policy. Conveniently enough, it came out at almost the same time as Quark's upgrade to QXP 3.2.

As you may have gathered along the way somewhere, I do not always subscribe to the "wisdom" espoused by other writers, but in this case I agree with the nearly unanimous industry sentiment, to wit, that PageMaker 5 was a vital step forward for the product. Where I diverged somewhat (and have been shown in the fullness of time to be correct, I hasten to add) is in thinking that the step came too late to make much of a difference.

Previous versions of PageMaker had their adherents, but for professional work most found it unacceptable. From 1990 on, at least, it had been apparent to all sentient beings that color publishing was set for takeoff and that programs that did not support it very well were about to get left at the gate. Stunningly, until this late 1993 upgrade, PM basically did not support printing with color graphics at all.

That was only the biggest of several problems. In spite of general ease of use, one could not have more than one PM document open at a time, an inexcusable omission, and too many layout changes had to be eased into place by eyeball, rather than with the menu-aided precision offered by QXP.

PageMaker 5 corrected all this. Today's PageMaker 6 is not nearly as big an advance over 5 as 5 was over 4. My rating of PageMaker 6 vs. QXP 3.3 would be very much the same as what you have just read, with one exception.

At the time I wrote, XTensions gave QXP a decided advantage. Since the review, however, Aldus was acquired by Adobe, and given Adobe's experience with plug-in filters for its Photoshop and Illustrator products, they easily comprehended the importance of emphasizing the development of such addons for PM.

The vast improvement in PM, as I noted in Column 9 in this book, has not done as much for product sales as you might expect. A confession may help you understand why.

As you have just read, I believe that for book work, PM is the program of choice. Its justification routine is much better than QXP's; it has automated indexing, and the complicated layouts that QXP excels in usually don't happen in books.

I wrote this, and I meant it. Therefore, I imagine you are thinking that this book was produced in PageMaker.

Dream on.

Like the huge majority of professionals, I use QXP. Even those of us who learn new programs, as I had to for this review, are more comfortable sticking with what they know best. Shameful, perhaps; slothful, definitely, but there it is. The inertia in the graphic arts industry is terrible. •

Adobe Type Manager Software that allows a computer screen to display accurate renditions of the typefaces that are in use in a document.

conditional search and replace A search-and-replace routine that takes into account extrinsic circumstances. In QXP one can search for occurrences of *U.S.* and change them to *USA* if and only if it is in a certain type size, but a true conditional search and replace, such as that in 89P, can go much farther. Such a routine could change it to *USA* in text, to *United States* if in a headline, and *The United States* at the start of a sentence.

database publishing Publishing that automatically integrates information that resides elsewhere. Its simplest incarnation would be a form letter that picks up the names of its recipients from a data file and generates as many copies of itself as are needed. It can range up to hideously complicated applications, such as magazines or catalogs that are custom-designed for the individuals who are to receive them, based on what a computer knows about their income and lifestyle.

em A large, fixed space, defined by various partisans as a) the actual width of the *M* character in a given typeface; b) the width of the largest character that could theoretically have been designed for the typeface; or c) a width equal to the pointsize of the type. In upwards of 90 percent of cases, all three definitions are identical, and as for the remainder, if you don't care about the difference I certainly don't.

en Half an em; under ordinary circumstances the width of a numeral.

format In code-driven typography, an editable string of commands that can be invoked at any time by a few keystrokes. If the format is later altered, all occurrences of it will update automatically on output.

H&J Hyphenation and Justification, generic term for computer assembly of text into lines. In spite of the name, the text need be neither justified nor hyphenated; ragged copy is said to go through H&J just as the hyphenated, justified copy you are reading now does.

justified Set flush to both the left and right margins, as the text you are reading is. Justification implies that the space between words will vary.

kerning Selective reduction of space between specific pairs of letters. Without kerning, the computer spaces out letters based on the assumption that they are all shaped like rectangles. This is a valid assumption if the letter in question is *H,* but not so valid if it is *Y,* and most emphatically not if the letter after the *Y* is *A.* Typefaces nowadays therefore incorporate a *kerning table* stating that all Y-A combinations—and possibly several hundred others—are to be closed up by a certain amount, which will depend on the typeface. Proper kerning not only makes type more legible, but also saves significant amounts of space on the page.

letterspacing Increasing or decreasing the space between characters on a given line, as in the first line of this definition. Letterspacing is normally considered a last resort to avoid a completely unacceptable line. Most H&J involves adjusting interword spaces only.

ligatures Characters that are joined composites of two or more letters. Nowadays ligatures are generally limited to combinations involving the letter *f* in serif typefaces. The standard ligatures in PostScript fonts are f-i and f-l, but book-work traditionally uses f-f, f-f-i, and f-f-l as well. Antique fonts sometimes have other ligatures, especially s-t and c-t. This book uses ligatures, and you can see examples of them wherever the word *justified* appears.

minicomputer A computer capable of supporting several independent slave terminals. Not as powerful as a *mainframe computer,* but a step up from the desktop computers today's artists use, which are technically *microcomputers.*

pi font A font that consists of non-alphanumeric characters, such as the Symbol font of mathematical, Greek, and technical characters included on most printers.

pica Twelve points, or approximately a sixth of an inch. Typographers have used this archaic system to express the width of columns of type for several centuries. Saying that the column is a certain number of inches wide is eminently sensible, but if you do it most typographers will look at you as though you had three heads.

ragged right Set flush to the left margin only, with the right margin being variable.

spaceband The character one gets by hitting the space bar on the keyboard; typographers use the term *band* to remind themselves that the character does not have a fixed width, but rather will vary from line to line.

straddling In tabular typography, a headline that encompasses more than one column.

superior and inferior figures In technical and mathematical typography, smaller figures that are positioned above or below the baseline. The 2 is a superior character in $e=mc^2$ and is an inferior character in H_2O.

thin space Fixed space equivalent to one-third of an em.

tracking Uniform reduction or increase of the space between characters, generally done for aesthetic or copyfitting purposes.

Zapf Dingbats An extensive pi font with many whimsical characters, included as part of the base package in most systems and printers today.

Epilogue

Would You Approve This Color?

Professional-level color turns out to be, strange as it may seem, the lack of any error big enough to let us call the overall appearance unprofessional.

The most frustrating aspect of our lives as computer artists is that our work is usually done for hire. It can be beautiful—in our opinion—but our client may not like it, and may accuse us of having done a bad job.

If you haven't noticed, the theme of this issue of *Computer Artist* is color correction, and as resident proselytizer on this complicated topic, I get a major article [the prologue of the present book] in addition to this, my usual column. The other piece talks about what is the best color. Here, we will discuss not what is *best*, but what is *reasonable*. Obviously, this is of great significance in deciding whether what we give our clients is of professional quality.

You are cordially invited, therefore, to look over my shoulder as I consider whether various images are professionally acceptable. In real life, I am fairly experienced in making this decision.

In a high-end color trade shop, the workflow goes in something like the following fashion. First, the scanner operator analyzes the original art, trying to see whether there is anything peculiar about it that may require a weird scan setting. Then, it is mounted on a drum, or a high-priced CCD scanner. The operator makes adjustments that should, among other things, insure proper highlight and shadow values, and hits the start button.

271

A

Once the scan is done, it is called up on a screen for review. Sometimes the scanner operator does this, sometimes somebody else. The reviewer either decides that the scan is good enough to work with, or sends it back for another try. If he chooses to work with it, he may apply curves and other global adjustments to fine-tune the image. Dust, scratches, and other such defects are also removed at this time.

Film and a contract proof are now pulled. Once they arrive, so will someone like me, to pass final judgment: send it out, or do it over.

The Case Against Change

The person giving final approval tends to be very prejudiced in favor of sending it out, for three major reasons, in increasing order of importance.

B

C

Economics. If I bounce the job it must be redone at the company's expense. Furthermore, it may delay a promised delivery.

Does it really matter, in the overall scheme of things? Many of these jobs are priced on the basis of "proof to satisfaction," and three or more correction passes are normal. If I expect the client to make changes anyway, I am less inclined to quibble about small problems.

Is it really my call? The most important player in the approval game is neither me, nor the scanner operator, but the person who evaluates the scan on screen and applies final curves to it. Being human, that person will handle images differently than I would. Being human, I may not appreciate this, and think I could have done better. However, rejecting the image based on personal taste could result in an endless cycle: if I reject it,

detest, a failure to hold important detail, or, most commonly, failure to achieve the desired numbers in four areas: highlight, shadow, fleshtones and neutral colors.

In picture series ABC, three different conceptions compete for favor. (In this series, as in all others in this column, the first scan is the starting point and the second two were done by students who were told to fix it up in one of my color-correction classes. No local selection or correction was allowed.)

All of the ABC group have respectable highlight and shadow values. The artists differ on how white the statue should be and how much contrast it should get. Personally, I like the sharp contrast of C and find A rather tepid, but can think of no reason to reject any of the three. It is entirely reasonable that one might want a soft, yellowish look in this image, so, if presented with A for a final okay, I'd approve it.

Similar contrast issues show up in DEF, but even if you like the overall feel of D, it is not professionally acceptable. From everything we know about the clothing little girls wear, the lace collar has to be white, not pink. The darkest background areas are also much lighter than they should be. This inaccurate shadow value accounts for the overall flat feel of this endeavor.

The artist in E found and fixed all of the above-named problems. Setting proper highlights and shadows created

the reproof will probably come out on the next shift, where my successor inspector may disagree with me and bounce it again, and his judgment will in turn be overruled by the inspector on the third shift, whereupon the third nonchargeable proof will come back to me the following day to be rejected again, etc., etc.

Worse yet, if I insist that the job be redone, and then the client receives it and orders up a move back in the direction of the image I rejected, I'll look like a real nincompoop.

All this points to a standard of reasonability rather than rectitude. The question is not whether *I* like the work, but whether it is possible that a thinking client may.

The Reasons to Say No

The main reasons to blackball an image, therefore, are things that are unquestionably bad: a clear defect, a move in a direction that the client is known to far more life in the picture. He also noted and corrected the red cast that afflicted the little girl's collar in the original.

Nevertheless, this image gets the gong. There is general agreement among professionals that in Caucasian flesh the yellow values should be at least as heavy as the magenta, and that there must be significant quantities of cyan. The artist did not comply with these rules. Nobody has pinker, softer flesh than a young child, but we still can't have magenta 10 or more points higher than the yellow.

Had the artist found a way around this difficulty, E would have been acceptable, even though it is not in F's quality league. F, an excellent correction of D, displays the power of global curves in isolating and enhancing local areas. Remember, no local selecting was allowed here: the extra snap in the face and hair came solely from applying curves to the entire picture.

For all the admirable technical prowess shown in F, there is nothing much wrong with E, other than the fact that the artist was so busy adjusting highlight and shadow that he forgot about proper fleshtone value. Unfortunately, this leaves the image with one of those well-known, well-defined, easily-corrected defects that differentiate a nice try from professional-level color.

The Eye vs. the Camera

The question of whether to remove a cast remains highly controversial in professional circles. At a trade conference of prepress executives in 1994, I posed the question of whether in a case like DEF, the pink cast should be removed, assuming that it is in the original photograph and not the result of a poor scan. Unbelievably, the vote split just about evenly. You can't ask much more of a basic question than that, and yet in this mature industry, there is no consensus.

DEF presents the cast removal question in its most pristine form. There is no artistic reason whatever to assume that the photographer wanted the cast. This is obviously not a studio shot; the chances are the cast was caused by fluo-

K

rescent lighting, accurately recorded as pink by both camera and scan.

The case against removing or minimizing the cast, usually advanced by chauvinistic photographers, is that computer artists should not be second-guessing them, period. The case for, usually advanced by inveterate retouchers, is that first, one might as well trust a three-card monte dealer, or perhaps even an art director, as a photographer; and second, that the purpose of the correction should be to convey not what the camera saw but what the eye *would* have seen.

The executives of prepress companies who said that their firms would leave the cast in did not understand their own procedures. Almost all professional scanner operators, upon analyzing the DEF image, would set their highlight based on the assumption that the girl's collar was a dead neutral white, *even if it had a slight cast in the original.* They would thus (inadvertently, perhaps) eliminate the cast in the lower ranges of the picture and minimize it elsewhere. They might, perhaps, not go as far as I would in seeking out other neutral areas in the picture and correcting them—but what they're doing is cast reduction, all the same.

Unlike a camera, the human visual system is highly adaptable, and shrugs off color casts in ambient lighting. This phenomenon, which color scientists call *chromatic adaptation,* explains why image F is so much more realistic-looking than either of its two competitors. If we were actually in the room with the child, we would ignore the pink lighting and see approximately the same colors we would outdoors on a sunny day.

These arguments convince me, and most successful retouchers, that, absent some indication that the photographer may have been trying for a particular look, casts should be minimized.

That is a fine general approach, but it has its pitfalls, as the artist in J found out. He measured the three faces in G, the original, and found that they were much yellower than a textbook would suggest. He therefore forced down the yellow and hiked the magenta and cyan until he achieved the "correct" values of J, ruining the image in the process.

As already noted, humans ignore color imbalances in ambient lighting, within reason. But a dark room with only the harsh yellow of an oil lamp is hardly what one would call reasonable lighting conditions. If we were there in person, we would surely see yellow. G is therefore acceptable. Perhaps we would

L

M

not see the cast quite as severely as the camera did, so I would accept H as well. J, however, is color theory misapplied, and I would order it redone.

Does the Cast Make Sense?

KLM, yet another in our series of photos taken under substandard lighting conditions, gives us a choice of casts.

A cast can be detected by measuring the values of things that we know are supposed to be neutral whites or grays. In a CMYK world, pure neutral colors, such as the woman's white jacket in GHJ, or the little girl's collar in DEF, should have equal magenta and yellow, and slightly more cyan. The black value is irrelevant. (If you are working in RGB, all three channels should have equal values.) In quasi-neutrals, such as the backgrounds in GHJ and KLM and the marble in ABC, a certain amount of variation is acceptable, but a major imbalance suggests a cast.

Without having an original chrome to look at, I distrust image K for being too red. From context, we know we are in a tropical area with dense greenery

that is blocking much of the sunlight. The green cast in L seems to me perfectly reasonable under the circumstances. Green light will be reflecting everywhere from the trees. The operator's priority was no doubt to improve the color of the greenery, which is not very agreeable in K.

In color correction it is sometimes possible to have one's cake and eat it too. In M, the artist managed not only to eliminate any cast, but also to maintain good grains in the wood and to build more contrast into the wooden statue.

Technically, therefore, it is a superior correction to L, and one I believe most viewers would prefer. I would, however, accept L as reasonable, as possibly being more atmospheric. Since I cannot imagine any artistic or photographic reason for a red cast to be desirable in this image—and I know the red cast is there by measuring the inking values in the area in front of the building—I would turn thumbs down on K.

Emphasizing the Obvious

In images C, F, and M, skillful use of curves caused the important objects in the image to show more apparent contrast, even though there was overall no more color-space to work with than in the competitive versions. It is not always apparent even to the best retoucher how to achieve this when the subjects are so complex. Accordingly, we must say that several of the alternatives are acceptable, at least as a first submit.

In NOP, however, correct technique is so obvious that one should perhaps be less tolerant of second-best. From the strict numerical point of view, all are within reason. They all have good highlights and shadows. N has a modest blue cast that should no doubt be minimized.

It would be ridiculous, though, to pretend that N and P are contenders in this contest. O's buildings are much more detailed and lifelike, and the buildings are what is important here.

This is the simplest kind of color correction. If manipulating each of four color curves is not your bag, in Photoshop, one can do it with an adjustment of the L curve in LAB. It can even be accomplished, although I hold my nose as I mention it, with Photoshop's Levels command. By whatever method, you will need to extend the lighter ranges of the image, at the expense of the darker tones. The move is based on the idea that everything that the buildings are what is important here and they both start out lighter than a midtone in all four colors.

True, the sky and the roof of the house at right are darker than this, but if they lose a little contrast we can live with it.

So, by one method or another, we increase the midtone value in all four colors. This will give the white buildings far more pop, as seen in O.

N and P have no gross technical defect, in the sense that some of the other images we have looked at have.

Since, however, they miss an obvious method to get better, I would not accept either one of them.

A Vote for Technique

It would be great if every computer artist had the skill to consistently produce corrections like M, F, and O. Even if you can't just reach back and serve one of those aces, however, it will usually suffice to just put the ball in play.

When artist and client agree that an image has gotten the best possible treatment, this is indeed a happy moment. The best way to get there in a hurry is to have good color correction technique. If you miss the best correction method, you may get there just the same, but it may take you an extra round of revises.

Nobody finds the best solution to every picture every time. Even if we miss some tricky method, even if our color is not as scintillating as some of the examples here, we can still achieve professional results merely by refraining from mistakes. ●

Notes and Credits

The Sources of the Images

Most of the images in this book come from royalty-free CDs of stock photography. Each major image is credited below, and is copyrighted by the firm or individual to whom it is attributed.

There is not very much uniformity in the industry as to how many photos are supplied per disk, and what formats they are in. Prices fluctuate and are therefore not listed here, but none of the CDs listed here cost more than $300 and some can be had for less than a tenth of that.

In alphabetical order, the images come from:

- **Artbeats**, 800-444-9392 or 503-863-4429. Artbeats specializes in backgrounds: textured images, such as marbled paper, wood, and stone. Images are provided at very high resolution, 30 mb or more, as RGB TIFFs, compressed losslessly.

- **Aztech New Media**, 416-449-4787, markets a 3,000-image collection, Photofile World Image Library, as a set of 24 CDs. The collection, which was formerly called World Bank, is organized country by country, with travel and culture shots dominating. Images are CMYK TIFFs of around 5 mb, suitable for printing at approximately 20 square inches or less.

- **CAM, Inc.**, 888-742-8871 or 954-419-9333, is the successor to Hammerhead Interactive, discussed in Column 8. It markets around 50 low-cost disks, in Photo CD format. Not generally available through mail order outlets, the disks can be ordered on CAM's Internet site, http://pictus.com.

- **Corel Corp.**, 800-591-0010, also available from many mail-order sources. Corel, as discussed in Columns 8 and 9, has been the most aggressive vendor by far in terms of the breadth of its library, with over 600 CDs currently available and more appearing every month, as well as its pricing. Images are supplied in Photo CD format, with recent releases having been scanned on higher-end devices.

- **Digital Stock Corp.**, 800-545-4514, also available from many mail order sources. Digital Stock is one of the high-end royalty-free vendors both in terms of quality and price, offering themed CDs on a variety of topics. Approximately 50 CDs are currently available. Though drum-scanned, the images are supplied in Photo CD format.

- For **Hammerhead Interactive**, see the listing for CAM, Inc.

- **Image Kit**, a 10-CD boxed set, is marketed by TDC Interactive, 1-800-832-0032. Aimed at art directors, the set is full of specialized, but useful, images, often at large sizes, such as the eye on page 134. Objects have Photoshop selection paths included; files are PICTs that expand to over 10 megabytes apiece. Single disks in the set are devoted to skies, water, and foliage.

- **PhotoDisc, Inc.**, 206-441-9355, also available from many mail-order sources. The company's CDs, which are at the high end of the price spectrum, generally contain 336 images, an unusually large number. The images themselves are JPEG-compressed RGB TIFFs, expanding to about 10 mb apiece, suitable for printing to about half a magazine or newspaper page.

- **Vivid Details, Inc.**, 800-948-4843, markets a dozen CD sets of very high resolution uncompressed CMYK textures and backgrounds, with titles such as *Leather, Slate,* and *Old Paint.* It does not plan to release further disk sets, in favor of adding new images for online sales; its Web site is http://www.vividdetails.com. The site features several thousand images, and not just backgrounds.

Prologue

The verdict of the jury that evaluated the images has been upheld on appeal. I show these images to my color correction classes, and as of this writing, over a hundred people have voted on the same best-or-worst basis that the original jury did. In all cases except DEF, the original jury results have been reaffirmed. As to DEF, I now know that my jury had an atypical reading. The two jurors who voted for E as best had evidently been drinking; only one person has voted for it since. My classes continue to favor D over F by nearly a three-to-two margin. Those who vote for D, as I did, invariably feel that E is the worst. Those who vote for F as best split 50–50 between D and E as worst.

The Munsell Color Perception test is available from the Macbeth Division of Kollmorgen Corp., 914-565-7660.

The picture of canoers (ABC) is from Corel's *Canoeing and Kayaking.*

The image of children (DEF) is from Digital Stock's *Babies and Children.* As to why it made its way into this piece, consult the Afterword to Column 2.

The pig image, GHJ, appears in Aztech New Media's Photofile World Image Library collection.

The familiar KL picture of the model in red is from the Kodak Photo Sampler CD, which is available free to qualified graphic arts professionals.

The castle and walls of MNO are from PhotoDisc 5, *World Commerce & Travel.*

The photograph of the woman in the bright blue costume (PQRS) is by Franklyn Higgs.

The sunbather of TUV is from the Corel Professional Photos Sampler.

Column 1

The full-page graphic on page 25 is based on an image from Corel's *Fitness.*

H.W. Fowler's classic, *Modern English Usage,* is available through Oxford University Press, or on the bookshelves of virtually all careful writers.

Information about the Pantone Matching System and other color-control products can be obtained from Pantone, Inc., 201-935-5500. Pantone swatch books and other reference materials may be purchased from many graphic sources.

TrapWise is available from Luminous Corp., 800-685-6736 or http://www.lumcorp.com; Full AutoFrame, from Scitex Corp. 617-275-5150; and DK&A Trapper (formerly Island Trapper) from DK&A, Inc., 619-488-8118.

The three fallacious explanations of trapping in books on QuarkXPress do exist, and for those with satisfactory reasons for wanting to know, I will identify them by e-mail, but have no intention of doing so in print.

The pizza image used in the 5-color trapping discussion is from Corel's *Cuisine.*

Column 2

The photographs of the parade float and of the white horse are by Franklyn Higgs. They were scanned at two different resolutions on a Dainippon Screen drum scanner.

Sports fans will understand that the reference to two work stoppages in professional leagues means that the column was written in Fall 1994.

The image of the reclining model showing register problems is from Corel's *Beautiful Women.*

The controversial image of the young seal is from the Corel Professional Photos Sampler CD.

The column I was referring to in which the seal image originally appeared was "Colors, Curves, and Horse-Trading," *Computer Artist,* August-September 1994. That column was later reworked into Chapter 5 of *Professional Photoshop.*

The piece in which another author asserted that Prologue image F was "certainly the best" of the three alternatives, foreshadowing my similar error with the seal image of Figure 2.6, appeared in *Color Publishing* magazine, November-December 1994.

The swindler I.O. Snopes offered up his wisdom in Faulkner's *The Town.*

Column 3

The images on page 64 come from two of the highly specialized Corel titles discussed in Column 8. The bridal picture is from *Weddings,* the frogman from *Navy SEALs.*

The quality control strip is that of the Graphic Arts Technical Foundation, GATF, 412-621-6949 or http://www.gatf.lm.com.

The picture of the three musicians, possibly the most reproduced image in the world, is in the Kodak Q-60 scanner quality-control set.

Copies of the full Specifications for Web Offset Publications are available for purchase from SWOP, Inc., 212-983-6042.

Ellery Queen's Challenge to the Reader is from *The Dutch Shoe Mystery.* Sherlock Holmes's contemptuous dismissal of bizarre phenomena is found in *The Red-Headed League.* Lord Peter Wimsey rejects the motive motif in *Busman's Honeymoon,* and Hercule Poirot expounds on the role of the grey cells in *Thirteen at Dinner.*

The picture of playing cards is from Image Kit's *Miscellaneous* CD.

The red car that illustrates problems with Separation setup comes from Corel's *Exotic Cars.*

Column 4

The graphic on page 103 is based on an image from ImageKit's *Illustrations* CD.

The image of the sailboarder is from Corel's promotional book and accompanying CD, *The World's Best Digital Photographs.* The image of the children comes from Digital Stock's *Babies and Children.*

Column 5

The collaged graphic of various curve and quasi-curve maneuvers on page 122 is composed of dialog boxes from the products of many different vendors.

The image of lettuce is from Corel's *Barbecue and Salads.*

The large eye comes from ImageKit's *People* CD.

Column 6

The opening graphic of a vase of roses is from Vivid Details' *Flowers* set, and the sailboat is from Corel's *Caribbean*.

The generalized attack on an image is fleshed out in my *Professional Photoshop* (John Wiley & Sons, 1995), as is the subject of black generation and how to exploit it.

The little girl in Figure 6.3 is my niece, Rebecca.

The picture of the leaves against a dark background is from Corel's *Foliage Backgrounds*.

Column 7

The opening image of a brook and forest is included in Kodak's promotional section of the installation CD for Adobe PageMaker.

The version of CIELAB that is used as Photoshop's native colorspace is one of several iterations of this means of specifying color, first propounded by the Commission Internationale de l'Eclairage in 1931. For those wishing technical information, Billmeyer and Saltzman, *Principles of Color Technology* (John Wiley & Sons, 1981) has an extensive section on LAB.

The cat is from Corel's *Cats & Kittens*.

The wine label is from Corel's *Grapes & Wine*. The gymnast in the red uniform is from Corel's *Amateur Sports*.

The seal is from the Corel Professional Photos Sampler.

If you were not able to work out the reference to how to solve the seal problem of Figures 2.6 and 2.7, here's the answer. One seal was properly white but lacked detail; one had good detail but a color cast. Both should have therefore been converted to LAB, and a third version created which used the L from the detailed seal and the A and B from the white one.

The redheaded model is from Corel's *Fashion*.

The rainforest image is from CAM's *Tropical Paradise*.

The grayish Canadian snowscape comes from Corel's *Scenics*.

The allusion to the lady from Niger refers to Edward Lear's limerick:

> There was a young lady from Niger,
> Who smiled as she rode on a tiger.
> They returned from the ride
> With the lady inside,
> And the smile on the face of the tiger.

Column 8

The image of the smoldering volcano on page 185, very apt for today's professional photography market, is based on an image from Digital Stock's *Fire & Ice*.

The extremely yellow Canada goose is from Corel's *Birds, Volume 2*. The woman on page 195 is from CAM's *Swimsuit Edition*, and the two images on page 194 are from CAM's *A Rose Is a Rose* and *Japan*.

The quotation on the antagonism generated by the new process is from a 1993 article by Scott Highton, chairman of the technology committee of the American Society of Media Photographers, in which he also stated, "ASMP has been strongly opposed to clip art photography disks and encourages all photographers considering participation in them to consider the damage that giving away unlimited usage of their photography will have on their own business, as well as the business of photography in general."

Column 9

The graphic on page 206 showing textures is made up of images from seven different vendors. All of these images are small parts of a much larger whole; in all cases there is at least enough additional background to fill a full page of a newspaper or magazine, and the ArtBeats and Vivid Details images have considerably more than that!

From top left to bottom right, the swatches are: "Mulberry Wine," from the ArtBeats *Marbled Paper Textures* set, Mimi Schleicher, artist; "Jamaican Rose," from the Vivid Details *Granite* set; a neon reflection on pavement from Corel's misnamed *Rainy Nights,* which consists exclusively of just such texture shots; pressed metal from Digital Stock's *Urban Textures*; a tan fabric from CAM's *Tartans*; a rippling sea from the ImageKit *Water* CD; and coffee beans from PhotoDisc 3, *Backgrounds and Textures.*

The PlateMaker plug-in is available through A Lowly Apprentice Productions, (619) 438-5790 or support@alap.com.

Visu Technologies currently has no phone number in the United States. Its e-mail address is visu@euronet.nl; its Web site is http://www.vgm-visu.nl; its phone in the Netherlands is (31) 20-669-3701.

MetaTools, whose KPT series of products are also available through many mail-order outlets, can be reached at 805-566-6200 or at http://www.metatools.com.

Fractal Design's Painter is available from most mail-order houses; the company is reachable at 408-688-8800.

Scitex can be reached at 617-275-5150, http://www.scitex.com.

Dicomed, which manufactures high-end digital cameras, is headquartered in Britain. It is reachable in the United States at 800-888-7979, or http://www.dicomed.com.

The vaporware referred to in the comment about Quark was a product called QuarkXPosure, a photo-manipulation package that was alleged to be able to give serious competition to Photoshop. It was due out in mid-1995, but as of a year later is on indefinite hold.

APS stands for Advanced Photography System, a film technology introduced in early 1996 by a consortium of Canon, Fuji, Kodak, Minolta, and Nikon. It allows digital data, such as a sound narration, to coexist with traditional film. A sensible advance, but unfortunately incompatible with existing cameras. This is what lit the fuses of many photographers, who charged it was all a plot to make them buy new equipment.

Column 10

Florence's Duomo, realized by Brunelleschi only a few years before Nicolas Jenson began his typographic work on the opposite coast of Italy, is shown on page 225 in an image based on one from Corel's *Portrait of Italy* CD. Points of similarity between fifteenth-century architecture and typeface design can be noted quite as easily as between 1970s fashion and typefaces.

Although most type designers today do their work in Fontographer, Robert Slimbach and the rest of the Adobe Originals Design Group use a proprietary system, supplemented by FontStudio, a program that is no longer being sold. Adobe, incidentally, acquired the rights to FontStudio as part of its acquisition of Ares Software; it is not inconceivable that it will be resurrected some day, particularly when one considers that Fontographer is a product of Adobe's arch-rival, Macromedia.

The major font resellers, who can supply virtually any of the faces discussed here, including those of Elsner & Flake, Emigre, Font Bureau, and TreacyFaces, are FontHaus, 800-942-9110; FontShop, 800-363-6687; Phil's Fonts, 800-424-2977; and Precision Type, 800-248-3668.

Emigre fonts are shown on-line at http://www.emigre.com.

Column 11

The quotations from Daniel Berkeley Updike come from his two-volume *Printing Types* (Harvard University Press, 1922).

Macromedia's Fontographer is available through all standard software suppliers. Ares Software, creator of FontChameleon, was acquired by Adobe in June 1996. The FontChameleon product was discontinued.

The reference in the Afterword is to Moye, *Fontographer: Type by Design* (MIS:Press, 1995).

Column 12

Adobe PageMaker and QuarkXPress are available wherever software is sold. Both companies have extensive on-line resources. Penta Software is reachable at 410-771-8973.

XChange, which markets Quark XTensions, is at 800-788-7557. Development of new XTensions, particularly Web-related, continues at a brisk pace.

Melville's *Moby Dick,* which was used to test the hyphenation and justification capabilities of the three programs, is in e-text along with many other classics, from Project Gutenberg, available through Walnut Creek CDROM, 800-786-9907.

Epilogue

With the exception of the familar DEF set, which is mine, all images come from Aztech New Media's Photofile World Image Library collection.

Computer Artist

Computer Artist magazine is a resource for computer-based designers, artists, imagers, and illustrators. This award-winning bimonthly provides information about trends and technology, offers step-by-step instruction in digital techniques, and showcases the best of today's electronic art. In addition to my column, each issue includes a profile of a leading computer artist, a "Behind the Art" section that tells the stories of successful commercial projects, and news on the latest hardware and software of interest to artists and designers. For subscription information, call 1-800-331-4463, ext. 252 (918-832-9252 outside the U.S.) For advertising information, call 603-981-9163.

Reaching the Author

My e-mail accounts are 76270.1033@compuserve.com; also DMargulis@aol.com.

A Note About the Type

The text face in this book is Apolline, designed by Jean-François Porchez and released by Agfa in 1995. This is technically a Venetian old style face, but it has the typical sturdiness of faces designed in the 1990s, as discussed in Column 10. For this book, I stripped out all width and kerning data for the font and created new values.

Index